ASSESSING THE BIOLOGICAL QUALITY OF FRESH WATERS

Proceedings of an International Workshop
held in Oxford, UK, on 16-18 September 1997

Sponsored by

FRESHWATER
BIOLOGICAL
ASSOCIATION

Institute of
Freshwater
Ecology

ENVIRONMENT
AGENCY

**Land & Water
Resources**
Research &
Development
Corporation

FRONTISPIECE. Jesus College Oxford, venue for the International Workshop held in September 1997. Jesus College was founded in 1571 on the site of White Hall – a hall for students dating from the 13th century.

PARTICIPANTS

Dr Karl-Jan Aanes, Norwegian Institute for Water Research, Brakkeveien 19, PO Box 173, Kjelsas, N-0411 Oslo, NORWAY

Dr Javier Alba-Tercedor, Departamento de Biología Animal y Ecología, Facultad de Ciencias, Universidad de Granada, 18071 Granada, SPAIN

Dr Patrick Armitage, Institute of Freshwater Ecology, River Laboratory, East Stoke, Wareham, Dorset, BH20 6BB, ENGLAND

Dr Torlief Baekken, Norwegian Institute for Water Research, Brakkeveien 19, PO Box 173, Kjelsas, N-0411 Oslo, NORWAY

Dr Michael Barbour, Tetra Tech Inc., 10045 Red Run Boulevard, Suite 110, Owings Mills, Maryland 21117, USA

Dr Alasdair Berrie, Freshwater Biological Association, River Laboratory, East Stoke, Wareham, Dorset, BH20 6BB, ENGLAND

Dr Philip Boon, Principal Freshwater Adviser, Scottish Natural Heritage, 2 Anderson Place, Edinburgh, EH6 5NP, SCOTLAND

Dr Ian Boothroyd, National Institute of Water and Atmospheric Research, Gate 10 Silverdale Road, PO Box 11-115, Hamilton, 2001, NEW ZEALAND

Dr Ulrich Braukmann, Landesanstalt für Umweltschutz, Baden-Wurttemberg, Postfach 210752, Karlsruhe, D-76157, GERMANY

Dr Cristina Cappelletti, Instituto Agrario di S. Michele all'Adige, Via E. Mach, 1, 38010 S. Michele all'Adige (TRENTO), ITALY

Mr Ralph Clarke, Institute of Freshwater Ecology, River Laboratory, East Stoke, Wareham, Dorset, BH20 6BB, ENGLAND

Dr Peter Davies, Freshwater Systems, 82 Waimea Avenue, Sandy Bay, Tasmania, 7005, AUSTRALIA

Prof. Dr Niels De Pauw, University of Ghent, Department of Applied Ecology and Environmental Biology, I. Plateaustraet 22, B-9000, Gent, BELGIUM

Dr Bob Dines, Environment Agency, Guildbourne House, Chatsworth Road, Worthing, West Sussex, BN11 1LD, ENGLAND

Dr Alastair Ferguson, Environment Agency, Rio House, Waterside Drive, Aztec West, Almondsbury, Bristol, BS12 4UD, ENGLAND

Dr Wojciech Fialkowski, Jagiellonian University, Dept of Hydrobiology, ul. Oleandry 2a, 30-063, Krakow, 30-063, POLAND

Dr Eirik Fjeld, Norwegian Institute for Water Research, Brakkeveien 19, PO Box 173, Kjelsas, N-0411 Oslo, NORWAY

Dr Nikolai Friberg, National Environmental Research Institute, Postbox 314, DK-8600 Silkeborg, DENMARK

Dr Mike Furse, Institute of Freshwater Ecology, River Laboratory, East Stoke, Wareham, Dorset, BH20 6BB, ENGLAND

Mr Konstantinos Gritzalis, National Centre for Marine Research, Institute of Inland Waters, Agios Kosmas, Hellinikon, Athens, 16604, GREECE

Mr Iain Gunn, Institute of Freshwater Ecology, Edinburgh Research Station, Bush Estate, Penicuik, Midlothian, EH26 0QB, SCOTLAND

Mr Peter Hale, IRTU, Industrial Science Centre, 17 Antrim Road, Lisburn, Co. Antrim, BT28 3AL, NORTHERN IRELAND

Prof. Charles Hawkins, Department of Fisheries and Wildlife, Watershed Science Unit and Ecology Center, Utah State University, Logan, Utah 84322-5210, USA

Mr Brian Hemsley-Flint, Environment Agency, Phoenix House, Global Avenue, Leeds, LS11 8PG, ENGLAND

Prof. John Hilton, Institute of Freshwater Ecology, River Laboratory East Stoke, Wareham, Dorset, BH20 6BB, ENGLAND

Dr Chris Humphrey, Wetland Management Section, Environmental Research Institute of the Supervising Scientist, Locked Bag 2, Jabiru, NT 0886, AUSTRALIA

Mr James Hunt, Environment Agency, Rio House, Waterside Drive, Aztec West, Almondsbury, Bristol, BS12 4UD, ENGLAND

Dr Richard Johnson, Department of Environmental Assessment, Biodiversity Section, Swedish University of Agricultural Sciences, Box 7050, S-750 07, Uppsala, SWEDEN

Dr Jackie King, Freshwater Research Unit, Department of Zoology, University of Cape Town, Private Bag, Rondesbosch 7700, SOUTH AFRICA

Dr Jiri Kokes, Water Research Insitute, Drevarska 12, Brno, 657 57, CZECH REPUBLIC

Mr Esa Koskenniemi, West Finland Regional Environment Centre, PO Box 262, Vaasa, 65101, FINLAND

Dr Michel Lafont, Cemagref, 3 bis Quai Chauveau, CP 220, Lyon, FRANCE

Dr Paul Logan, Environment Agency, Kings Meadow House, Kings Meadow Road, Reading, Berkshire, RGI 8DQ, ENGLAND

Mr Ray Martin, School of Computing, Staffordshire University, Beaconside, Stafford, ST18 0DG, ENGLAND

Dr Alexander Milner, School of Geography, University of Birmingham, Edgbaston, Birmingham, B15 2TT, ENGLAND

Ms Nicki Mitchell, Department of Zoology, University of Adelaide, Adelaide 5005, AUSTRALIA

Dr Catia Monauni, Instituto Agrario di S. Michele all'Adige, Via E. Mach, 1, 38010 S. Michele all'Adige (TRENTO), ITALY

Dr Otto Moog, Department of Hydrobiology, University of Agriculture, Max Emmanuel Strasse 17, A-1180 Vienna, AUSTRIA

Dr Dorian Moss, Institute of Terrestrial Ecology, Monks Wood, Abbots Ripton, Huntingdon, Cambridgeshire, PE17 2LS, ENGLAND

Dr John Murray-Bligh, Environment Agency, Kings Meadow House, Kings Meadow Road, Reading, Berkshire, RG1 8DQ, ENGLAND

Dr Richard Norris, CRC for Freshwater Ecology, University of Canberra, Canberra 2601, AUSTRALIA

Prof. Jay O'Keeffe, Institute for Water Research, Rhodes University, PO Box 94, Grahamstown, 6140, SOUTH AFRICA

Dr Ana María Pujante, Departamento de Biología Animal, Universitat de València, Dr Moliner 50, 46100 Burjassot, València, SPAIN

Prof. Vincent Resh, Department of Environmental Science, Policy & Management, Division of Insect Biology, 201 Wellman Hall, University of California, Berkeley, CA 94720, USA

Dr Trefor Reynoldson, National Water Research Insitute, Environment Canada, Canada Centre for Inland Waters, 867 Lakeshore Road, Burlington, Ontario, L7R 4A6, CANADA

Dr David Rosenberg, Department of Fisheries and Oceans, Freshwater Institute, 501 University Crescent, Winnipeg, Manitoba, R3T 2N6, CANADA

Mr Leonard Sandin, Swedish University of Agricultural Sciences, Department of Environmental Assessment, Box 7050, S-750 07, Uppsala, SWEDEN

Dr Ursula Schmedtje, Bayerisches Landesamt für Wasserwirtschaft, Lazarettstrasse 62, 80636 Munchen, GERMANY

Dr Nick Schofield, Land and Water Resources, Research and Development Corporation, 97 Northbourne Avenue, GPO Box 2182, Canberra, ACT 2601, AUSTRALIA

Mr Justen Simpson, CRC for Freshwater Ecology, University of Canberra, Canberra 2601, AUSTRALIA

Dr Nikolas Skoulikidis, National Centre for Marine Research, Institute of Inland Waters, Agios Kosmas, Hellinikon, Athens, 16604, GREECE

Mr John Steel, Environment Agency, Lambourn House, Howbery Park, Wallingford, Oxon, OX10 8BD, ENGLAND

Dipl-Ing Ilse Stubauer, Department of Hydrobiology, University of Agriculture, Max Emmanuel Strasse 17, A-1180 Vienna, AUSTRIA

Dr Roger Sweeting, Freshwater Biological Association, The Ferry House, Far Sawrey, Ambleside, Cumbria, LA22 0LP, ENGLAND

Dr Gloria Tapia, Institute of Freshwater Ecology, River Laboratory, East Stoke, Wareham, Dorset, BH20 6BB, ENGLAND

Dr Piet Verdonschot, Institute for Forestry and Nature Research, PO Box 23, Wageningen, 6700 AA, THE NETHERLANDS

Dr Gerardo Vina-Vizcaino, Corporate Environmental Group, BP Exploration Co., Carrera 9A No 99-02 Piso 4, Santate de Bogota DC, COLOMBIA

Prof. William Walley, School of Computing, Staffordshire University, The Octagon, Beaconside, Stafford, ST18 0DG, ENGLAND

Dr John Wright, Institute of Freshwater Ecology, River Laboratory, East Stoke, Wareham, Dorset, BH20 6BB, ENGLAND

FOREWORD

For over a century, biologists have investigated the complex relationships between the environmental features of river systems and their animal and plant communities. Much of the early work was on fish and, typically, river zones were classified on their dominant fish species for the purpose of fishery management. The importance of macroinvertebrates, not only as a source of fish food but for assessing the quality of running waters, also started to gain recognition. For much of the 20th century, our knowledge of the macroinvertebrates occurring in fresh waters and their ecological requirements expanded at an ever-increasing rate. At the same time, many different procedures for detecting pollution, based on macroinvertebrates, were developed within Europe and elsewhere.

Within the UK, several alternative techniques were available by the late 1970s, designed to provide biologists with simple but effective procedures for explaining biological results to non-specialists. Nevertheless, the time was right to explore the option of developing a more flexible system for bioassessment with application throughout the country. In 1977, a small team of invertebrate zoologists was assembled at the River Laboratory of the Freshwater Biological Association (FBA) in Dorset, and so began the "River Communities Project" which eventually lead to the development of RIVPACS. The team was in a strong position to benefit from the painstaking work of the many biologists who had worked in this field before them. In particular, mention should be made of the taxonomic work undertaken by staff of the FBA (and others) whose taxonomic keys have appeared within the Scientific Publications series of the Association, and the academic and Water Authority scientists whose biological, physical and chemical data and expertise were crucial for the long-term success of the project.

As a result of twenty years of research, made possible by long-term financial support and the growing recognition of the value of biological monitoring for assessing river quality, it was apparent that an authoritative and up-to-date account of the development of the River InVertebrate Prediction And Classification System (RIVPACS) would be a valuable text for both pure and applied freshwater ecologists in the UK. However, bioassessment systems for aquatic environments have been designed and are being developed in many countries throughout the world, based on macroinvertebrates and other major faunal or floral groups. Hence, the idea of an international workshop of invited specialists was born.

An international committee was formed to organise the workshop, and 59 scientists active in the field of bioassessment, drawn from 23 countries, gathered for the three-day meeting, which was held at Jesus College, Oxford, in September 1997. As an established, independent seat of learning in a cosmopolitan city on the River Thames, it seemed a most appropriate venue. The workshop created its own momentum and each participant contributed to this book, either by writing a chapter or by contributing ideas to the workshop discussions.

The book is intended to be a comprehensive account of the rationale and development of some major advances in bioassessment at the turn of the 21st century. It summarises major developments of RIVPACS, provides an up-to-date account of the current system and explores problem areas and opportunities. In addition, it provides a showcase for a number of scientists throughout the world who have adopted similar procedures and adapted them to their own requirements. Following the workshop, it has taken two years to edit and co-ordinate the contributions into as seamless a text as possible.

Most of the authors and the editors are well known and have been working in freshwater biology for many years. During this time many of their organisations have gone through considerable changes and are almost unrecognisable now compared with the time when the early work was initiated. It is a tribute to their commitment that the work has continued. Recognition of the importance of this research by the UK's Natural Environment Research Council, the National Rivers Authority (now the Environment Agency) and Environment Australia (through the Land and Water Resources Research & Development Corporation) has ensured that funding for both the work and the international workshop has been forthcoming.

As a result of its long-standing reputation in the field of freshwater biology and limnology, and because much of the UK work on RIVPACS has been carried out under its auspices, the FBA was asked to publish this book. It now joins the Association's impressive list of publications.

Biological quality assessment methods based on the use of reference sites are being developed and used throughout the world. Procedures for setting site-specific targets for the fauna to be expected in the absence of environmental stress (the so-called reference condition) are described in several chapters of this book. The applicability of reference conditions other than the near-pristine are also considered for circumstances where the latter cannot be achieved or where staged measurements of progress are needed.

It is intended that this book will provide a significant stimulus for further investigations based on the reference condition approach.

Roger Sweeting

EDITORIAL PREFACE

The original idea for an International Workshop came from Roger Sweeting. After early consultations, it was agreed that the workshop would be organised and funded by a partnership of three organisations: the Environment Agency, the Institute of Freshwater Ecology and an Australian consortium comprising Environment Australia and the Land and Water Resources Research and Development Corporation. We would like to acknowledge the practical help received from each one of the sponsoring organisations, not only in terms of financial support but also in the provision of time and manpower to ensure the success of the workshop and this publication.

An organising committee took responsibility for the scientific, social and financial aspects of the workshop and for deciding on the form of the publication. The committee included representatives from the Environment Agency (Roger Sweeting (Chairman), Bob Dines, Brian Hemsley-Flint, Paul Logan, John Murray-Bligh and John Steel), the Institute of Freshwater Ecology (John Hilton, John Wright and Mike Furse) and an Australian representative (Peter Davies). Several planning meetings were held at the IFE River Laboratory in Dorset, in Reading and at Jesus College, Oxford, prior to the workshop. We would like to thank each member of the committee for discharging their particular responsibilities with enthusiasm and good humour.

Participation in the International Workshop was by invitation, and the committee proposed potential contributors from around the world, with the emphasis on scientists working on biological river-quality assessment, classification or modelling. The formal presentations were also by invitation, but many delegates offered poster presentations or software demonstrations and these were accommodated in a special evening session. We thank all those who accepted the invitation to participate in the workshop.

Five parallel workshop sessions were devised by the organising committee, including a variety of important and controversial issues. Each session had a chairman who accepted responsibility for presenting a brief report to the full workshop and for writing an account of the discussions and conclusions of their session. The chairman was allocated a rapporteur to take headline notes during the discussions. We would like to thank everyone who contributed to these sessions by sharing their ideas and moving the debate forward.

The location for the workshop, Jesus College, Oxford, provided a major attraction for many participants and we are grateful to Ken Pain, Assistant Bursar, for provision of facilities for the scientific sessions, the accommodation, food and, in particular, the arrangements for the workshop banquet. We also thank Nicki Mitchell who worked behind the scenes prior to the workshop and, together with Gloria Tapia and Iain Gunn, helped the organising committee to ensure that everything ran smoothly.

We are grateful to Professor Gwynfryn Jones, Director of the Freshwater Biological Association at the time, for readily accepting the proposal that the FBA would publish manuscripts based on the workshop presentations and discussions, in the form of an FBA Special Publication. John Wright, David Sutcliffe and Mike Furse accepted editorial responsibilities for the scientific content of each written contribution, and David Sutcliffe also acted as copy-editor and production manager for the FBA. During the production of this volume it was decided to present the contents as a book containing a sequence of twenty-four main chapters, with a single comprehensive list of references. This format replaced the earlier concept of separate contributions collected under a common title, like earlier FBA Special Publications reporting the proceedings of scientific meetings. The change in presentation, though modest, has necessitated some alterations to authors' manuscripts in order to present a reasonably consistent text throughout the book, although one inconsistency may be noted. Usage of words ending in –ise rather than -ize is now common in the UK, and as most of our contributors used the former spelling this has been favoured except in some chapters emanating from North America, where –ize is the normal spelling and has been retained. We thank the contributors for their forebearance during the protracted process of achieving what we hope will be seen as a useful and coherent summary of the development and application of various techniques in the developing field of biological assessment for managing a variety of riverine and lacustrine habitats.

The editors would like to thank the invited speakers for their written contributions, presented herein as Chapters 1 to 18, and also the internal and external referees for their valuable advice. Special thanks are proffered to Mike Barbour and Chris Yoder who, after the workshop, agreed to write Chapter 19 on the multimetric approach as used in the USA, in order to give better coverage of a topic raised during the workshop. The editors are also grateful to all of the chairmen for their efforts both during and after the workshop, and to all those participants who commented on early drafts summarising the workshop sessions. We also record our thanks to Roger Sweeting, who did much to initiate and sustain interest in the workshop and helped to see it through to final publication.

Finally, we would like to thank Mrs Rosalie Sutcliffe, who undertook the unenviable task of compiling the reference list and the indexes.

John Wright, David Sutcliffe and Mike Furse

Some terms commonly employed by biologists working with RIVPACS.

Taxon (plural *taxa*)	A type of organism, irrespective of the taxonomic level at which it is defined (e.g. *Ephemera danica, Ephemera* sp. or Ephemeridae).
Standardised taxa	The level to which all macroinvertebrates recorded at the RIVPACS III reference sites have been identified. See Wright, Blackburn *et al.* (1996) for the list of 637 standardised taxa in the 614 site Great Britain dataset.
Number of taxa (= *N-Taxa*)	Number of BMWP taxa present in a sample.
Family	A group of organisms that are considered to be naturally related genera based on taxonomic research worldwide (e.g. genera of mayflies within the family Baetidae).
BMWP families (= *BMWP taxa*)	Taxa that are used in the Biological Monitoring Working Party system. With the exception of the class Oligochaeta, all BMWP taxa are families, as defined by Maitland (1977). Each BMWP family is allocated a value in the range 1 to 10, according to known tolerance to organic pollution. Highest scores are given to families intolerant of organic pollution (e.g. Ephemeridae and Perlidae score 10) and *vice versa* (e.g. Chironomidae score 2 and Oligochaeta score 1). A number of families of freshwater macroinvertebrates are not incorporated into the BMWP system.
BMWP indices	The three indices are: BMWP score, number of BMWP taxa (also referred to as number of taxa or N-Taxa) and the average score per taxon (ASPT)
BMWP score	The BMWP score is the sum of the values of the BMWP families recorded in the sample. A standard RIVPACS sample must be taken if the result is to represent the "Observed fauna" in an Observed/Expected ratio.
ASPT	Average Score Per Taxon. The ASPT is the BMWP score for a sample divided by the number of BMWP taxa in the sample. ASPT is a biotic index of organic pollution.
Observed taxa	List of taxa obtained by the standard RIVPACS sampling protocol. The listing can be of standardised taxa, families or BMWP families.
Expected taxa	RIVPACS predicts the taxa that would be expected at an unstressed site if the standard RIVPACS sampling protocol was used. The prediction is based on a small set of environmental variables. The listing of expected taxa has attached probabilities of capture for each taxon, and these probabilities are taken into account when comparing the expected taxa with the observed taxa captured at the same site (see text for detailed protocol).
O/E ratio (= *EQI*)	Ratio of the Observed to the Expected fauna. The ratio may relate to the number of standardised taxa, families or BMWP families. Most frequently it is expressed as one or more of the three BMWP indices. O/E ratio is the same as the Ecological Quality Index (EQI).

CHAPTER 1

An introduction to RIVPACS

JOHN F. WRIGHT

Institute of Freshwater Ecology, River Laboratory, East Stoke,
Wareham, Dorset, BH20 6BB, UK

Summary

RIVPACS (River InVertebrate Prediction And Classification System) is a software package developed by the Institute of Freshwater Ecology (IFE). The primary application is to assess the biological quality of rivers within the UK. RIVPACS offers site-specific predictions of the macroinvertebrate fauna to be expected in the absence of major environmental stress. The expected fauna is derived by RIVPACS using a small suite of environmental characteristics. The biological evaluation is then obtained by comparing the fauna observed at the site with the expected fauna.

RIVPACS also includes a site classification based on the macroinvertebrate fauna of the component reference sites. New sites, judged by their fauna to be of high biological quality, may be allocated to classification groups within the fixed RIVPACS classification. This has potential for evaluating sites for conservation.

In this chapter, the origins and history of the RIVPACS approach are described, including major scientific and operational developments over the life of the project. RIVPACS III is described in detail and predictions at different taxonomic levels are demonstrated. The value of the reference dataset for river management and conservation is examined, and the chapter concludes with a brief consideration of some future challenges.

Introduction

Background

The initial four-year project which eventually lead to the development of RIVPACS started in October 1977, funded by the Natural Environment Research Council and the Department of the Environment. The project had two major objectives: (1) development of a biological classification of unpolluted running-water sites in Great Britain, based on the macro-invertebrate fauna, and (2) assessment of whether the macroinvertebrate community at a site could be predicted using physical and chemical features.

Careful decisions were made on the choice of reference sites, the field and laboratory procedures and the methods for analysis (Wright, Moss *et al.* 1984). Decisions made over 20 years ago on the field-sampling protocol and the level of identification used at reference sites have determined the present field-sampling protocol (Murray-Bligh, Furse *et al.* 1997) and resulted in a wide range of prediction options in RIVPACS III (Wright, Moss *et al.* 1997).

However, the long-term success of the project depended upon the initial demonstration of a strong relationship between the environmental features and faunal characteristics of the original 268 reference sites (Wright, Moss *et al.* 1984). This was essential for an operational

system that would be capable of delivering reliable predictions of the fauna over a wide range
of river types. During RIVPACS development, practical issues of concern to end-users were
addressed, to ensure that biological monitoring gained a higher profile alongside chemical
monitoring. A number of these issues, including quality assurance, presentation of biological
results, and methods for detecting spatial and temporal change, are described in later chapters
of this volume.

The accumulated experience of the IFE team, together with the new ideas being explored by
several groups in other countries (e.g. Reynoldson, Bailey *et al.* 1995; Norris 1996), make this
the ideal time to assess current achievements and examine some future challenges.

The context for RIVPACS

Biological monitoring is required, in addition to chemical monitoring, because the ultimate
consequences of environmental stress can only be determined by an appraisal of the biota. The
16th Report of the Royal Commission on Environmental Pollution (1992) dealt with
Freshwater Quality and their first recommendation was that *"The regulatory authorities should
endeavour to develop a general classification scheme based on biological assessment for use
throughout the UK in the 1995 and subsequent river quality surveys"*. The question of which
major taxonomic group to use for site appraisal has been addressed on many occasions
(Hellawell 1986). Although it would be wise to retain an open mind when designing a
monitoring programme for a new region (Ormerod, Rundle *et al.* 1994), the advantages of
using macroinvertebrates have made them the favoured group in most surveillance and
monitoring studies (Rosenberg & Resh 1993b). Wallace & Webster (1996) review the essential
role played by macroinvertebrates in the functioning of stream ecosystems.

The effects of stress in running waters can be detected at many different levels of
organisation, ranging from biochemical and physiological effects on individuals, through the
response of a population, to community responses and ecosystem effects (Sutcliffe 1994). A
comprehensive monitoring programme may include a number of these elements. Bunn (1995)
pointed out that the ecological consequences of stress are best examined at higher levels of
organisation, but these assessments detect impacts after the event. A future challenge will be
the integration of the community approach with early warning techniques based on lower
levels of organisation. In the meantime, biological surveillance of communities, with special
emphasis on characterising taxonomic richness and composition, is perhaps the most sensitive
tool now available for quickly and accurately detecting alterations in aquatic ecosystems
(Cairns & Pratt 1993).

It would be invaluable to understand the processes that result in the observed patterns of
community structure in unstressed river systems. This would provide a firm basis for
interpreting the mechanisms leading to changes in the structure and functioning of
communities under stress. At present, this knowledge is very restricted (Hildrew 1992) because
a wide variety of ecological and evolutionary processes, historical events and geographical
circumstances, contribute to the patterns of species richness and composition observed in
nature (Cornell & Lawton 1992; Schluter & Ricklefs 1993). As a consequence, lotic
community responses to a range of environmental stresses are well documented, but the
processes of community change are poorly understood.

Hellawell (1986) proposes three major categories of environmental stress. These are natural
stresses (e.g. droughts and floods), imposed stresses (e.g. sewage pollution, toxic waste and
pesticides) and environmental manipulation by man (e.g. reservoir construction, channel
modification and the transfer of water between catchments). The macroinvertebrate fauna may
be affected by each one of these stresses, and the fauna at any given site may be the end result

of more than one category of stress.

A review of the longer-term trends expected in stressed ecosystems is given by Odum (1985). These include a consideration of energetics, nutrient cycling, community structure and general system-level trends. At the community level, Odum suggests that the proportion of r-strategists will increase, the size of organisms will decrease, lifespans will decrease, food chains will shorten and, typically, species richness will decrease, allowing some taxa to dominate. He hypothesises that functional properties such as community metabolism are more robust than species composition and other structural properties. Perry (1994) also discusses the idea that functional attributes such as production, respiration and nutrient cycling may be more robust than structural attributes, including species composition and richness. If this is true, then monitoring structural changes may give earlier warning of the effects of environmental stress than the measurement of functional attributes.

In RIVPACS, the emphasis is on the prediction of taxonomic composition and richness. In RIVPACS III, attempts have also been made to predict $\log_{10}$ categories of abundance at family level in order to detect early signs of structural change before substantial loss of taxa.

In order to develop a general system in which the fauna may be used to detect environmental stress, three features must be present. First, a mechanism is required for predicting the "expected" fauna at a given unstressed site, in order to provide a "target" community. Second, the procedure must be applicable to a wide range of sites. Finally, there must be an appropriate procedure for comparing the observed fauna with the expected fauna.

The RIVPACS approach

The basic concept and use of reference sites

RIVPACS offers a prediction of the "expected" fauna at a given site, with stated environmental features, through a procedure which draws on information from a series of appropriate sites of high biological quality. In practice, no rivers in Great Britain are unaffected by human activity in the catchment or in the river channel itself. Thus, there is a need to identify those rivers and sites that are minimally impacted and the best examples of their type. At the outset, detailed discussions took place between biologists throughout Great Britain and the IFE team, in order to generate a list of potentially suitable river systems. Before sampling began, a river and site-selection procedure was devised, based on geological, physical and chemical factors to ensure a wide coverage of different river types (Wright, Moss *et al.* 1984; Chapter 20).

The funding arrangements following the initial study necessitated a step-by-step approach to building a comprehensive series of minimally stressed reference sites. Increasing experience of the fauna to be expected at high quality sites, coupled with more severe criteria for site acceptance (Wright, Furse *et al.* 1995), resulted in a comprehensive set of "reference sites" (Hughes 1995; Reynoldson, Norris *et al.* 1997) with high capability for setting a target of the fauna to be expected at a given site. The benefits and difficulties associated with the acquisition and use of reference sites are discussed by Reynoldson & Wright in Chapter 20. Prior to each major analysis, macroinvertebrate and environmental data were collated for each reference site. An essential feature of the RIVPACS approach is the classification of reference sites using the macroinvertebrate fauna. Thus, sites with similar macroinvertebrate assemblages are brought together and no assumptions are made about the environmental features that influence species occurrence. This approach differs from the strategy adopted in the Rapid Biological Assessment method used in the USA, in which environmental attributes that indicate "relatively undisturbed" sites are the basis for selecting a series of reference sites in a given ecoregion or sub-ecoregion (Omernik 1995). For this, it is assumed that reference sites in the defined region have relatively similar macroinvertebrate assemblages which may be used to calculate an array of measures or metrics that define the expected condition, and against which the biological condition of the test sites may be determined (Barbour *et al.* 1995; Chapter 19).

Predicting the expected fauna

The next stage in RIVPACS was to determine whether classification groups defined on biological criteria were also coherent with respect to a series of environmental attributes. This was investigated using multiple discriminant analysis (MDA) (Klecka 1975). Ideally, the environmental attributes should be relatively stable over time and unaffected by environmental stress. A description of this procedure, and details of the effectiveness of the technique for demonstrating the relationship between the biological and environmental features of the reference dataset, are given by Moss in Chapter 2.

The detailed techniques whereby environmental features for a new site were used in RIVPACS to predict the expected fauna of that site, are also presented in Chapter 2. Essentially, this was a two-stage operation. First, the probability of the new site being in each one of the classification groups was determined. In practice, a site would normally have a high probability of occurrence in one or a few classification groups and all others would not make a significant contribution. Second, a novel technique was used to predict the probability of occurrence of individual taxa at the site (Moss, Furse *et al* 1987). This required information on the frequency of occurrence of taxa in each classification group and the probabilities of classification group membership for the new site.

Comparing the observed and expected fauna at each site

RIVPACS offers a comparison between the fauna captured at the site using the standard field protocol and the expected fauna derived by prediction. The observed fauna is represented by positive occurrences of taxa, whereas the expected fauna is displayed as probabilities of capture ranging from 100% probability to the percentage probability requested by the user. The latter is normally 0.1% for family-level predictions, but frequently 50% for species-level predictions. At family level, the ratio of the observed to the expected number of taxa is easily computed, and provides the first indication of whether the fauna matches expectation. Examples of observed/expected (O/E) ratios are given later.

Some practical considerations

Sampling methods

Perhaps the most crucial decisions made at the outset of the project were how to sample, where to sample, and when to sample. Early consultations with Water Authority and River Purification Board biologists indicated that pondnet sampling was widespread but that local procedures varied in detail. In some regions, sampling was confined to riffles because the detection of organic pollution was a priority and riffle assemblages were known to be sensitive to this form of stress (Balloch *et al.* 1976). In other regions, a variety of habitats were included in the sampling procedure. The need for a simple and flexible sampling procedure for use at a wide range of locations, a classification of reference sites based on comprehensive faunal assemblages, and a prediction system capable of detecting a wide range of environmental stresses, indicated that a single habitat protocol would be inappropriate. On the other hand, separate sampling units for each major habitat at a given site would increase sampling effort and result in non-uniform effort across the sites. It was concluded that a reasonably comprehensive species list for each site would be obtained from a timed pondnet sample in which all major habitats were sampled, approximately in proportion to their occurrence. The procedure for each reference site involved a 3-minute pondnet sample plus a 1-minute manual search in each of spring (March–May), summer (June–August) and autumn (September–November), in order to capture the major components of the fauna.

Using this procedure, in a pilot study, three biologists each took two samples at four sites on one river (Furse, Wright *et al.* 1981). Clustering and ordination of species-level data gave strong site-faithfulness for the six samples from each site, despite the fact that there were significant inter-operator differences in the number of taxa captured (p <0.05) and the study was confined to one season.

At a small number of deep lowland sites, sampled later in the project, a standard pondnet (900 μm mesh, 230x255 mm frame, 275 mm bag depth) on a 1.5 m handle was ineffective. In these cases, a light-weight version of the Medium Naturalist's dredge (Holme & McIntyre 1971; Furse, Moss *et al.* 1986) was used in the deep water in conjunction with pondnetting of marginal areas. Further details of all field procedures may be found in Murray-Bligh, Furse *et al.* (1997).

Reference sites and identification protocols

In the initial programme, sampling sites were chosen at *ca* 5, 10, 20, 30 and 40 km from source and thereafter at 20 km intervals downstream, because rate of change in community composition is greater near the source of each stream (Verneaux 1976). The precise location of each sampling site was always chosen in consultation with the local biologist. Later in the project, further advice was taken on the geographical areas and river types which required greater representation and on the availability of both deep lowland and small stream sites, to make the system more comprehensive and reliable.

The involvement of regional biologists in selecting reference sites and collecting field samples was crucial in building each new version of RIVPACS. In addition, it was essential that samples from reference sites were subjected to a standard laboratory protocol and identified to the same taxonomic level. For this reason, all samples were preserved and sent to the River Laboratory where the IFE team was responsible for processing the samples (Furse, Wright *et al.* 1981) and identifying the fauna to a specified taxonomic level. Where closely related species or genera could not be distinguished consistently, they were represented as a taxonomic "group". Prior to the analyses, the combined seasons taxon lists for each reference site were subjected to a "standard edits" program which standardised the precision of the faunal listings, thus ensuring valid comparison between sites (Wright, Blackburn *et al.* 1996). For each reference site in each season, $\log_{10}$ categories of abundance at family level (i.e. <10, <100, <1000 and 10,000 individuals per family) were recorded to supplement the presence/absence data in the standardised taxon lists.

Classification of reference sites

The procedure chosen for classifying the reference sites by their macroinvertebrate assemblages was two-way indicator species analysis (TWINSPAN) (Hill 1979a), a divisive polythetic technique. Gauch & Whittaker (1981) compared a number of hierarchical procedures (agglomerative and divisive) and took the view that TWINSPAN was an appropriate technique for complex, "noisy", large or unfamiliar datasets. Initially, the standardised taxon lists based on three seasons combined sampling were used to develop site classifications because they demonstrated higher predictive ability than alternative classifications. The latter included the standardised lists for single seasons (qualitative data only), combined/single season classifications at family level (qualitative or $\log_{10}$ categories of abundance) and at BMWP family level (qualitative only) (Furse, Moss *et al.* 1984). Further information on the Biological Monitoring Working Party (BMWP) score system for the appraisal of running-water sites (National Water Council 1981) will be presented later.

Recently, a number of other classification techniques have been used to provide a suitable framework for developing prediction systems (Chapter 2; Moss, Wright *et al.* 1999; Norris 1996). Despite this, TWINSPAN remained the method of choice in RIVPACS III because alternative procedures failed to divide this substantial dataset into classification groups that were coherent with respect to the environmental attributes chosen for prediction (Wright, Furse *et al.* 1995; Wright, Moss *et al.* 1997).

The classification forms a framework for the prediction system, but also may be used to classify new sites based on taxon lists obtained in spring, summer and autumn, using the standard protocol. TWINSPAN offers a "key" to the classification based on a limited number of "differential" taxa that are diagnostic for each division in the classification (Hill 1979a). This key was used to classify new sites in RIVPACS I. However, in RIVPACS II and RIVPACS III, an improved procedure has been adopted (Rushton 1987) in which the full taxon list for a new site is used to generate probabilities of classification group membership. This procedure may be used with standardised taxon lists or BMWP family-level data.

Environmental variables for prediction

Initially, a large number of environmental attributes were acquired for each site. Whereas some variables were time invariant (e.g. altitude, slope, distance from source), others varied with the seasons (e.g. river width, depth, substratum) and for the latter, mean values were derived from observations taken in three seasons. In contrast, chemical variables were represented as annual mean values derived from the best available data.

Although 28 environmental variables were used in the first analyses that linked environmental features to site groups based on faunal characteristics (Wright, Moss *et al.* 1984), it was apparent that many of the variables were highly correlated and therefore redundant. Moss, Furse *et al.* (1987) used a modified list of 28 variables but demonstrated that a subset of these was capable of delivering a practical system. In consequence, changes were made to successive versions of RIVPACS in the search for a limited suite of environmental variables that could deliver a reliable prediction system. The importance of quantifying errors in the measurement of environmental variables is emphasised in Chapter 3 and some thoughts on alternative variables for prediction are considered at the end of this chapter.

Stages in the development of RIVPACS

Initial stages

The major developments and outputs from each phase of the RIVPACS project are presented in Table 1.1. Between 1977 and 1981, the initial field sampling programme was designed and undertaken in collaboration with colleagues in the water industry. IFE staff then identified the macroinvertebrate fauna and collated the environmental data for 268 reference sites, before analyses commenced. A TWINSPAN classification of sites, using standardised species-level data for three seasons, was developed to 16 groups. MDA was then used to predict the group membership of the 268 sites, based on 28 environmental variables. In an internal (re-substitution) test, 76.1% of sites were classified correctly (Wright, Moss *et al.* 1984). Fifteen additional classifications were also constructed, using data from single/combined seasons and different taxonomic levels. These included qualitative data at species, family and BMWP family level, and also family $\log_{10}$ category data. In each case, predictive ability based on the same 28 variables was lower than the species-level combined seasons classification (Furse, Moss *et al.* 1984).

Table 1.1. *Historical review of RIVPACS development, 1977-1997. See the text for further details.*

Dates	No. sites	Main developments	Major outputs
1977-1981	268	Formulation of standard field procedures. Production of a site classification based on the fauna. Demonstration of the strong link between biological and environmental features using MDA.	
1981-1984	370	Increase in geographical coverage of reference sites. Development of a new procedure for predicting the probability of taxon occurrence.	
1984-1988	370	Incorporation of biological indices from the BMWP system into the prediction system.	RIVPACS I tested by water industry biologists.
	438	Increase in the number of deep lowland rivers and small streams. Development of a new classification/prediction system using 438 sites in 25 classification groups (basis for RIVPACS 11).	
1989-1990	438	Operational development of RIVPACS II.	RIVPACS II used in 1990 River Quality Survey.
1991-1995	438	Development of a banding system to summarise results of 1990 River Quality Survey. Comprehensive testing of RIVPACS II using an independent dataset of high quality sites.	
	614+70	Increase in reference sites to give comprehensive coverage in Great Britain, plus a new senes of 70 reference sites for Northern Ireland. Investigation of alternative procedures for site classification and prediction of the fauna, using environmental attributes.	
		Development of a new classification and prediction system for Great Britain and Northern Ireland, based on the enlarged dataset (RIVPACS III).	RIVPACS III used in 1995 General Quality Assessment Survey.
1995-1997	614+70	Development of new procedures for detecting statistically significant temporal and spatial changes.	RIVPACS III+.

The successful demonstration of a strong link between faunal composition and the environmental features of the 268 reference sites led to further funding. The objectives for the next phase (1981–1984) included greater representation of rivers in Wales and Scotland, and lowland rivers in England, reducing the number of variables for prediction and refining the prediction procedure. At first, the environmental variables were used to predict probabilities of classification group membership only. In this phase, a novel technique was devised for predicting the probabilities of capture of individual taxa, based on their frequency of occurrence in the relevant classification groups (Moss, Furse *et al.* 1987). The same paper demonstrated that reducing the number of predictive variables from 28 to 11 (or even 5) resulted in only a modest loss of accuracy.

RIVPACS I

By 1984, a 370-site classification to 30 groups and a revised prediction system were in place. As before, the classification used species-level data and predictions were made at this taxonomic level. However, in addition to species-level predictions, other taxonomic levels could be generated by downgrading outputs to family or BMWP family level. The BMWP system is based on selected families of macroinvertebrates. Each family within the system is allocated a score in the range 1 to 10 according to its known tolerance to organic pollution, the most pollution-intolerant families being allotted the highest scores (Armitage, Moss *et al.* 1983). The BMWP score for a site is the sum of the scores of the BMWP families present in the sample, and the average score per taxon (ASPT) is simply the BMWP site score divided by the number of BMWP taxa. Expected values for BMWP score, number of BMWP taxa and ASPT were calculated from the expected probabilities of the BMWP families, and therefore observed/expected ratios were available for each BMWP index. These ratios were particularly suited to the requirements of water industry biologists engaged in routine biological monitoring. In 1986, the classification and prediction system was implemented on a simple microcomputer and made available to water industry biologists throughout Great Britain for testing under the acronym RIVPACS I. The software gave predictions at species, family and BMWP family levels and offered four reduced sets of predictive variables for appraisal. As a result of the testing exercise, the value of the prediction system was widely recognised and gave further impetus to the project.

Between 1984 and 1988, further sites on deep lowland rivers and on small streams (<5 km from source) were added, to give a total of 438 reference sites that were used to develop a new classification with 25 groups. The variables for prediction were reappraised and Water Authority/River Purification Board biologists requested single and paired season predictions. There was also progress in developing procedures for site evaluation based on observed to expected (O/E) ratios and the use of banding to distinguish unstressed sites (with O/E ratios close to unity) from stressed sites (with progressively lower O/E ratios). Note that the O/E ratio for each BMWP index is sometimes referred to as the Ecological Quality Index (EQI), as in Chapters 4 to 6 of this volume.

RIVPACS II

The newly formed National Rivers Authority (NRA) decided to fund development of the 438-site classification and prediction system into an operational version (RIVPACS II) for use in the 1990 River Quality Survey. RIVPACS II ran on IBM and IBM-compatible Personal Computers in addition to mainframe computers, and offered a number of significant improvements over the previous test version (Cox, Furse *et al.* 1991). It retained interactive predictions but, more importantly, it offered a datafile-operated system to make the prediction procedures more efficient. It also offered a menu of six sets of environmental variables for prediction (Wright *et al.* 1993), the choice of single, paired and three seasons combined predictions, plus a new variable taxonomic level (customisation) to provide compatibility with the requirements of local laboratories. Finally, it incorporated the improved method for the classification of new sites first suggested by Rushton (1987) (see Chapter 2).

RIVPACS II was used at almost 9000 sites in the 1990 River Quality Survey throughout England, Wales and Scotland, and on a more experimental basis in Northern Ireland, where there were no local reference sites (Sweeting, Lowson *et al.* 1992). The survey was conducted at BMWP family level and the initial output was as O/E ratios for the three BMWP indices. A banding system was then devised to distinguish good quality from progressively stressed sites in order to satisfy the reporting requirements of the national survey (Wright *et al.* 1993). Further discussion of the merits and difficulties inherent in devising a banding system may be found in Clarke, Furse *et al.* (1996).

This large-scale use of the system, and further detailed tests undertaken by the IFE, indicated that RIVPACS II performed effectively on many rivers. Nevertheless, there was a need to include additional river types, improve geographical coverage and increase the number of small stream sites to ensure that a future system could deliver reliable predictions throughout the country. The IFE tests also confirmed some inadequacies in prediction of the fauna (e.g in chalk streams) and demonstrated that a more rigorous protocol was required for accepting reference sites. Such problems were to be expected with a new methodology, but the potential advantages of this approach warranted the time and effort needed to refine the system (Royal Commission on Environmental Pollution 1992).

RIVPACS III

An upgraded version of the system was required for the 1995 General Quality Assessment (GQA) Survey, and data were collated for an additional 245 reference sites in Great Britain (Wright, Furse *et al.* 1995). These included sites of high biological quality previously sampled by the IFE, and further sites recommended by local biologists in order to make the dataset more comprehensive. The system was further enhanced by including 70 sites in Northern Ireland. As before, all species-level identifications were undertaken by IFE staff.

A large number of exploratory analyses were undertaken before RIVPACS III was finalised (Wright, Furse *et al.* 1995; Chapter 2). An early attempt to include all UK sites within a single classification was abandoned when it became apparent that the more restricted fauna in Northern Ireland would compromise both the Great Britain and Northern Ireland components of an all-inclusive system. Parallel classification and prediction systems were therefore developed for Great Britain and Northern Ireland within RIVPACS III. The enlarged dataset of 663 sites for Great Britain was progressively reduced, using several different procedures to ensure high quality in the final dataset. First, a series of criteria for site acceptance were applied to all sites. They included a minimum BMWP score of 100, a minimum of 30 standardised taxa and a nearest neighbour dissimilarity value not exceeding 0.55 (Belbin 1992). Next, during a series of classification and prediction exercises, sites that proved to be poor examples within their classification group (demonstrated by O/E ratios or BMWP indices) were rejected. Finally, five sites that had a surprisingly high taxon richness for their geographical location were removed because they were judged to be disruptive to a general prediction system (Wright, Furse *et al.* 1995*)*. By this route, the dataset for Great Britain was reduced to 614 reference sites, of which just 386 of the original 438 RIVPACS II sites were retained.

Before developing RIVPACS III, Moss, Wright *et al.* (1999) demonstrated that several widely different approaches to site classification had potential as the starting point for a prediction system. However, when the 614-site Great Britain dataset became available, it was clear that a TWINSPAN classification would provide the best basis for the new prediction system (Wright, Furse *et al.* 1995; Chapter 2). Nevertheless, one important modification was implemented. Whereas RIVPACS II was based on qualitative species data, in RIVPACS III, qualitative species data plus family data (with $\log_{10}$ categories of abundance) were used to characterise each site (Wright, Furse *et al.* 1995; Wright, Moss *et al.* 1997). This new procedure, which used more information on the fauna, succeeded in creating more coherent site groupings of chalk stream sites, where problems had been encountered in RIVPACS II.

RIVPACS III+

The structure and major features of RIVPACS III are examined in the next section. However, one further development of the software, described by Clarke in Chapter 3, is listed in Table 1.1. RIVPACS III+ represents a major step forward through the incorporation of error terms for the O/E ratios used to assess site quality, and provides a mechanism for detecting statistically significant spatial and temporal differences between the macroinvertebrate assemblages of

Figure 1.1. Classification of the 614 reference sites for Great Britain into 35 groups in RIVPACS III. The number of sites in each group is shown above each group number (the latter are given in **bold type**.) Four major blocks of sites are also indicated.

sites. In this way, it mirrors the objective procedures developed by the NRA for reporting chemical quality (National Rivers Authority 1994).

A review of RIVPACS III

Classification of sites

As previously indicated, two parallel classification and prediction systems were developed within RIVPACS III, based on 614 sites in Great Britain and a further 70 sites in Northern Ireland. In this review, attention will focus on the Great Britain component of the system. The 614 reference sites were divided into 35 classification groups, based on faunal composition (Fig. 1.1). Group size varied from six to 39 sites with a mean value of 17.5 sites per group, as in RIVPACS II. The steps leading to this end-result are presented elsewhere (Wright, Furse *et al.* 1995). Whereas RIVPACS II displayed a progression from upland to lowland groups, the RIVPACS III classification was more complex. Nevertheless, the 35 groups could be partitioned into four major blocks to provide a framework for interpreting the classification.

The 145 sites in Groups 1 to 9 were headwater and small stream sites which occurred throughout most of Great Britain, although central and south-eastern England were poorly represented. Groups 10 to 17, with 154 sites, were predominantly medium to large upland sites found mainly in Scotland and northern England. Groups 18 to 24 included 136 medium to large river sites in northern England, Wales and south-west England. Finally, Groups 25 to 35, with 179 sites, were lowland streams and rivers in the south and east. One feature of this large lowland block was the inclusion of three small stream groups (29, 31, 32) that occurred in the area where sites in Groups 1 to 9 were sparse. Thus, the additional small stream sites affected the overall structure of the earlier classifications. Nevertheless, the strong environmental contrasts between the north and west compared to the south and east were still apparent in the sequence of macroinvertebrate assemblages in Groups 10 to 17, 18 to 24 and 25 to 35 (Fig. 1.2).

The mean standardised taxon richness for the 35 classification groups varied from 47 taxa in Group 5 to 109 taxa in Group 18 (Fig. 1.3). In general, richness was lower in the small stream groups (47–75 taxa per group) and in the upland groups (50–83 taxa) compared to the intermediate (72–108 taxa) and lowland groups (70–98 taxa). It was apparent that a wide variety of rivers in south Wales, and southern and eastern England, were capable of supporting taxon-rich assemblages. Species composition changed progressively across the classification but the frequency of occurrence of some non-insect groups was lower in the small stream (Groups 1–9) and upland (Groups 10–17) sections of the classification (Wright *et al.* 1998a).

At BMWP family level, the mean BMWP score per classification group varied from 255.2 in Group 18 to 123.5 in Group 5. The range for mean number of BMWP taxa varied from 40.1 taxa (Group 25) to 20.7 (Group 5), and ASPT ranged from 6.98 (Group 11) to 4.82 (Group 34).

System for predicting expected fauna at sampling sites

When the 614 sites in RIVPACS III were subjected to an internal MDA test using the standard environmental variables (Option 1 in RIVPACS III, Table 1.2), 51.6% of the sites were predicted to the "correct" group based on the re-substitution procedure. In this test, a correct prediction occurs when the classification group in which a site is placed with the highest probability of group membership, by MDA, is the same as the classification group in which the site was placed in the original TWINSPAN classification. Clearly, this is a severe test because there are 35 possible groups into which the site may be placed using the relevant environmental features in the MDA equations. If the classification is viewed as an artificial division of a

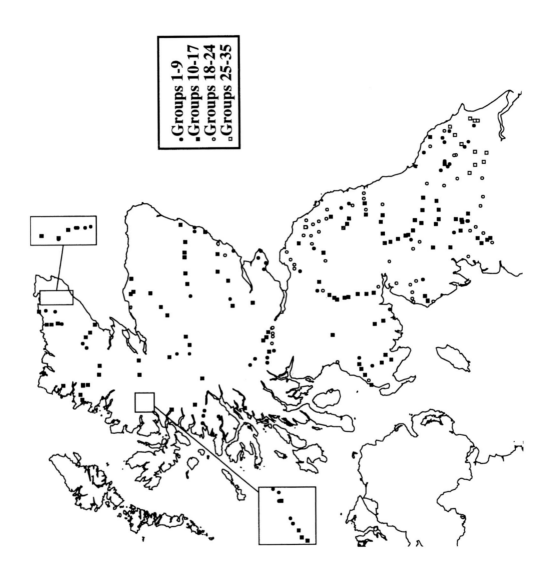

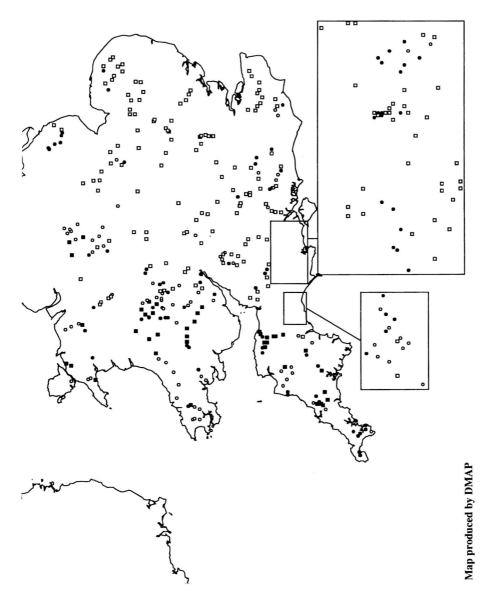

Map produced by DMAP

Figure 1.2. The location of the RIVPACS III classification Groups 1–9, 10–17, 18–24 and 25–35, in Great Britain.

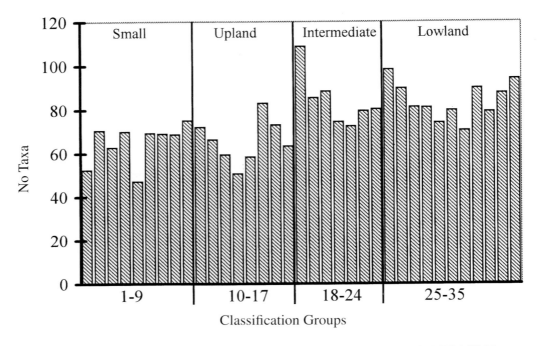

Figure 1.3. Mean standardised taxon richness for the 35 classification groups in RIVPACS III.

continuum of sites, then cases in which the second highest probability of group membership corresponds to the correct group should also be of value in the prediction system. A further 18.1% of sites were in this category.

Following a detailed assessment of O/E ratios and chi-squared tests to confirm that the correct taxa were being predicted (Wright, Furse *et al.* 1995), it was clear that RIVPACS III was setting higher standards for the expected fauna and BMWP index values than RIVPACS II, and performing at least as well as the previous system despite the fact that it now encompassed a wider range of river systems.

Table 1.2. *The five environmental options available for prediction in RIVPACS III.*
Option 1 is recommended for use in Great Britain.

All five options require the following eight variables:

Distance from source (km)	Altitude (m)
Mean substratum (phi units)	Discharge category (9 categories, cumecs)
Mean water width (m)	Mean water depth (cm)
Latitude (°N)	Longitude (°W/°E)

Two to four additional variables are also required, according to the option chosen.

Variable	Option 1	Option 2	Option 3	Option 4	Option 5
Alkalinity (mg CaCO$_3$l^{-1})	+	+	–	+	–
Slope (m km^{-1})	+	–	+	+	–
Mean air temperature (°C)	+	+	+	–	+
Air temperature range (°C)	+	+	+	–	+

The suite of environmental variables for prediction and the taxonomic options available in RIVPACS III are closely similar to those in RIVPACS II (Wright *et al.* 1994) but in each case one or two changes have been made. The 12 environmental variables recommended for use in Great Britain (Option 1) remain unchanged (Table 1.2) but Option 6 from RIVPACS II has been deleted. The latter required the use of chloride as a predictor variable, but because high chloride could be an indicator of environmental stress, it was deemed inappropriate for use in RIVPACS.

The environmental data for a given site can be used to predict any or all of the taxonomic levels and seasonal options previously available in RIVPACS II (Table 1.3). One addition to RIVPACS III is the facility to test a new experimental index (Q14) (Wright, Furse *et al.* 1995), designed to detect early signs of environmental stress prior to major loss of taxon richness, as expressed through low O/E ratios. The index requires $\log_{10}$ abundance data for single seasons and operates on pollution-sensitive BMWP families with scores in the range 4 to 10. The Q14 index measures the observed loss of abundance for each family in relation to expectation, and a threshold value based on the reference dataset is used to indicate environmental stress.

Table 1.3. *The taxonomic, seasonal and prediction options available in RIVPACS III.*

(1) 3 = three seasons combined; 2 = any two seasons combined; 1 = spring, summer or autumn.

Taxonomic level	Seasonal options[1]	Type of prediction
Species	3, 2 or 1	Presence/absence only
All families	3, 2 or 1	Presence/absence only
Customised	3, 2 or 1	Presence/absence only
BMWP	3, 2 or 1	Presence/absence+biological indices
All	1 only	$\log_{10}$ categories of abundance+Q14 index

In RIVPACS III, predictions can be made either interactively or in batch mode if the biological and environmental data are held in computer files. The observed fauna can then be compared with the expected fauna derived from RIVPACS using O/E ratios, and further categorisation of the results into bands can be made when required.

Examples of predictions based on RIVPACS III

This section includes three predictions to demonstrate the flexibility of the system. Each one is for a different location on the Moors River in Dorset, south-west England. Some sections of this river have been scheduled as a Grade 1 Site of Special Scientific Interest (SSSI) (Ratcliffe 1977) because they support rich assemblages of macrophytes and macroinvertebrates. However, other sections have been polluted by industrial and domestic effluents during a period of progressive urbanisation. An extensive survey of the macroinvertebrate fauna of this river in the mid-1980s (Wright, Welton *et al.* 1988) provides the data for these predictions.

1. A species-level prediction for an unstressed site

The Kings Farm site, in the middle reaches of the Moors River, is of high biological quality and forms one of the 614 reference sites in RIVPACS III. This species-level prediction demonstrates the procedure for comparing the observed with the expected fauna. Figure 1.4 lists the environmental data required for Option 1 of RIVPACS III in order to predict the probabilities of classification group membership. A site with these environmental features has the greatest affinity with Group 33, followed by Groups 32, 25 and 30. RIVPACS uses information on the probabilities of group membership, together with the frequency of

MOORS RIVER AT KINGS FARM

Mean width (m)	3.9	Altitude (m)	19
Mean depth (cm)	48.8	Distance from source (km)	17.0
Substratum (%)		Slope (m km⁻¹)	1.4
Boulders + cobbles	0	Discharge category	3
Pebbles + gravel	9	Mean air temperature (°C)	10.57
Sand	16	Annual air temp. range (°C)	12.39
Silt and clay	74	Latitude (°N)	50.51
Mean substratum (phi)	6.01	Longitude (°W)	1.51
Alkalinity (mg l⁻¹ CaCO₃)	161.7		

Classification groups predicted using the above data:-

Gp 33 = 72.1% ; Gp 32 = 17.8% ; Gp 25 = 4.3% ; Gp 30 = 3.8%.

Predicted taxa, in decreasing order of probability of capture:-

*	97.5%	Glossiphonia complanata (L.)		75.3%	Procladius sp.
	97.4%	Micropsectra group	*	74.6%	Lumbriculus group
*	97.1%	Erpobdella octoculata (L.)	*	72.0%	Polycelis nigra group
*	95.8%	Gammarus pulex (L.)	*	72.0%	Microtendipes sp.
*	94.9%	Elmis aenea (Muller)		70.6%	Gyraulus albus (Muller)
*	94.5%	Hydracarina		70.2%	Centroptilum luteolum (Muller)
*	94.3%	Cricotopus group	*	69.5%	Limnephilus lunatus Curtis
*	92.6%	Pisidium nitidum Jenyns	*	68.9%	Caenis luctuosa group
*	90.4%	Pisidium subtruncatum Malm		66.1%	Anisus vortex (L.)
*	89.8%	Psammoryctides barbatus (Grube)	*	65.2%	Ephemerella ignita (Poda)
*	88.6%	Asellus aquaticus (L.)	*	64.5%	Oulimnius tuberculatus (Muller)
*	87.4%	Potamopyrgus jenkinsi (Smith)	*	64.4%	Hydroptila sp.
	87.2%	Sphaerium corneum (L.)		63.3%	Bithynia tentaculata (L.)
*	86.1%	Aulodrilus pluriseta (Piguet)	*	62.4%	Eukiefferiella group
	86.0%	Paratanytarsus group		61.7%	Valvata piscinalis (Muller)
*	85.4%	Thienemannimyia group	*	59.9%	Ancylus fluviatilis Muller
*	85.0%	Limnodrilus hoffmeisteri Claparede	*	59.8%	Crangonyx pseudogracilis Bousfield
*	83.1%	Helobdella stagnalis (L.)	*	57.8%	Piscicola geometra (L.)
	81.4%	Sialis lutaria (L.)		56.1%	Potamothrix hammoniensis (Michaelsen)
*	81.1%	Ceratopogonidae	*	54.7%	Polycentropus flavomaculatus (Pictet)
	78.5%	Polypedilum sp.	*	52.0%	Halesus sp.
*	78.1%	Baetis vernus Curtis		51.9%	Sigara falleni (Fieber)
*	78.1%	Lymnaea peregra (Muller)	*	51.4%	Rhyacodrilus coccineus (Vejdovsky)
*	77.7%	Physa fontinalis (L.)	*	50.7%	Baetis rhodani (Pictet)
	77.6%	Sigara (Sigara) sp.	*	50.5%	Prodiamesa olivacea (Meigen
*	75.5%	Stylaria lacustris (L.)			
*	75.3%	Potamonectes depressus (Fabricius)			

At 50% probability level: $\dfrac{\text{observed no.taxa}}{\text{expected no.taxa}} = \dfrac{39.0}{39.0} = 1.00.$

Figure 1.4. Species-level prediction for a site of high biological quality (Kings Farm, Moors River, Dorset, south-west England). Observed taxa are shown with an asterisk. See the text for further details.

occurrence of taxa in the relevant classification groups, to generate the taxa expected in the absence of environmental stress (Chapter 2). In practice, the list of expected taxa is presented in decreasing probability of capture and, if requested, can include all of the 637 taxa in the reference dataset for Great Britain. However, for species predictions, the list is frequently terminated at the 50% probability level (Fig. 1.4), to avoid printouts with large numbers of low probability taxa.

The taxa captured at Kings Farm by the standard sampling protocol (i.e. the observed fauna) are held in a separate biological file, but the RIVPACS printout identifies each observed taxon within the expected taxon listing using an asterisk. At sites of high quality, most taxa predicted with a high probability of capture should be observed at the site, but at the 50% probability level, only around one in two of the expected taxa should be observed after employing the standard protocol. To compare the observed fauna with the expected probabilities over the 100 to 50% probability range, the asterisks are summed to give the number of observed taxa (39), and all probabilities between 100 and 50% are summed to give the expected number of taxa (39.0) (see Fig. 1.4). At the 50% probability level, the O/E ratio for this site is unity, indicating that the site is of high biological quality.

2. BMWP family predictions at stressed sites

Chemical pollution and other forms of environmental stress affect individual species of macroinvertebrates. However, in Britain, the need for rapid appraisal of sites by non-specialists led the BMWP to develop a monitoring system based on selected families of macroinvertebrates (National Water Council 1981). As previously explained, expected values for the three BMWP indices can now be computed within RIVPACS for a given site with stated environmental features. When stress leads to the loss of some sensitive (higher scoring) families, then lowering of the O/E ratios for BMWP score, number of scoring taxa and ASPT will result.

A sampling site at Hurn, in the lower reaches of the Moors River, was subject to both organic and pesticide pollution in the mid-1980s. The environmental data for the site, the probabilities of group membership and the expected probabilities of family occurrences over the range 100 to 50% are presented in Fig. 1.5. Although most of the families expected with a very high level of probability (100 to 95%) are present, there is under-representation of all other families listed to 50% probability. In particular, several families of Trichoptera, Plecoptera and Ephemeroptera are missing. These detailed results are valuable to the local biologist when searching for evidence of the cause of the problem. However, it is also important to devise simple procedures for converting lists of taxa into a form which may be communicated to non-biologists and the public. This is achieved using BMWP indices.

In calculating BMWP family-level indices, the standard practice is to sum all the expected probabilities from 100% to 0.1%, and not simply for the 100 to 50% probability range illustrated in Fig. 1.5. For this reason, it is also critical to record the total number of families collected by the standard sampling protocol. At Hurn, four of these families had expected probabilities of occurrence below 50%. Figure 1.5 includes the O/E ratios for the three BMWP indices derived by RIVPACS from the observed and expected BMWP families. Whereas 24 BMWP taxa were observed, the expected number was 35.2, resulting in an O/E ratio well below unity (0.68). The O/E ratio for BMWP score was even lower (0.52), implying the loss of high scoring taxa, and this was confirmed by the O/E for ASPT which was also low (0.76). Although these results indicate an environmental problem, formal procedures are required to integrate the results from the O/E ratios and generate a quality band. These procedures are critical for reporting national surveys, targeting sites for remedial action, and for documenting changes over time. Some important considerations in the development of a scientifically credible banding system are presented by Clarke in Chapter 3, and a practical system devised for reporting the 1995 General Quality Assessment Survey is described by Hemsley-Flint in Chapter 4.

3. Abundance-based index (Q14)

So far, the emphasis has been on recognising the loss of individual species or BMWP families as a means of detecting stress. In practice, changes in the abundance of taxa also occur in response to stress, most notably when organic enrichment creates favourable conditions for a

MOORS RIVER AT HURN

Mean width (m)	11.3	Altitude (m)	10
Mean depth (cm)	30.3	Distance from source (km)	30.0
Substratum (%)		Slope (m km⁻¹)	0.9
Boulders + cobbles	4	Discharge category	4
Pebbles + gravel	66	Mean air temperature (°C)	10.61
Sand	22	Annual air temp. range (°C)	12.32
Silt and clay	8	Latitude (°N)	50.46
Mean substratum (phi)	-1.38	Longitude (°W)	1.49
Alkalinity (mg l⁻¹ CaCO₃)	92.7		

Classification groups predicted with the above data:-

Gp 19 = 57.7% ; Gp 30 = 9.4% ; Gp 28 = 7.1% ; Gp 25 = 6.3% ; Gp 32 = 4.7%
Gp 26 = 4.4% ; Gp 27 = 4.2%.

Predicted taxa, in decreasing order of probability of capture:-

*	100.0%	Chironomidae			78.3%	Hydroptilidae
*	100.0%	Oligochaeta			76.6%	Haliplidae
*	100.0%	Elmidae			74.5%	Leuctridae
*	100.0%	Baetidae		*	74.3%	Lymnaeidae
*	99.8%	Sphaeriidae			73.2%	Polycentropodidae
*	99.7%	Hydropsychidae			72.2%	Sialidae
*	99.7%	Simuliidae			71.5%	Leptophlebiidae
*	99.2%	Gammaridae		*	70.4%	Asellidae
*	97.4%	Hydrobiidae			70.0%	Sericostomatidae
*	97.2%	Tipulidae			65.9%	Gyrinidae
	96.8%	Ephemerellidae			61.6%	Goeridae
*	94.1%	Erpobdellidae		*	57.3%	Planariidae
	93.7%	Limnephilidae		*	57.3%	Planorbidae
*	90.4%	Leptoceridae			51.1%	Psychomyiidae
	89.7%	Caenidae		*	50.7%	Piscicolidae
*	87.3%	Glossiphoniidae		*	50.5%	Hydrophilidae
	86.5%	Dytiscidae				
	82.3%	Rhyacophilidae	[*	48.2%	Valvatidae	
*	81.3%	Ancylidae		*	33.1%	Physidae
	80.4%	Heptageniidae		*	28.0%	Calopterygidae
	79.8%	Ephemeridae		*	18.9%	Taeniopterygidae]

Summary of BMWP Indices:-

	No.Taxa	BMWP Score	ASPT
Observed (O)	24	108	4.50
Expected (E)	35.2	208.9	5.93
O/E	0.68	0.52	0.76

Figure 1.5. BMWP family-level prediction for a stressed site (Hurn, Moors River, Dorset, south-west England), including the use of BMWP indices. See the text for further details.

restricted number of low-scoring BMWP families. In this case, many of the sensitive taxa have already disappeared and therefore O/E ratios based on presence/absence data are capable of exposing the problem without the need for quantitative data. There is a greater need for a procedure that can detect early effects of stress before loss of taxa leads to low O/E values derived from presence/absence data. RIVPACS III includes an experimental abundance-based index (Q14) that operates on single season family data with attached $\log_{10}$ categories of abundance. This index uses the proportional deficit of observed abundances below those expected for taxa with a BMWP score of 4 to 10, and ignores high abundance of BMWP taxa with a score of 1 to 3. In early tests it proved to be highly discriminatory amongst sites at the higher end of the quality spectrum but tended not to differentiate between sites with only low-scoring taxa. Ideally, it should be used at sites that are in a good quality band based on presence/absence data but where there are concerns over the early onset of environmental stress. The Q14 value below which stress may be indicated is based on the lower 5-percentile value of the index, using single season data for the 614 reference sites in RIVPACS III.

The Q14 index is demonstrated for a site below Palmersford Sewage Treatment Works, which is located between Kings Farm and Hurn. A preliminary combined season BMWP family-level prediction using presence/absence data indicated that the site just qualified as Biological Class A, based on criteria developed by the IFE and used in the 1990 River Quality Survey (Sweeting, Lowson *et al.* 1992). Figure 1.6 lists the observed and expected $\log_{10}$ abundance categories for the appropriate BMWP families in spring and includes the Q14 index, as determined by RIVPACS. The Q14 value of 32.43 is well below the critical limit of 42 and suggests that the site is stressed despite the previous Class A rating based on presence/absence data. However, more testing is required to fully determine the utility of this index.

The macroinvertebrate reference dataset

The biological data for the 614 reference sites included in RIVPACS III forms a unique historical record of the fauna at a wide range of running-water sites across Great Britain, because of the quality of the sites, the use of standard protocols in the field and laboratory, and the reliability of identifications. All the samples have been retained for future reference.

Taxon richness in the reference dataset

After combining the data for three seasons and applying the standard edits program, the standardised taxon richness varied between 31 and 134 taxa across the 614 reference sites. However, at over 80% of the sites, the number of standardised taxa per site fell within the range 50 to 99 (Wright *et al.* 1998a). Whereas extremely taxon-poor sites were confined to physically harsh environments in upland areas of Scotland and northern England, the most taxon-rich sites encompassed a wide range of river types in south Wales, southern England and East Anglia.

Wright *et al.* (1998b) present frequency distributions of the number of taxa per site at standardised "species", family and BMWP family levels. They also demonstrate that there were very highly significant correlations between the number of species and families ($r = 0.890$) and between the number of species and BMWP families ($r = 0.854$), as might be expected. During national and local surveys, a substantial number of sites in Great Britain are sampled at family or BMWP family level using the RIVPACS protocol. In view of these correlations, the data may contain valuable information for the early detection of species-rich sites of interest to the statutory nature conservation organisations within Great Britain.

The standardised taxon list for the 614 reference sites in Great Britain includes 637 "species", of which 142 are non-insects and 495 are insects (Table 1.4 and the Appendix). A

MOORS RIVER D/S PALMERSFORD STW

Mean width (m)	5.8	Altitude (m)	12
Mean depth (cm)	101.1	Distance from source (km)	25.0
Substratum (%)		Slope (m km^{-1})	1.0
Boulders + cobbles	0	Discharge category	4
Pebbles + gravel	2	Mean air temperature (°C)	10.61
Sand	27	Annual air temp. range (°C)	12.30
Silt and clay	72	Latitude (°N)	50.48
Mean substratum (phi)	6.17	Longitude (°W)	1.50
Alkalinity (mg l^{-1} CaCO$_3$)	98.5		

Classification groups predicted using the above data:-

Gp 33 = 82 % ; Gp 32 = 11 % ; Gp 25 = 2.4 % ; Gp 35 = 1.6 % ; Gp 30 = 1.5 %.

Comparison of expected (EXP) and observed (OBS) BMWP family log categories of abundance:-

EXP	OBS		EXP	OBS	
1.95	2	Gammaridae	.42	1	Coenagriidae
1.69	1	Baetidae	.42	0	Tipulidae
1.60	0	Elmidae	.37	0	Ephemeridae
1.54	0	Caenidae	.30	0	Psychomyiidae
1.45	0	Limnephilidae	.29	0	Calopterygidae
1.06	1	Leptoceridae	.29	0	Dendrocoelidae
1.01	2	Dytiscidae	.24	0	Sericostomatidae
.98	0	Simuliidae	.23	0	Goeridae
.96	2	Planariidae	.20	0	Rhyacophilidae
.83	0	Haliplidae	.20	0	Molannidae
.79	0	Corixidae	.19	2	Gyrinidae
.64	0	Polycentropodidae	.17	1	Piscicolidae
.60	1	Hydropsychidae	.16	0	Heptageniidae
.60	0	Hydroptilidae	.15	0	Neritidae
.60	0	Ancylidae	.15	0	Nemouridae
.55	0	Leptophlebiidae	.14	0	Hydrophilidae
.49	0	Ephemerellidae	.14	0	Lepidostomatidae
.46	0	Sialidae	.14	0	Notonectidae

Q14 = 32.43 (values below 42 may indicate stress).

Figure 1.6. BMWP family-level prediction using $\log_{10}$ category abundance data and the Q14 index for a site below Palmersford Sewage Treatment Works, Moors River Dorset, south-west England. See the text for further details.

full listing of the taxa, together with their frequency of occurrence in the 614 site dataset, is given by Wright, Blackburn *et al.* (1996). Apart from its value to river biologists as a source of information on the taxa most likely to be encountered in lotic waters, the list also flags threatened species with Red Data Book status (Shirt 1987; Bratton 1991) and rare species accorded "Nationally Scarce" status within Great Britain. Nationally Scarce taxa should be known from 100 or fewer 10x10 km squares of the National Grid (Bratton 1991). The RIVPACS III dataset includes 14 Red Data Book species (1 Gastropoda, 1 Bivalvia, 3 Ephemeroptera, 4 Coleoptera, 4 Trichoptera and 1 Diptera) and a further 47 which currently have the status of Nationally Scarce species (1 Gastropoda, 4 Bivalvia, 1 Ephemeroptera, 1 Plecoptera, 2 Odonata, 28 Coleoptera, 1 Megaloptera, 7 Trichoptera and 2 Diptera). (Note: In Wright, Blackburn *et al.* (1996), 15 RDB species were listed including two Gastropoda. A

Table 1.4. *Contribution of each major taxonomic group of freshwater invertebrates to the 637 standardised taxa recorded at the 614 RIVPACS III sites in Great Britain. Further details are given in the Appendix on page 24.*

(1) Taxonomic groups that are not identified to species.

(2) The level of identification varies from family to family.

Non-insects	No. of taxa	Insects	No. of taxa
Spongillidae[1]	1	Ephemeroptera	37
Hydridae[1]	1	Plecoptera	27
Tricladida	9	Odonata	13
Chordodidae[1]	1	Hemiptera	28
Ectoprocta[1]	1	Coleoptera	104
Gastropoda	29	Megaloptera	3
Bivalvia	22	Neuroptera	2
Aeolosomatidae[1]	1	Trichoptera	98
Oligochaeta	51	Lepidoptera[1]	1
Hirudinea	14	Diptera[2]	182
Hydracarina[1]	1		
Crustacea	11		
Totals:	142		495

careful re-examination of the single specimen of *Segmentina nitida* Müller (RDB1), which is now in poor condition, has failed to provide conclusive corroboration of the earlier identification and this must therefore be rejected). Over the past 20 years, the large scale of the sampling programme and the careful attention to species identifications has resulted in two Oligochaeta, three Ephemeroptera and one member of the Diptera being added to the British list.

There are further opportunities to utilise this dataset by examining the biological information in relation to environmental attributes. These could include the variables used in prediction, chemical determinands collected by the Environment Agency and the Scottish Environment Protection Agency, and further geological, geomorphological and other variables which may be accessed through a Geographic Information System.

Some future challenges

Refinement of RIVPACS is an on-going process, and each of five workshops held at Oxford (see Chapters 20 to 24) has focused on a topic which contributes to this process. In this concluding section, the emphasis is on items where progress is anticipated in the near future.

Early warning indices

Q14 is just one of fourteen indices devised by Ralph Clarke (see Wright, Furse *et al.* 1995) to provide early warning of major change in family abundance prior to substantial loss of families. Caution is required in the development and use of such indices because the RIVPACS sampling protocol is effort-dependent and takes account of all habitats, rather than involving quantitative sampling on one defined habitat. Nevertheless, some procedures which compare the observed and expected $\log_{10}$ abundance categories of families in a single season show promise, and further testing of abundance indices will attempt to identify those best able to detect the early stages of environmental stress.

New environmental features for prediction

The strong link between the environmental features of the reference sites and their biological assemblages has always been critical to the success of RIVPACS. Early in the project, care was taken to choose a limited set of environmental variables for prediction which were easy to acquire and had high predictive capability. Recently, the emphasis has been on the acquisition of a comprehensive set of reference sites that pass severe criteria for acceptance. It is now time to consider whether catchment characteristics, such as geological, soil, geomorphological and hydrological factors, can increase the reliability of the prediction system. It should be possible to obtain some attributes through a Geographic Information System. If the value of additional variables or alternatives to existing field-collected variables can be demonstrated, then a future version of RIVPACS may have broader application.

A link between RIVPACS and the River Habitat Survey

At present, RIVPACS is more successful at predicting species composition than the particular species richness to be expected at an individual site, when using the standard sampling protocol. In other words, the system generates the list of taxa with attached probabilities of occurrence, but local factors will influence the species richness observed at the site under study. At high quality sites the observed to expected ratio can be either above or below unity, and only when the ratio falls to a stated value below unity is the site regarded as stressed. In the RIVPACS classification, sites with similar species composition are grouped together, but within a given classification group the taxon richness varies from site to site. This is the result of genuine differences in the environmental conditions at the sites, the impact of natural stresses such as recent floods and droughts prior to sampling, and the fact that the sites will vary somewhat in their biological quality. The prediction methodology, in drawing on information from many sites across several classification groups, minimises the problems which would otherwise be encountered if the expected fauna was derived from a small number of local reference sites.

The addition of new predictive variables that describe local habitat features seems unlikely to offer a major breakthrough in the prediction of taxon richness in RIVPACS, which currently offers a general system for predicting the typical fauna to be expected across a very wide range of running-water sites under stated environmental conditions. An alternative approach might involve a detailed appraisal of the physical habitat of the 614 reference sites, to investigate variation in O/E ratios above and below unity. One possible route would be to link RIVPACS and the River Habitat Survey (RHS) approach (Raven, Fox *et al.* 1997) developed by the Environment Agency. In this method, the physical features of a series of semi-natural reference sites have been used to develop a classification (= typology) of rivers. This is the basis for predicting the semi-natural character of a river segment from map-derived data. Comparison of the observed physical character of the segment with the predicted semi-natural character provides an assessment of habitat quality. A comparison between habitat quality derived through the RHS and biological quality derived from RIVPACS could be instructive and offer a starting point for detailed investigations on site features that promote species richness.

Patterns in faunal composition

As previously indicated, the 614 reference sites represent a unique dataset and it is important to extract the maximum information, given the enormous effort required to assemble it. RIVPACS depends on the correlation of site attributes with faunal composition, for the purpose of prediction. The end-product is a system with considerable practical application, but it cannot explain the processes responsible for the observed patterns of faunal change along and between river types. In truth, this is a major challenge also requiring the use of experimental techniques. Nevertheless, the reference dataset provides an opportunity to investigate patterns in faunal composition among and within river types, in order to gain a wider perspective on the structure and functioning of minimally impacted sites.

Interpreting the cause of stress

Finally, although RIVPACS has well-developed methodologies for detecting stressed sites, interpretation of the cause of stress is still largely in the hands of the biologist with local knowledge and time to examine the differences between the list of observed and expected taxa. Clearly, there is potential for the development of new techniques for interpretation of results. These might include the development of new indices sensitive to specific forms of stress, an expert system for interpreting the differences between the observed and expected fauna, or the parallel use of ecotoxicological techniques to aid interpretation.

Acknowledgements

A number of organisations have provided financial support for the development of RIVPACS over the past 20 years. They include the Natural Environment Research Council, the Department of the Environment, the Scottish Office, the Welsh Office, the Department of the Environment (Northern Ireland), the National Rivers Authority and the Environment Agency. The RIVPACS team is grateful to each one of these organisations. The project also benefited from site data collected under contract to the former Nature Conservancy Council. Finally, it is a pleasure to acknowledge that RIVPACS is the end-product of a team effort by scientists at the River Laboratory of the Freshwater Biological Association and more recently the Institute of Freshwater Ecology, scientists from the Institute of Terrestrial Ecology, and biologists from the Environment Agency, the Scottish Environment Protection Agency and the Industrial Research & Technology Unit in Northern Ireland. I also thank an external reviewer and colleagues for helpful comments on the manuscript.

Appendix:– List of 22 major taxonomic groups of macroinvertebrates containing 117 families (and numbers of "standardised taxa"; total = 637) from the 614 reference sites for running-waters in Great Britain used in RIVPACS III (see Table 1.4 in this chapter; Wright, Blackburn *et al.* 1996; Wright *et al.* 1998a, 1999b).

Porifera
  Spongillidae (1)
Coelenterata
  Hydridae (1)
Tricladida
  Planariidae (5)
  Dugesiidae (2)
  Dendrocoelidae (2)
Nematomorpha
  Chordodidae (1)
Ectoprocta
  Ectoprocta (1)
Gastropoda
  Neritidae (1)
  Viviparidae (1)
  Valvatidae (3)
  Hydrobiidae (1)
  Bithyniidae (2)
  Lymnaeidae (5)
  Physidae (3)
  Planorbidae (11)
  Acroloxidae (1)
  Ancylidae (1)
Bivalvia
  Margaritiferidae (1)
  Unionidae (2)
  Sphaeriidae (18)
  Dreissenidae (1)
Aphanoneura
  Aeolosomatidae (1)
Oligochaeta
  Naididae (20)
  Tubificidae (22)
  Enchytraeidae (2)
  Haplotaxidae (1)
  Lumbriculidae (5)
  Lumbricidae (1)
Hirudinea
  Piscicolidae (1)
  Glossiphoniidae (7)
  Hirudinidae (1)
  Erpobdellidae (5)
Hydracarina
  Hydracarina (1)
Crustacea
  Argulidae (1)
  Asellidae (2)
  Corophiidae (1)

Crangonyctidae (1)
Gammaridae (4)
Niphargidae (1)
Astacidae (1)
Ephemeroptera
  Siphlonuridae (2)
  Baetidae (13)
  Heptageniidae (5)
  Leptophlebiidae (6)
  Ephemerellidae (2)
  Potamanthidae (1)
  Ephemeridae (3)
  Caenidae (5)
Plecoptera
  Taeniopterygidae (3)
  Nemouridae (9)
  Leuctridae (6)
  Capniidae (2)
  Perlodidae (3)
  Perlidae (2)
  Chloroperlidae (2)
Odonata
  Platycnemididae (1)
  Coenagrionidae (5)
  Calopterygidae (2)
  Gomphidae (1)
  Cordulegastridae (1)
  Aeshnidae (2)
  Libellulidae (1)
Hempitera
  Mesoveliidae (1)
  Hydrometridae (1)
  Veliidae (1)
  Gerridae (1)
  Nepidae (1)
  Naucoridae (1)
  Aphelocheiridae (1)
  Notonectidae (3)
  Corixidae (18)
Coleoptera
  Haliplidae (11)
  Noteridae (1)
  Dytiscidae (36)
  Gyrinidae (6)
  Hydraenidae (11)
  Hydrophilidae (22)
  Scirtidae (4)
  Dryopidae (2)

Elmidae (11)
Megaloptera
  Sialidae (3)
Neuroptera
  Osmylidae (1)
  Sisyridae (1)
Trichoptera
  Rhyacophilidae (4)
  Glossosomatidae (2)
  Philopotamidae (3)
  Polycentropodidae (9)
  Ecnomidae (1)
  Psychomyiidae (6)
  Hydropsychidae (9)
  Hydroptilidae (6)
  Phryganeidae (2)
  Limnephilidae (19)
  Molannidae (1)
  Beraeidae (3)
  Odontoceridae (1)
  Leptoceridae (23)
  Goeridae (3)
  Lepidostomatidae (3)
  Brachycentridae (1)
  Sericostomatidae (2)
Lepidoptera
  Pyralidae (1)
Diptera
  Tipulidae (31)
  Psychodidae (19)
  Ptychopteridae (1)
  Dixidae (5)
  Chaoboridae (1)
  Culicidae (1)
  Thaumaleidae (1)
  Ceratopogonidae (1)
  Chironomidae (86)
  Simuliidae (19)
  Stratiomyidae (3)
  Empididae (4)
  Dolichopodidae (1)
  Rhagionidae (3)
  Tabanidae (2)
  Syrphidae (1)
  Ephydridae (1)
  Sciomyzidae (1)
  Muscidae (1)

CHAPTER 2

Evolution of statistical methods in RIVPACS

DORIAN MOSS

Institute of Terrestrial Ecology, Monks Wood, Abbots Ripton, Huntingdon, PE17 2LS, UK

Summary

Statistical methods were required in RIVPACS for classifying running-water sites according to their observed fauna and for predicting the macroinvertebrate fauna at a number of different taxonomic levels. Variations of a basic method were tested and refined during the development of RIVPACS, in parallel with the expansion of the reference biological and environmental datasets.

For RIVPACS I and II, TWINSPAN was used for classification of the reference sites. This was followed by a prediction procedure based on the use of multiple discriminant analysis (MDA), and a novel method for predicting the probability of occurrence of individual taxa. Successive methods for determining the classification group or groups to which new sites should be allocated, based on their fauna, are also described.

Prior to the development of RIVPACS III some alternative methods for site classification, and a novel approach to prediction using logistic regression, were examined. These methods were tested internally on the RIVPACS II dataset and on an independent dataset. Although some of these methods showed promise, the method eventually chosen for RIVPACS III was a variation on the original TWINSPAN/MDA methodology.

Introduction

The purpose of this chapter is to provide technical information on the evolution of the RIVPACS methodology over a period of almost 20 years. It includes some alternative approaches to the classification of reference sites which were evaluated at different stages of the project, and the techniques for using site classifications based on biological data, together with environmental datasets, in order to predict the macroinvertebrate fauna. RIVPACS has undergone progressive development, and each version has been a significant improvement on its predecessor. In tracing the evolution of methods, this paper focuses on the methodological investigations that preceded RIVPACS III, but begins with a summary of the methods used in earlier versions of the system (Table 2.1).

Methods used in the preliminary version

The initial objectives of the project were twofold: to classify unpolluted running-water sites based on their macroinvertebrate fauna, and to assess whether the type of macroinvertebrate community at a site might be predicted using physical and chemical features (Wright *et al.* 1981). The original 268 reference sites on 41 rivers were chosen to include a wide range of physical and chemical conditions. They were believed to be free from the effects of serious pollution, and were judged to be of high biological quality by water industry biologists.

Table 2.1. *Year of completion and numbers of sites and classification groups for each version of RIVPACS.*

GB = Great Britain; NI = Northern Ireland.

Version	Year	No. of sites	No. of groups
Preliminary	1981	268	16
RIVPACS I	1984	370	30
RIVPACS II	1988	438	25
RIVPACS III (GB)	1995	614	35
RIVPACS III (NI)	1995	70	7

Initially, 94 rivers were categorised by length, altitude at source, geology of the catchment, discharge, temperature, pH and conductivity, and 41 were then selected to represent the full range of these conditions. Wright (Chapter 1) has described how the spring, summer and autumn biological samples at each site were collected and identified. The dataset therefore included the opportunity to combine data for one, two or three seasons. It also allowed a number of different taxonomic levels of precision to be considered, ranging from the use of all the identifiable species (combined with some higher taxa in cases where specific identification was not possible), to the use of BMWP family-level data.

At the outset of the project, a new procedure (TWINSPAN) had just been developed by Hill (1979a). This method, originally devised for the classification of vegetation communities, was based on qualitative or quantitative plant lists collected from quadrats ("rélévées"). TWINSPAN, or two-way indicator species analysis, analyses data on the occurrence or abundance of species in samples. The samples (and also the species) are classified by making successive divisions on the basis of ordinations of the samples/species matrix, using the method of correspondence analysis. Depending on the number of divisions requested, the result is 2, 4, 8, 16, etc. classification groups, unless a minimum group size for further division has been set and reached. TWINSPAN also identifies "differential species" for each division, which are highly characteristic of one and not the other side of that division, and it uses those differential species to construct a key to the classification. The key can be used to allocate further samples to one of the classification groups.

To fulfil the first objective of the project, a site classification using TWINSPAN was taken to level 4 in order to extract 16 classification groups from the 268 sampling sites, based on species lists from all three seasons combined. At this time, the differential species key was proposed as a method for the classification of new sites, the objective being to classify their communities in the framework of the 16 TWINSPAN groups. This was thought to have potential value for evaluating high quality sites for conservation.

The second objective involved investigation of whether it was possible to predict the biological community from physical and chemical variables. Initially, the aim was to use the values of the environmental variables from the reference sites in an attempt to predict the classification group to which each site had been allocated in the TWINSPAN classification. The technique used was multiple discriminant analysis (MDA) (Fig. 2.1).

Twenty-eight environmental variables were selected for this exercise and MDA was then used for prediction to classification group. The species-level classification based on three seasons combined data resulted in 76.1% of the reference sites being classified to the "correct" group using this technique. Additional TWINSPAN classifications based on single season data at species level or lower levels of identification using combined seasons data (Furse, Moss *et*

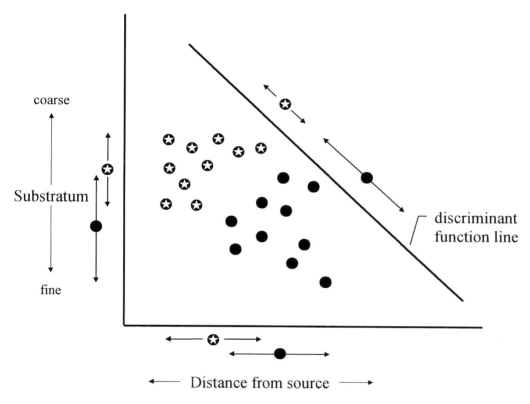

Figure 2.1. An illustration of the method of multiple discriminant analysis (MDA). Two groups of samples (✪ and ●) are plotted schematically by their values of two environmental variables: substratum and distance from source. The two groups cannot be separated by either environmental variable alone. However, when they are projected onto the discriminant function line, they form discrete groups and so can be distinguished by their position along this line. The same principle is applied in multi-dimensional space to separate n groups using k variables.

Table 2.2. *A comparison, by season and taxonomic level, of the percentage of the 268 sites in the preliminary version of RIVPACS that were predicted to their correct biological classification group by multiple discriminant analysis. Results are based on 16 classification groups and 28 environmental variables.*

Taxonomic level	3 seasons combined	Spring	Summer	Autumn
Species qualitative	76.1	61.9	63.4	69.0
All families quantitative	53.7	–	–	–
All families qualitative	58.2	–	–	–
BMWP families qualitative	60.1	–	–	–

al. 1984) invariably resulted in a lower percentage of reference sites predicted to the correct group (Table 2.2).

Further developments in RIVPACS I and II

In the next phase of the project, samples from 102 additional sites in Scotland, Wales and on lowland rivers in England, were added to make the database more comprehensive. Species-level, combined seasons data from 370 sites on 61 rivers were subjected to TWINSPAN analysis, resulting in a classification to 30 groups. MDA based on 31 environmental variables resulted in 74.3% of the reference sites being predicted to the correct group (Wright, Moss *et al.* 1984).

A novel prediction method (Moss, Furse *et al.* 1987) was then developed to predict the probability of capturing individual taxa at a new site, based on the following procedure (also see Fig. 2.2 for a graphical worked example).

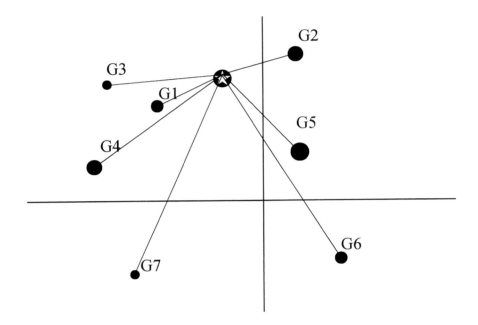

Data for example:

Group	Distance from test site	Group size	Probability that test site belongs to group	Frequency of occurrence of x in group	Contribution to probability that x is found at test site
1	2.3	4	0.27	0.75	0.2025
2	2.5	5	0.30	0.60	0.1800
3	3.8	3	0.10	0.00	0.0000
4	5.3	5	0.08	0.20	0.0160
5	3.7	6	0.21	0.83	0.1743
6	7.4	4	0.02	0.25	0.0050
7	7.4	3	0.02	0.33	0.0066
				Total probability	0.5844

Figure 2.2. Prediction of the probability of occurrence of a given taxon X at a test site (refer to the text for explanation). ✪ indicates the location of the test site in two-dimensional discriminant space. ● G7 indicates the location of the centroid of group 7 in two-dimensional discriminant space.

(1). Using discriminant functions from MDA, discriminant scores in k dimensions were calculated for the test site.

(2). Distances in discriminant space from the test site to each TWINSPAN group centroid were calculated.

(3). The minimum distance (d_{min}), to the closest centroid, was checked to ensure that it would allow a valid prediction (the criterion was $d_{min} < chi^2_k$).

(4). It was assumed that the probability of membership of a group decreases exponentially with the distance from the group mean, and should also be weighted by group size.

(5). The probability of occurrence of a given taxon at the test site was calculated as the sum, taken over all groups, of the product: [(estimated probability that the site is a member of the group) multiplied by (proportion of members of that group in which the taxon occurs)].

Investigation of the contribution of the individual environmental variables to the discriminant analysis, based on the species-level combined seasons classification, showed that many of these variables were redundant. There would therefore be an acceptably small decrease in the percentage of correct predictions if they were based on a carefully selected subset of variables. Thus, the use of eleven physical and chemical variables still resulted in the prediction of 62.7% of reference sites to the correct group (Table 2.3). Use of smaller subsets of variables, subsets that excluded chemical variables, and three additional test classifications based on family-level identification (but still using 31 environmental variables), all demonstrated lower ability in prediction to group. In view of the lower performance of the family-based classifications compared to the species classification using 31 variables, and the disadvantages inherent in using multiple classifications, future tests focused on the species-level classification. The latter, although capable of being used to predict species composition, could also be used to predict at lower taxonomic levels by degrading the outputs to the required taxonomic level.

Table 2.3. *A comparison of the percentages of 370 sites, in the 30 biological classification groups of RIVPACS I, that were predicted to the correct group by MDA, using different numbers of physical and chemical variables.*

(1) Including both physical and chemical variables. (2) Physical variables only.

Taxonomic level	Number of environmental variables				
	31[1]	11[1]	5[1]	11[2]	5[2]
Species qualitative	74.3	62.7	49.7	56.8	48.1
All families quantitative	61.1	–	–	–	–
All families qualitative	59.5	–	–	–	–
BMWP families qualitative	58.1	–	–	–	–

The classification and prediction system was programmed on a BBC microcomputer and released, as RIVPACS I, for testing by all Water Authorities, River Purification Boards and the Department of the Environment (Northern Ireland). The prediction option offered the use of either five or eleven environmental variables, with a choice between physical variables only (for sites where the chemical parameters might have been affected by pollution, or had not been measured) or a combination of physical and chemical variables. Four taxonomic levels (species, family quantitative, family qualitative, BMWP families qualitative) were offered for prediction of the fauna. Once the required environmental variables for a site had been entered using the keyboard, the program read the data, performed the calculations and printed out the predictions of group membership and the expected taxa in decreasing order of probability of capture, down to a pre-selected level. In this first version, it was not possible to use environmental variables held on disk. In addition, the comparison of the observed fauna with the expected fauna had to be done manually.

The classification module used the TWINSPAN key, based on species-level identifications, and asked the user to respond to the presence or absence of each differential species at the site under consideration, using the keyboard. The progress of the site classification through each division was shown graphically on the screen, using a dendrogram of the classification structure. The module also offered site classification based on the other three taxonomic levels, and in this case the differential taxa were derived retrospectively and imposed upon the species classification.

In the late 1980s, several changes were made to the system, leading up to the development of RIVPACS II. The reference dataset was expanded to 438 sites on 76 rivers, with the addition of 80 new sites on small streams, large lowland rivers and rivers in Scotland. At the same time, 12 sites from the previous 370 were omitted because on reappraisal they were found to be aberrant in some way and therefore had the potential to distort the new classification. TWINSPAN was again used to develop the 438-site classification to 25 groups. The prediction procedure using MDA was the same as for RIVPACS I. After some initial analyses using a total of 28 environmental variables, a series of tests on smaller subsets of variables was initiated before the decision was taken to propose the use of just eleven environmental variables.

In practice, when the National Rivers Authority (NRA) funded the Institute of Freshwater Ecology (IFE) to develop an operational version of the new system as RIVPACS II, a menu of six alternative subsets of environmental variables was requested in order to retain some flexibility. In computing terms, the major advance was the upgrade to meet the new era with the widespread use of personal computers, and RIVPACS II was therefore made available on PC and mainframe computers. It was also programmed to read environmental and biological data from disk and output the results in digital formats, and this made it more efficient for use in the biological component of the 1990 River Quality Survey.

One further modification was made to the classification module based on biological data. There was some doubt over the reliability of the TWINSPAN key, in so far as it relied on the occurrence of a limited number of differential species to classify new sites. An alternative procedure for biological site classification was implemented, as proposed by Rushton (1987). In contrast to the TWINSPAN key, Rushton's procedure utilised the full list of taxa captured at a new site. In his approach, all sites within the RIVPACS classification are ordinated using DECORANA or detrended correspondence analysis (Hill 1979b). The centroids of each RIVPACS classification end-group are then calculated, based on the distribution of their component sites in multi-dimensional ordination space. In DECORANA, the ordination axes scores of each site are functions of the scores of each of the individual taxa present at them, and *vice versa*. The ordination of the RIVPACS reference sites, therefore, provides a set of standardised ordination scores for each taxon present in one or more of the same sites. Thus, the coordinates of any new site in the same ordination space may be calculated from the component scores of the taxa captured there, using standard RIVPACS sampling procedures. The probability of a site with those taxa present being a member of each RIVPACS end-group can be calculated probabilistically using the same procedures as those used in MDA (Klecka 1975). Separate algorithms were developed for biological site classifications based on the presence/absence of taxa at each of BMWP family and species level.

Methods investigated for the development of RIVPACS III

Traditional methods

Following the completion of RIVPACS II, the NRA supported a major contract to the IFE to undertake exhaustive testing of the current system, to expand its scope by including a wider range of sites within the reference dataset, and to investigate alternative classification and prediction techniques. Sites in Northern Ireland were also included for the first time. In the remainder of this chapter the investigations on alternative techniques are described.

RIVPACS III is based on 614 sites in Great Britain and a separate set of 70 sites in Northern Ireland that was analysed independently. However, for three reasons, the methodological investigations were made on a dataset of 410 sites obtained from the 438 RIVPACS II sites. First, 28 RIVPACS II sites were omitted because more rigorous analysis indicated that they fell short of the standard required of reference sites and they might have influenced the comparisons between alternative techniques. Second, a series of sites of high conservation value intended for inclusion in RIVPACS III were withheld, so that they could be used as independent test sites during the appraisal of alternative methods. Finally, some additional sites that were being sampled for eventual inclusion in RIVPACS III, including headwater streams outside the scope of RIVPACS II, were not available in time for the tests.

Initially, 17 different classification and prediction exercises were undertaken (Moss, Wright *et al.* 1999), many of them using the PATN multivariate analysis package (Belbin 1992). In addition to the original TWINSPAN method, the techniques included several different algorithms for the combination of samples into groups based on the between-sample similarity matrix, and several methods for ordination of samples in multi-dimensional space followed by clustering of the samples based on the ordination scores.

Several of these methods were successively eliminated using the following assessment criteria.

(1). Since the prediction method depends on distinctions between the taxa typical of each group, the range of group sizes should avoid the inclusion of groups containing a large proportion of all sites, and should ensure an adequate minimum group size.

(2). The percentage of sites allocated to the "correct" group by MDA should be assessed using an internal test on the same set of reference sites (by either the re-substitution or the cross-validation method) and an external test on the independent set of test sites.

(3). The percentage of variation between the groups (compared with within-group variation) should be maximised for each environmental variable, and also for the number of taxa, BMWP score, average score per taxon (ASPT), and biological ordination axes based on DECORANA ordination (Hill 1979b).

(4). Average within-group biological similarity should be maximised to avoid having biologically heterogeneous groups. However, it was necessary to avoid circularity in the assessment.

(5). Similarity of observed and expected fauna should be maximised.

Some methods "chained" to give one very large group of over 100 sites and several groups with only one site. These classifications would not provide sufficient distinction for the prediction method and were rejected on this criterion. After all the criteria had been applied, six methods were chosen for further investigation. They are listed in Table 2.4 together with background information on their performance in the initial tests. The next stage entailed

Table 2.4. *The characteristics of six different classification methods tested during the development of RIVPACS III. All methods, except the first, were based on 410 sites and 24 classification groups.*

(1) Result from analysis of variance of DECORANA scores.

(2) Agglomerative hierarchical clustering option FUSE in PATN, based on the Bray-Curtis similarity matrix.

(3) Unweighted pair-group mean arithmetic averaging with clustering parameter $\beta = -0.5$.

(4) Semi-strong hybrid scaling.

(5) Detrended canonical correspondence analysis (in CANOCO) on biological data plus 14 environmental variables.

Method	Group size range	SD of group size	% sites correctly allocated by MDA	% biological variation within groups[1]
TWINSPAN (RIVPACS II); 438 sites	6 – 36	8.16	56.6	–
TWINSPAN; 410 sites	7 – 34	7.93	57.3	85.5
PATN FUSE[2] UPGMA[3]	9 – 28	5.59	61.2	84.4
PATN FUSE Ward's fusion	6 – 51	9.82	65.9	83.8
PATN SSH[4] 6 dimensions+k-means clustering	10 – 30	5.31	57.3	86.5
CANOCO DCCA[5] k-means clustering	8 – 36	5.93	63.4	87.8

development of the full prediction system based on MDA for each one of these six methods, in order to give predicted taxa as in previous versions of RIVPACS, and not just prediction to classification group as had been done for the initial 17 methods.

Logistic regression

A seventh method, which was completely different from all the others, was also investigated. This relied on logistic regression equations to estimate the probability of occurrence of each taxon separately. It avoided the need for a site classification and MDA.

For each taxon i (in practice, each BMWP family) the probability P_i that taxon i is found at a site was predicted from the environmental variables as follows.

(a). Detrended canonical correspondence analysis (DCCA) was applied to the species-level data from 410 sites in order to calculate the first four environmental axes (C_1, C_2, C_3 and C_4) based on the combination of biological data and 13 environmental variables. This gave site ordination scores and regression coefficients based on environmental variables alone. DCCA was run using the CANOCO program (Ter Braak 1985).

(b). Logistic regression coefficients were calculated to fit the probability of occurrence of taxon i, depending on the values of C_1, C_2, C_3 and C_4 and the squared/product terms C_1^2, C_2^2, and (C_1 x C_2). The dependent variable took the value 1 for those sites where taxon i was captured, and 0 where it was not found.

(c). Tests were made on the independent sites; i.e. C_1, C_2, C_3 and C_4 ordination scores were calculated for test sites. From (a) above, logistic regression estimates of P_i were calculated for each taxon on each site. From (b) above, observed/expected (O/E) ratios were calculated for number of BMWP families, BMWP score and average score per taxon (ASPT). Goodness of fit was assessed by a chi-squared test on numbers of BMWP families observed and predicted at each site, banded in 10-percentile ranges of expected probability.

Results of methodological tests

The tests comparing the seven methods chosen for further investigation were made using an independent dataset of 101 sites of high nature conservation value. Note that whereas results for BMWP family and species level were available for methods 1 to 6, method 7 (logistic regression) was only undertaken at BMWP family level in view of the large number of species involved.

Mean O/E ratios derived from the 101 test sites (Table 2.5) were used to compare the performance of the TWINSPAN methodology based on 438 sites in 25 groups (method 1, RIVPACS II) with the same method using the reduced dataset of 410 sites in 24 groups (method 2). At BMWP family level, the mean O/E ratios for each of the three indices were closer to unity in the reduced dataset (method 2) compared to method 1, suggesting that the more rigorous approach to site selection brought some benefits to the prediction system. In contrast, at species level, the differences, though small, were slightly in favour of method 1.

Table 2.5. *A comparison of the observed/expected (O/E) ratios (means and standard deviations) from the seven classification/prediction procedures based on 101 independent test sites.*

Classification methods:- (1) TWINSPAN on 438 sites; (2) TWINSPAN on 410 sites; (3) PATN FUSE UPGMA with $\beta = -0.5$; (4) PATN FUSE with Ward's fusion algorithm; (5) PATN SSH in 6 dimensions, followed by k-means clustering; (6) CANOCO DCCA on 14 variables, followed by k-means clustering; (7) Logistic regression.

Measure	Method 1	Method 2	Method 3	Method 4	Method 5	Method 6	Method 7
O/E No. of BMWP families							
Mean	1.0577	1.0217	1.0224	1.0302	1.0176	1.0229	1.0632
SD	0.1727	0.1598	0.1589	0.1620	0.1542	0.1681	0.1735
O/E BMWP score							
Mean	1.0777	1.0354	1.0333	1.0456	1.0292	1.0407	1.0767
SD	0.2077	0.1879	0.1820	0.1892	0.1768	0.1929	0.1982
O/E ASPT							
Mean	1.0155	1.0111	1.0093	1.0142	1.0099	1.0164	1.0111
SD	0.0746	0.0708	0.0703	0.0783	0.0725	0.0713	0.0698
O/E No. of taxa (species)							
Mean	1.0090	0.9845	0.9798	0.9899	0.9783	0.9764	–
SD	0.1913	0.1888	0.1895	0.1784	0.1825	0.1909	–

The comparisons between methods 2 to 6 (Table 2.5), all based on 410 site classifications, but with widely different procedures for the initial classification, demonstrated that their predictive capabilities using MDA were relatively similar. Logistic regression (method 7) generally fell within the range of performance offered by the other methods, particularly when method 1 was included. However, in general it did not perform as well as methods 2 and 5, although it was very slightly more consistent for ASPT.

Table 2.6. *A comparison of the Pearson correlation coefficients between the observed and expected (= predicted) values of the number of BMWP families, BMWP score, ASPT and number of species for 101 test sites, using methods 1 to 7 (see Table 2.5).*

Measure	Method 1	Method 2	Method 3	Method 4	Method 5	Method 6	Method 7
No. of BMWP families	0.3784	0.4594	0.4650	0.4576	0.4713	0.3555	0.3780
BMWP score	0.3910	0.4812	0.5181	0.5138	0.5455	0.4613	0.4617
ASPT	0.7674	0.7969	0.7964	0.7486	0.7823	0.7859	0.8039
No. of taxa (species)	0.4156	0.4007	0.4414	0.5077	0.4544	0.3704	–

An alternative approach was to calculate correlation coefficients between observed and expected number of taxa, BMWP score and ASPT values (Table 2.6). The correlation coefficients for BMWP indices reinforced the argument that method 2 using the reduced dataset was more reliable than method 1, and the differences between methods 1 and 2 at species level were marginal. Closer examination of the results for methods 2 to 6, suggested that method 6 (based on DCCA) performed least well, with poor correlations between observed and expected values for number of families, BMWP score and number of species but not for ASPT, where its performance was similar to that of most other systems.

Method 5 (semi-strong hybrid scaling (SSH) followed by k-means clustering) provided the most consistent results overall, in that it performed best in terms of correlation coefficients for number of BMWP families and BMWP score, and second best for number of species. Although fifth for ASPT, it still offered high predictive capability for this index. Given that this method also had a limited range of group sizes (10 to 30 sites per group with low standard deviation), these various indicators suggested that a system based on this technique might offer reliable predictions across a wide range of sites.

The chi-squared test permitted a detailed comparison between the individual taxa predicted and those observed at each of the 101 test sites. As before, the test was possible at BMWP family level for methods 1 to 7 and at species level for methods 1 to 6 only. Summaries of chi-squared results (Fig. 2.3) give the number of sites at which significant differences were recorded for each method and three statistical significance levels. As in the earlier comparisons, the differences between methods were relatively small, but method 2 (TWINSPAN) and method 5 (SSH followed by k-means clustering) were the most promising in that they had marginally lower numbers of sites with significant chi-squared values at both BMWP family and species level. Again, logistic regression (method 7) fell within the range of methods 2 to 6 at BMWP family level.

To simplify interpretation, the chi-squared results for each site were linked to their O/E ratios (Fig. 2.4). By banding sites according to the O/E ratios from low to high values, it became apparent not only which methods had few significant differences, but also how the O/E bands related to significant chi-squared values. Some high and some low O/E values can be expected with any prediction system, although they are minimised in the ideal system. If there are significant differences, as shown by the chi-squared tests, in the distributions of observed

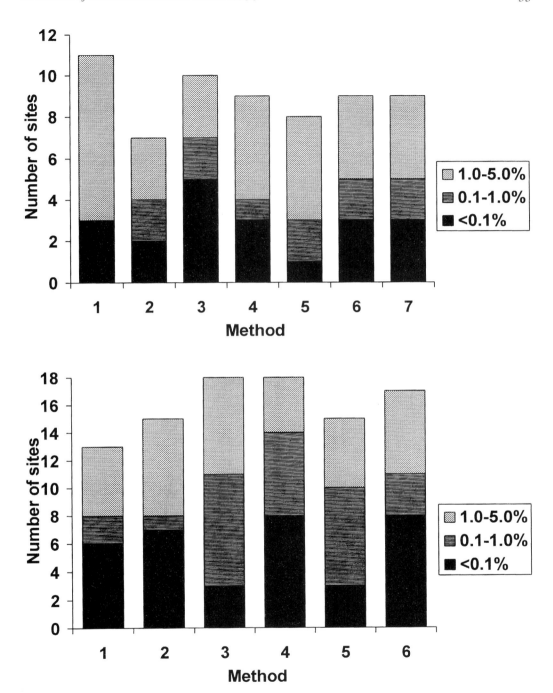

Figure 2.3. Numbers of sites (out of 101) with significant departures from good fit according to the chi-squared test, categorised by the significance levels for each method (<0.1%, solid bars; 0.1–1.0%, horizontal shading; 1.0–5.0%, stippled). *Above:* BMWP families. *Below:* Species.
Methods: 1 = TWINSPAN on 438 sites (RIVPACS II); 2 = TWINSPAN on 410 sites; 3 = PATN FUSE UPGMA; 4 = PATN FUSE Ward's fusion; 5 = PATN SSH k-means; 6 = DCCA k-means; 7 = Logistic regression.

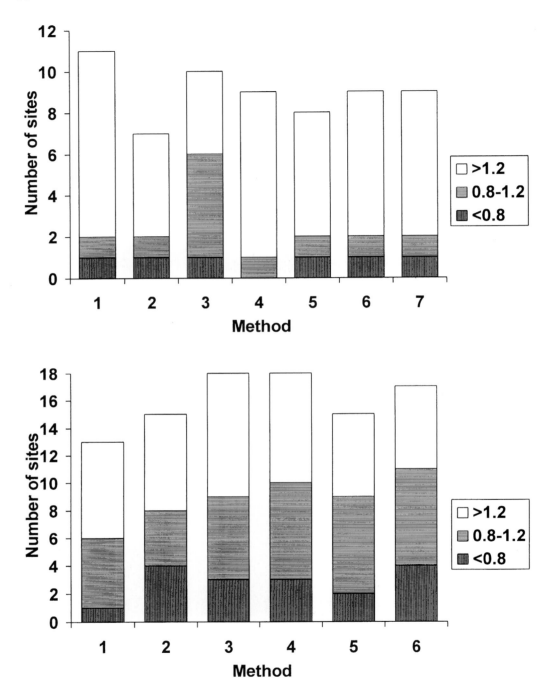

Figure 2.4. Numbers of sites (out of 101) with significant departures at the 5% level from good fit according to the chi-squared test, categorised by observed/expected ratio bands for each method (O/E <0.8, vertical shading; O/E 0.8–1.2, horizontal shading; O/E >1.2, unshaded blocks). *Above:* BMWP families. *Below:* Species.
Methods: 1 = TWINSPAN on 438 sites (RIVPACS II); 2 = TWINSPAN on 410 sites; 3 = PATN FUSE UPGMA; 4 = PATN FUSE Ward's fusion; 5 = PATN SSH k-means; 6 = DCCA k-means; 7 = Logistic regression.

and expected values when O/E ratios are closer to unity (i.e. in the range 0.8–1.2), this implies a more serious deficiency in predictive capability. This is because it suggests that taxa predicted with a high probability of occurrence are being under-recorded and taxa predicted with a low probability are being found more frequently than expected. In considering the need to minimise differences between the observed and expected fauna when O/E ratios are near to unity, only method 3 (UPGMA) performed badly at BMWP family level, while method 2 out-performed methods 2 to 6 at species level.

Conclusions

The prediction system for each method was tested by computing the probability of occurrence of both BMWP families and species (3 seasons combined) for an independent series of 101 sites. These sites encompassed locations throughout Great Britain, and include a number of river types and geographical locations beyond the scope of the RIVPACS II database. The test was therefore a demanding one, not only for RIVPACS II, but for the other options based on the slightly reduced dataset. The tendency for the mean O/E value for each BMWP index to be slightly above unity (Table 2.5) was probably due to the presence of a number of sites of higher than average biological quality which had been selected for their nature conservation interest.

Table 2.7. Summary conclusions on RIVPACS III test methods:
an overall assessment of the independent test results.

Method	O/E ratios	Chi-squared tests	Comments
TWINSPAN	Good	Good	Consider further
PATN FUSE UPGMA	Intermediate	Poor	
PATN FUSE Ward	Intermediate	Intermediate	
PATN SSH+k-means	Good	Good	Consider further
CANOCO DCCA+k-means	Intermediate	Intermediate	
LOGISTIC	Poor	Intermediate	No classification

In summary (Table 2.7), there was very little to choose between the original TWINSPAN method and that based on SSH followed by k-means clustering, although the latter was, if anything, slightly to be preferred. However, when the final RIVPACS III Great Britain dataset of 614 sites had been completed, tests using SSH gave unsatisfactory results. The classification groups were too heterogeneous. Thus, similar sites, especially those on chalk streams, were sometimes widely separated in the classification, and the MDA results were very much poorer than those from the TWINSPAN classification. This was probably due to the large number of headwater sites in RIVPACS III, which were successfully isolated by TWINSPAN but not by SSH. By contrast, the dataset for Northern Ireland, comprising more homogeneous sites, gave good results with SSH (Wright, Gunn *et al.* 1995). The final decision for the development of RIVPACS III was therefore to continue to use TWINSPAN, but for the first time to use both species (presence/absence data) and family abundance data together in the TWINSPAN classification (Wright, Moss *et al.* 1997). This approach was shown to be more effective at bringing the chalk stream sites together into coherent groups, a problem that had been identified within RIVPACS II because it relied on presence/absence species data alone. In order to be consistent in methodology for both parts of the UK, this approach was also used for the Northern Ireland dataset.

CHAPTER 3

Uncertainty in estimates of biological quality based on RIVPACS

RALPH CLARKE

Institute of Freshwater Ecology, River Laboratory, East Stoke, Wareham, Dorset, BH20 6BB, UK

Summary

RIVPACS derives estimates of the macroinvertebrate fauna to be expected at a river site in the absence of environmental stress. Biological quality indices can be derived from statistics which measure some aspect of lack of agreement between the observed and the expected fauna. To assess the significance of spatial or temporal differences in the values of an index requires knowledge and quantitative estimates of the sources of variation and errors in both the observed and expected fauna, jointly referred to as the uncertainty; this topic is discussed.

Detailed procedures are proposed to assess the uncertainty in quality indices based on the ratio of observed (O) to expected (E) values of the BMWP indices. Studies involving a replicated sampling programme across a range of types and qualities of site were used to derive estimates of sampling variation, sample processing biases and the effect of errors in measuring the environmental predictor variables.

The latest version of the RIVPACS software package, RIVPACS III+, uses statistical simulations which integrate these sources of variation to provide an assessment of the uncertainty in (1) O/E values, (2) the assignment of sites to quality bands, (3) spatial and/or temporal differences in O/E values and (4) potential changes in quality band.

Introduction

The philosophy of a RIVPACS-type approach to assessing the biological quality of river sites is to compare the observed fauna with the expected or "target" fauna. The expected fauna is predicted from the environmental characteristics of the site using a set of reference sites which are believed to be unpolluted or unstressed (Wright, Moss *et al.* 1984; Wright *et al.* 1993).

Any measure of agreement, or lack of it, between the observed and expected fauna can be used to define an index of biological quality for river sites. Many quality indices can be proposed, based on either the presence/absence or abundance levels of individual taxa. Indices may involve a comparison of taxonomic diversity or taxonomic composition, assessment of the observed status of certain key "indicator" taxa, or be based on the statistical likelihood of the observed fauna given the expectation (for further details on possible indices, see Clarke, Furse *et al.* 1996). In Great Britain, the most common use of RIVPACS to assess biological quality for both national and local surveys involves quality indices based on the ratio, O/E, of observed (O) to expected (E) values of the number of BMWP (Biological Monitoring Working Party) families and the average score per taxon (ASPT) of BMWP families (Armitage, Moss *et al.* 1983; Wright *et al.* 1993).

Whatever quality index is chosen (e.g. see Hewitt 1991), irrespective of whether a

RIVPACS-type approach is involved, it is vital to have some idea of the errors or chance variation that can influence the value of the index for any particular site. It is convenient to refer to the combined effect of all sources of variation in the index value for a particular site at a point in time as the uncertainty. Without some knowledge of the level of uncertainty, an index of biological quality is of little value. Three main questions need to be considered.

First, what are the potential errors in an estimate of biological quality for a site; for example, can we derive some form of confidence limits? Second, if the range of possible values for an index is subdivided into quality bands to provide a simple summary of the results, what are the chances that a site is assigned to the wrong band? Finally and perhaps most crucially, how can we assess whether there is a significant or real difference in the biological quality estimates obtained for two samples? They could be from the same site on different sampling occasions, or from two different sites, perhaps one upstream and one downstream of a potential impact. These questions are relevant to all methods of biological quality assessment, and not just the RIVPACS-type approach involving a comparison of the observed with expected fauna.

Quality index values for RIVPACS reference sites

In attempting to assess the uncertainty or errors in the comparison of the observed with the expected fauna, it is important to realise that although the RIVPACS reference sites are variously thought of as "clean", "unpolluted", "unstressed" or "top quality", they are not perfect. They represent the best sites available in the population for each physical type of site and provide a realistic target fauna for each type of river site. Most importantly, it must be remembered that the reference sites are not all of the same quality, however that is defined. Figure 3.1 shows the distribution of the estimated qualities of the 614 reference sites used in the RIVPACS III software package, based on the O/E ratios of their observed to expected values of ASPT (see Chapter 1). The expected value for any site, including the reference sites themselves, is a weighted average of "environmentally similar" reference sites. Therefore, by definition, the average O/E value for the reference sites must be around one, but roughly half of the reference sites will be better than average and tend to have O/E values greater than one, and roughly half will have values less than one.

The overall variation in the O/E values for the reference sites includes both that due to errors in the whole system of estimating biological quality, and true or real variation in the quality of the reference sites. Therefore, in a sense, the overall variance in the quality index values for the reference sites provides an upper limit to the errors or uncertainty in the index values for unstressed or high quality sites. But to use this overestimate of the index errors may result in only very large differences in biological quality being detected. This error term would also be inappropriate for assessing improvements in poorer quality sites with fewer taxa.

One good use of the distribution of quality index values for the reference sites could be in setting quality band limits. In the absence of other objective criteria, it makes sense to treat the reference sites as covering the quality range of the highest quality band of sites and then use the lower (say) 5 percentile of the values as the lower limit of the top band for all sites. An extension of this approach, called the 5M banding system, was used by the former National Rivers Authority for their national River Quality Survey in 1990 (Sweeting, Lowson *et al.* 1992).

The range of values obtained for the reference sites can also help to assess the usefulness of any type of quality index. If the range is relatively large for supposedly high quality sites, then the index may be insensitive to, or unable to differentiate between, moderate to high levels of stress. For example, the lower 5 percentile limit of O/E based on the number of BMWP taxa for three seasons combined in samples from the RIVPACS III reference sites, is 0.78. It has been suggested that a better overall measure of the biological quality of a site in a given year would

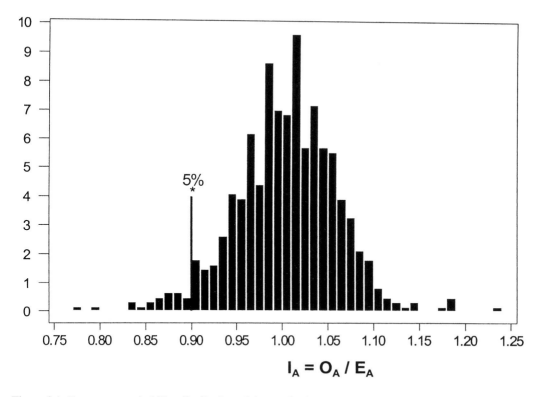

Figure 3.1. Percentage probability distribution of the quality index based on O/E for ASPT, viz. $I_A = O_A/E_A$, for the 614 reference sites used in RIVPACS III. * denotes the lower 5 percentile.

be to use the minimum of the three O/E ratios for the RIVPACS single season samples (spring, summer, autumn) for the site in that year. However, because single season samples are based on less information and are more susceptible to sampling variation, the lower 5 percentile value of this index for the RIVPACS reference sites is 0.57, necessitating either a very broad top quality band or high rates of misbanding for good quality sites.

Quality bands and the effect of errors

Having derived biological quality index values for river sites, further simplification of the results into a few quality bands may be helpful in the presentation of national summary statistics, and for local decision-making in river management (National Rivers Authority 1994).

The decision on how many bands to have and where to place the band limits often depends on managerial requirements for operational planning, but should also depend on statistical aspects, such as acceptable misbanding rates. Having more bands gives finer apparent discrimination of quality but greater actual misbanding rates. Figure 3.2 shows the probability of misbanding a site of any particular true quality according to the size of the errors or uncertainty in the index values, expressed as a percentage of the width of the quality bands (see Clarke, Furse *et al.* 1996 for the mathematical derivation). When the standard deviation of the errors in the index values is only 10% of the width of a band, then sites whose true quality lies in the middle of the band would never be misbanded. Sites whose true quality lies on the border of two bands will always have at least a 50% chance of being placed in the wrong band.

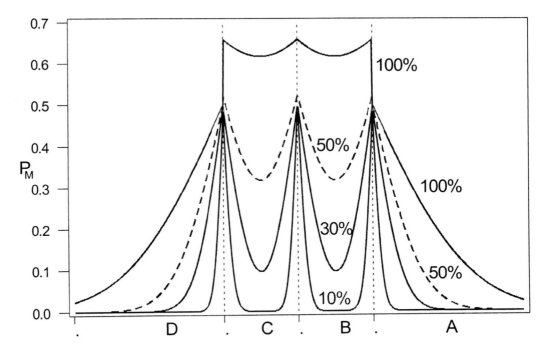

Figure 3.2. Plot of the probability (P_M) of misbanding a site versus its true quality index value (I_E) for a range of standard errors (δ) in the observed index value (I_O). For illustration, the quality index has been divided into four bands (A, B, C, D) with the middle two bands each of width W. Plots are shown for δ = 10%, 30%, 50% and 100% of W, where the broken line indicates the 50% plot.

Table 3.1. *Mean and range of misclassification rates (P_M; see Fig. 3.2) for sites whose true qualities are in a middle (i.e. not top or bottom) quality band for a range of error standard deviations (δ) in their observed quality index values, where δ is expressed as a percentage of the width of each middle band.*

δ (%)	Mean % misclassification	Range
10	8	0 – 50
30	24	10 – 50
50	39	32 – 52
100	63	62 – 66

With error standard deviations of 10% of band width, the overall misclassification rate for sites in a middle band, such as bands B or C in Figure 3.2 (assuming an even spread of true qualities), is only 8% (Table 3.1). If, however, the error standard deviation is 50% of the band width, then even the sites in the centre of a middle band have a roughly one in three chance of being placed in the wrong band and roughly 40% of all sites in the band will be misplaced into either a higher or lower band. If the error standard deviation is equal to the band width (i.e. 100%), as is likely if the index is divided into numerous bands, then all sites whose true quality lies within a middle band will more likely than not be placed in the wrong band (Table 3.1). The probability of misbanding a site from the top or bottom bands (bands A or D in Figure 3.1) is only half that for middle bands, or only one-quarter if the (top or bottom) band width is twice that of the middle bands.

Sources of uncertainty in observed and expected fauna for new sites

Variation in the observed fauna

The sources of variation in the observed fauna fall into the following four categories.

(O1): Sampling variation. Within each site there will still be spatial heterogeneity in the microhabitats for macroinvertebrates. An earlier study found that one standardised 3-minute RIVPACS sample typically contains 50% of the species and 60% of the families found amongst six replicate samples (Furse, Wright *et al.* 1981). Thus taxonomic richness and composition will vary between samples taken during the same period.

(O2): Sample processing errors. When sorting the material in a new sample and identifying the taxa, some taxa may be missed or misidentified. This may lead to bias and underestimation of the O/E ratio for number of taxa at the site.

(O3): Natural temporal variation. The taxa present at a site, not just in the sample, will vary naturally over time for reasons other than stress or pollution.

(O4): Effects of pollution or environmental stress on the fauna. It may be difficult to differentiate between *(O3)* and *(O4)*. For example, a reduction in river discharge may be due to differences in weather or due to abstraction; the former cause may be considered natural and the latter a man-induced stress. This highlights the problem of deciding whether RIVPACS predictions should be based on the discharge during the period of biological sampling or on some long-term "fixed" historical average for the site.

Errors in the expected fauna

The errors in the estimates of the expected fauna are potentially of four kinds, enumerated below.

(E1): Having an inadequate set of reference sites, with either too few sites in general or poor coverage of certain environmental types.

(E2): Not involving all relevant environmental variables. However, the best environmental variables for predicting the fauna may include some, such as certain chemical variables, which can be a cause of the stress or pollution which RIVPACS is trying to assess, and hence these must be excluded.

(E3): Not choosing the "best" multivariate statistical method to estimate the expected fauna for sites.

(E4): Errors in measuring the environmental variables for new sites.

Statistical approach used in RIVPACS

In RIVPACS, the statistical approach *(E3)* was to use TWINSPAN (Hill 1979a) to derive a biological classification of the reference sites, followed by multiple discriminant analysis (MDA) of the resulting site groups, using a small suite of environment variables (Moss, Furse *et al.* 1987). Moreover, by estimating the expected probability of occurrence of a particular taxon as a weighted average of its probability of occurring in each of the possible classification groups, rather than just in the most probable group, we are effectively "smoothing" the estimates and making them less dependent on the precise classification of the reference sites. Moss, Wright *et al.* (1999) compare alternative techniques for classifying sites prior to MDA and also assess the use of logistic regression for deriving predicted probabilities of taxa occurrence directly, without the prior need of a site classification.

Ideally we aim to minimise the effects of (*O1*), (*O2*) and (*E1*) to (*E4*) in order to maximise the efficiency of detecting real changes in quality. In practice it is difficult to disentangle the various sources of error. The data from the reference sites used to set the targets actually comprise the observed fauna that is subject to natural sampling variation. Also, as stated above, the reference sites are not all of the same quality.

Assessment of uncertainty in RIVPACS III+

After much thought, the following philosophy and approach to assessing uncertainty was adopted and developed into the latest version of the RIVPACS software package, RIVPACS III+ (Clarke, Cox *et al.*, 1997). First, the choice of reference sites (*E1*), environmental variables (*E2*) and prediction method (*E3*) are all treated as an integral part of the definition of the quality index; thus the only errors in the expected fauna and values are assumed to arise from errors in measuring the environmental variables for new sites (*E4*). The O/E or other indices of site quality tend to be estimated from unreplicated samples. Therefore, appropriate estimates of the typical effects of sampling variation (*O1*) and sampling processing errors (*O2*) need to be quantified for a wide range of types and qualities of site. The sampling variation for all qualities of site cannot be estimated from the variances for the high quality reference sites.

This chapter describes our research to quantify each of these sources of uncertainty, and includes details of our methods for synthesising the results into an overall numerical simulation approach in order to quantify the uncertainty in RIVPACS O/E indices of biological quality.

Replicated field study assessing sampling variation

Estimates of sampling variation and errors due to measuring the environmental variables were obtained from a replicated sampling study of 16 sites (Furse, Clarke *et al.* 1995). The study sites were selected in a stratified random manner from those in the former National River Authority's (NRA) 1990 River Quality Survey of over 5000 sites (Sweeting, Lowson *et al.* 1992), covering a wide range of qualities of site (A, B, C, D) from each of a wide range of physical site types. Each site was sampled in each of the three RIVPACS seasons (Spring (March–May), Summer (June–August) and Autumn (September–November)). On each occasion, three biological samples were taken, two by one individual from the IFE and one by a local NRA biologist. Care was taken to avoid effects of depletion or disturbance of the fauna for samples 2 and 3, and no trends related to sample order were subsequently detected. All of the biological samples were sorted and identified by experienced IFE staff, so all variation was assumed to be due to sample differences, rather than sample sorting and identification errors. The RIVPACS environmental predictor variables were also recorded independently for each site on each occasion by two IFE and two NRA staff .

From a detailed analysis of the replicate samples, we found that the square root of the observed number of taxa gave roughly constant sampling variability and standard deviation ($SD_{\sqrt{T}}$). This did not depend on the type or quality of site, but only on the number of seasons (1, 2 or 3) involved in the overall sample (Table 3.2). From the observed number of taxa (O_T) in any particular sample, approximate 95% confidence limits for the true mean taxonomic richness per sample at the site are given by: $(\sqrt{O_T}-1.96\ SD_{\sqrt{T}})^2$ to $(\sqrt{O_T}+1.96\ SD_{\sqrt{T}})^2$. (Goodness of fit tests showed that sampling variation of the square root of number of taxa approximated a normal distribution. In practice, this means that if, say, 15 BMWP families (taxa) are found in a single seasons sample, another sample from the same site at the same time could have anywhere between 12 and 19 taxa (Table 3.3). If 15 taxa are found in a combined

Table 3.2. *Estimated sampling standard deviations for the square root of the observed number of BMWP taxa, and the observed ASPT, for samples based on single season samples, or two or three seasons combined samples.*

Sampling standard deviation	No. of seasons involved in sample		
	1	2	3
$SD_{\sqrt{T}}$ = Sampling SD of $\sqrt{}$(no. of taxa)	0.228	0.164	0.145
SD_A = Sampling SD of ASPT	0.249	0.161	0.139

Table 3.3. *Examples of the 95% confidence limits for the number of BMWP taxa observed in a sample, based on 1, 2 or 3 seasons combined samples, for true means of 5, 15 or 30 taxa.*

No. of seasons in the combined sample	Mean no. of taxa observed	95% CL	
		Lower	Upper
1	5	3	7
2	5	4	7
3	5	4	6
1	15	12	19
2	15	13	18
3	15	13	17
1	30	25	35
2	30	27	34
3	30	27	33

seasons sample (i.e. spring, summer and autumn), then the sampling confidence limits are tighter at 13 to 17 taxa.

Differences between two samples taken by the same biologist, compared with differences between samples taken by different personnel, showed that about 12% of the total sampling standard deviation in observed number of taxa (and 4% of sampling SD for ASPT) is due to differences between personnel in sampling. Thus inter-operator effects are small and this implies that, providing personnel are adequately trained in field-sampling procedures, the same estimate of sampling variance can be used irrespective of who took the sample(s).

The within-site sampling standard deviation for ASPT did not depend on either the quality or type of site in any consistent manner and was not correlated with either the average ASPT for the site or the number of taxa on which ASPT was based. For practical purposes, the sampling variation of ASPT can be assumed to follow a normal distribution, with a constant standard deviation (SD_A) which depends only on the number of seasons (1, 2 or 3) included in the overall sample (Table 3.2).

Within-site sampling variation in observed BMWP score is very highly correlated with that for observed number of taxa. In contrast, sampling variation in observed number of taxa and observed ASPT are only moderately correlated and, for practical purposes, can be treated as varying independently between samples within any one site. Sampling variation in observed BMWP score can thus be derived from the simulations of the sampling variation in observed number of taxa and observed ASPT, of which it is the product (i.e. BMWP score = number of taxa x ASPT).

Sample sorting and identification errors

In processing RIVPACS samples, there may be a tendency for some taxa to be missed or misidentified by less experienced biologists. Since 1990, the Environment Agency has operated quality control and quality assurance schemes for all RIVPACS-type sampling in England and Wales (see Chapter 5). Under this scheme, IFE staff audit and re-analyse a proportion of the RIVPACS samples taken by the Agency.

To assess sample processing errors (*O2*), the results for 200 of these audited samples from each of 1990 and 1992 were re-analysed. On average, 1.5 to 4 taxa were missed per sample; this varied between NRA regions and improved between 1990 and 1992. The number of taxa incorrectly recorded as present was much lower, averaging only 0.25 per sample. We refer to the average net underestimation of the number of taxa in a sample as the bias. It was found to be reasonable to assume a Poisson distribution for the (net) number of taxa missed in individual samples, so that, for example, when the average number of taxa missed is 2.0, anywhere between 0 and 5 or very occasionally up to 8 taxa can be missed from individual samples. Our aim was to derive simple rules which could be incorporated into error terms that correct for biases in the taxa recorded for a sample.

Processing errors also affect ASPT in that the ASPT of the missed taxa tends to be slightly higher than the observed ASPT. We were able to derive the following simple relationship, relating the ASPT of the missed taxa ($ASPT_{miss}$) to the number of taxa (O_T) recorded as present (standard errors of regression coefficients in brackets):

$$ASPT_{miss} = 4.29 [0.50] + 0.077 [0.024] \ O_T \qquad (1)$$

Equation (1) estimates that the mean ASPT of the missed taxa ranges from around 4.5, when five taxa are recorded as present, to over 6.5 when more than 30 taxa are recorded.

What are the implications of sample processing errors for biases in the index values based on combined seasons samples? We found that roughly half (49%) of the BMWP taxa missed in one season's sample are recorded in a second season's sample from that site. Also, *ca* one-third (37%) of taxa missed in one season's sample were not recorded in either of the other two seasons samples for a site. Thus, when *ca* two taxa are, on average, missed per sample, the net underestimation is also *ca* two taxa for both two and three season combined samples. (Note that if the bias per single sample was much higher, then this result for combined season samples would not apply).

Errors in the expected values due to errors in measuring
the environmental predictor variables

The effect of errors in measuring the environmental predictor variables, on the expected fauna, was assessed by two approaches. First, we used a computer-based sensitivity analysis to estimate the effect, on RIVPACS O/E values, of varying the values of environmental variables by (say) 10 or 30% standard errors (SE) in repeated simulations for the RIVPACS reference sites. It was found that stream width, depth, slope and distance from source can all be measured with up to 20–35% SE without more than 5% of sites changing their O/E values by more than 0.02 for taxa O/E and 0.01 for ASPT O/E (Clarke, Furse *et al.* 1996). The RIVPACS expected (and hence O/E) values are more sensitive to changes in alkalinity (tolerable measurement standard errors were generally around 15%, but as low as 5% for values >150 mg $CaCO_3$ l⁻¹) and mean substratum (tolerable SE equals 1.0–1.5 phi units).

The second means of assessing such measurement errors was from the replicated field study. Each of the four recorders' values for the environmental variables were used to derive independent estimates of the expected (E) values for each site. Surprisingly, the size of error in E values did not depend significantly (p >0.05 in ANOVA tests) on either the number of seasons involved in the biological sample or the physical type of site. Variation between biologists in their recording of stream width, depth and substratum were all well within the acceptable tolerance limits determined from the above sensitivity analysis. Effects of within-season and inter-annual temporal variation could not be assessed, nor could the effect of error in mean annual alkalinity values (the alkalinity variable used in RIVPACS). This study provided the best available estimates of the standard errors for RIVPACS expected values due to measurement errors (estimated SE equals 0.53 for number of taxa, 4.3 for BMWP score and 0.081 for ASPT) but, as implied, these may be underestimates.

Integration of uncertainty terms to generate simulated values of O/E

In the RIVPACS III+ software package (Clarke, Cox *et al.* 1997), all the above sources of variation and error have been integrated in computer simulations of the potential values of the O/E indices for one or more samples. The simulations (default of 500) can be performed for an individual sample to estimate confidence limits for the O/E index of quality for the site, or simultaneous simulations for pairs of samples can be used to estimate the statistical significance and confidence limits for the difference in their quality.

For example, if O and E respectively denote the actual observed number of taxa and the estimated expected number of taxa for a sample, then the O/E value of the sample for simulation k is given by:

$$Q_k = [(\sqrt{O}+R_O)^2+B] / (E+R_E) \qquad (2)$$

where R_O = random term due to sampling variation, B = random Poisson bias term, R_E = random normal term due to errors in environmental variables. The frequency distribution of the simulated values (Q_k) provides confidence limits for the observed sample's O/E index of quality. To compare the O/E values for two samples (1 and 2), simulated O/E values (Q_{k1} and Q_{k2}) are calculated for each sample in each simulation. The frequency distribution and confidence limits of the simulated differences ($D_k = Q_{k2}-Q_{k1}$) can be used to indicate whether the O/E values for the two samples are statistically significantly different. (The exact procedures used in the statistical simulations are given in the Appendix at the end of this chapter).

Example of the method

The method is best demonstrated by an example showing the frequency distribution of the simulated potential values of O/E, based on number of taxa for two samples, 1 and 2 (Fig. 3.3). The observed or "face value" of O/E for sample 1 was 0.94, with estimated 95% confidence limits of 0.75 to 1.12 (Fig. 3.3a). This suggests that although the site from which sample 1 was taken may have as few as 75% of the expected number of taxa, because of the uncertainty in the O/E values the site actually may be of very high quality, with even more taxa than expected (O/E >1). Sample 2 appears to be from a poorer quality site, with a "face value" O/E of 0.75 and estimated confidence limits of 0.60 to 0.84 (Fig. 3.3b). Notice that the confidence limits for sample 2 are both lower and narrower; this is because the sampling variation for the observed number of taxa is less, in absolute terms, for poorer quality sites (Table 3.3).

Do the two sites really differ in quality? The observed difference in O/E (sample 2 minus sample 1) is –0.19, with 95% confidence limits of –0.40 to –0.01 (Fig. 3.3c). In fact, only 1.5% of simulated differences were positive, indicating a two-sided test significance at the p = 3% probability level for the null hypothesis of no difference in O/E for number of BMWP taxa. The two samples and each of the simulated values have also been assigned to quality bands ('a', 'b' and 'c') based on limits at O/E values of 0.85 and 0.70 (Fig. 3.3a and 3.3b). Furthermore, the O/E values for each simulation for the pair of samples (1 and 2) can be cross-classified according to their assigned quality band for each of the two samples (Fig. 3.4). On their observed or "face value" O/E, sample 1 would be placed in band 'a' and sample 2 in band 'b'. From the simulated O/E values, there is an estimated probability of 84.9% that the site from which sample 1 was taken is of quality band 'a'. The site from which sample 2 was taken has only a small likelihood (1.3%) of being in quality band 'a', is most likely (69%) to be in band 'b', but has a 29.7% chance of being in quality band 'c'. The most likely joint banding of the sites is that site 1 is band 'a' and site 2 is band 'b' (59.0%), which is also their observed joint banding.

From these two-way banding cell probabilities obtained from the simulations, we can estimate the probability of a change in band. From Figure 3.4 we see that in 10% of simulations both samples were assigned to the same band 'b'. There is also a small (1%) chance that both samples could be from the top band 'a'. However, it is most likely (with estimated probability of 59.0+5.1 = 64.1%) that site 2 is one band worse than site 1, and there is an estimated 25% chance that site 1 is band 'a' while site 2 is two bands worse.

Comparison of estimates of standard deviation of reference site O/E values

It is interesting to compare the approach for estimating uncertainty in O/E values proposed here, and used in the RIVPACS III+ software package, with possible alternative methods. Using the simulation methods described above (referred to as method (1)), the uncertainty standard deviation (SD) in simulated O/E values, averaged across the 614 RIVPACS reference sites, was 0.056 when based on number of taxa and 0.027 for ASPT (Table 3.4). One other

Table 3.4. *Comparison of four alternative estimates of the uncertainty standard deviation (SD) of the O/E values, based on the number of BMWP taxa and ASPT for 614 RIVPACS III reference sites.*

Method (1) = mean SD obtained by simulation of O/E values (see the text, and assuming no biases); as used in RIVPACS III+.

Method (2) = SD of observed O/E values.

Method (3) = mean mathematical SD, given expected probabilities for individual taxa; as in Clarke, Furse *et al.* (1996).

Method (4) = mean SD by simulation of O/E values as in method (1) but assuming twice the observed standard error in expected values due to measurement error.

Method	Number of taxa	ASPT
(1)	0.056	0.027
(2)	0.138	0.057
(3)	0.088	0.040
(4)	0.063	0.035

Figure 3.3 (*on facing page*). Frequency histogram of the distribution of the error-inclusive simulated values of O/E for number of BMWP taxa for (a) sample 1 and (b) sample 2; X denotes the actual observed value for each sample. The O/E values have been classified into three potential quality bands, a, b and c, with limits at 0.85 and 0.70. (c) shows the frequency distribution of the simulated values of the difference in O/E values (sample 2 minus sample 1). The horizontal bar lines denote the 95% confidence limits in each case.

(a) Sample 1: O/E = 0.94

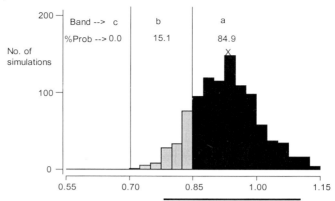

(b) Sample 2: O/E = 0.75

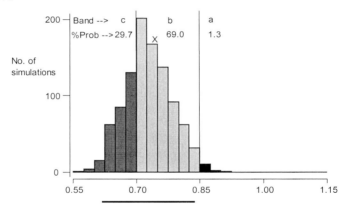

(c) Difference in O/E = -0.19

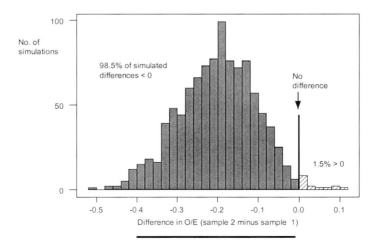

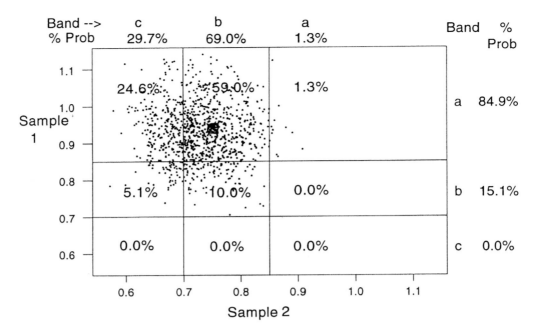

Figure 3.4. Two-way joint distribution of the simulated values of O/E for number of BMWP taxa for samples 1 and 2 (as in Fig. 3.3); ⊠ denotes the actual observed values of 0.94 and 0.75 respectively. Dots denote joint values for individual simulations (n = 1000). Quality bands (a, b and c) for O/E values are as in Fig. 3.3. The percentages (% Prob) of simulated values falling in each band are given for each sample separately and jointly.

simple approach (method (2)) is to use the SD of the observed O/E values for the 614 sites. As stated previously, this will give overestimates of the errors because they include real variation in quality of the reference sites. An alternative approach (method (3)) uses the mathematical SD conditional on the expected probability of each taxon, as used in RIVPACS II (Clarke, Furse *et al.* 1996), but this still includes variability between clean sites of the same physical type. As we may have underestimated errors in the expected (E) values due to errors in measuring the environmental predictor variables, another estimate is given (method (4)) based on assuming that the error SD for E values is twice that normally used in RIVPACS III+. This estimate of the uncertainty SD for O/E values of the reference sites is still less than, but now more similar to, that of the mathematical conditional expectation approach (Table 3.4).

Alternative methods (2) and (3) only provide estimates of the uncertainty in estimates of quality for high quality sites like the RIVPACS reference sites; they are not based on any evidence of the uncertainty in index values for poorer quality sites. Very importantly, only the approach proposed here (and used in RIVPACS III+) is able to derive estimates of errors and uncertainty in assessments for poorer quality sites.

Discussion

This simulation approach to assessing errors and uncertainty in quality indices is a useful beginning, especially for assessing the likelihood of changes in quality across the whole spectrum of types and qualities of river sites. RIVPACS III has now been updated to the

RIVPACS III+ software package to include these assessments of uncertainty in BMWP O/E ratios. This simulation approach could be adapted to assess uncertainty for any other indices based on a comparison of the observed and the expected fauna. It could also be used to estimate the precision and accuracy of O/E-type indices in other countries where the RIVPACS approach is being used, such as the River Health Monitoring Program throughout Australia (see Chapters 8 to 10).

Obviously, it may be argued that BMWP O/E indices based only on the presence/absence of families are not the ideal means to assess biological quality and detect the effects of stress. However, any alternative quality index is of limited use unless one has some idea of the errors and uncertainty in its values. The approach proposed here could be modified to assess the errors in indices based on abundance data. For example, preliminary studies have been made on measures of rank correlation, and Bray–Curtis-type similarity coefficients, between the observed and expected abundances and a measure of proportional loss of expected abundances of all except pollution-tolerant taxa. The assessment of the uncertainty in these abundance-based quality indices is one of the next stages of our research in collaboration with the Environment Agency in the UK.

Errors due to the inadequacy of the set of reference sites, the choice of environmental predictor variables, and the statistical method of estimating the expected fauna, have not been incorporated into RIVPACS III+. But, within the constraint of using BMWP O/E ratios, tests made with alternative statistical methods as part of the development of RIVPACS III (see Chapter 2, and Moss, Wright *et al.* 1999) indicate that the prediction method used in RIVPACS III is as good as any other.

More importantly, I believe it is not possible to completely disentangle inadequacies in the prediction system from real variation in quality within the reference sites. Thus the choice of reference sites, predictor variables and even prediction method are, in a sense, part of the definition of biological quality. What matters then is whether the chosen approach to assessing quality and change in quality is a useful, practical and understandable tool.

Acknowledgements

This research was funded jointly by the UK Environment Agency (formerly the National Rivers Authority) and the Natural Environment Research Council.

An Appendix to Chapter 3 follows on pages 52 to 54

Appendix:– Statistical simulation procedures used to assess uncertainty in RIVPACS O/E indices of biological quality at river sites

The term "sample" refers to the total sample for which the BMWP index values are calculated; this can be a single season sample, or a two or three seasons combined sample.

(a). Simulated observed values

O_T, O_A = observed number of taxa and ASPT recorded for the sample,

$O_S = O_T O_A$ = observed BMWP score recorded for the sample,

$O_{Tr} = (\sqrt{O_T} + Z_{Tr} SD_{\sqrt{T}})^2$ = observed number of taxa for simulated sample r,

$O_{Ar} = O_A + Z_{At} SD_A$ = observed ASPT for simulated sample r,

where Z_{Tr} and Z_{Ar} are random number deviates from a standard Normal distribution with a mean of zero and a variance of one; $SD_{\sqrt{T}}$ and SD_A are as in Table 3.2 of the main text.

$O_{Sr} = O_{Tr} O_{Ar}$ = observed BMWP score for simulated sample r.

(b). Simulated biases

Let M_1, M_2, M_3 denote the user-supplied estimates of the average bias due to sample sorting and identification errors for spring, summer and autumn single season samples respectively. Let $k_1 = 1$ if the overall sample of interest involves spring and 0 (zero) if it does not; similarly for k_2 (summer) and k_3 (autumn).

Let U $= M_1 k_1 + M_2 k_2 + M_3 k_3$.

Let U_T = expected net underestimation of BMWP taxa in overall sample
       = expected overall bias.

For single season samples: $U_T = U$.
For two season combined samples: $U_T = 0.51\ U$.
For three season combined samples: $U_T = 0.37\ U$.
Special case: when no taxa were recorded in the sample (i.e. $O_T = 0$),
       assume none were missed (i.e. $U_T = 0$).

U_{Tr} = net underestimate of number of taxa for simulated sample r;

U_{Tr} is estimated as a random deviate from a Poisson distribution with a mean of U_T.

U_{Ar} = ASPT of the U_{Tr} missed taxa for simulated sample r

       = $4.29 + 0.077\ O_T + Z_{br}(2/\sqrt{U_{Tr}})$

where Z_{br} is a random deviate from a standard Normal distribution with a mean of zero and a variance of one. (It is unlikely, but mathematically possible, to derive values of $U_{Ar} > 10$. Such values are reset to 10. Similarly, any values of $U_{Ar} < 1$ are reset to 1).

$U_{Sr} = U_{Tr} U_{Ar}$ = underestimate of BMWP score for simulated sample r.

$O_{Tbr} = O_{Tr} + U_{Tr}$ = bias-corrected observed number of taxa for simulated sample r.

O_{Sbr} = $O_{Sr} + U_{Sr}$ = bias-corrected observed BMWP score for simulated sample r.

O_{Abr} = O_{Sbr} / O_{Tbr} = bias-corrected observed ASPT for simulated sample r.

(c). Simulated expected values

E_T, E_A and E_S = expected number of taxa, ASPT and BMWP score for sample,

E_{Tr} = $E_T + 0.53 Z_{eTr}$ = expected number of taxa for simulated sample r,

E_{Ar} = $E_A + 0.081 Z_{eAr}$ = expected ASPT for simulated sample r,

where Z_{eTr} and Z_{eAr} are random number deviates from a standard Normal distribution with a mean of zero and a variance of one.

$E_{Sr} = E_{Tr}E_{Ar}$ = expected BMWP score for simulated sample r.

(d). Simulated O/E ratios

For each simulated sample r, the simulated O/E ratios, ignoring or uncorrected for any biases due to sample sorting and identification errors, are:

$Q_{Tr} = O_{Tr}/E_{Tr}$, $Q_{Ar} = O_{Ar}/E_{Ar}$, and $Q_{Sr} = O_{Sr}/E_{Sr}$

for number of taxa, ASPT and BMWP score respectively. These are known as the "face value" O/E ratios, in the sense that these would be the quoted values in the absence of any knowledge of errors.

The equivalent O/E ratios corrected for bias are:

$Q_{Tbr} = O_{Tbr}/E_{Tr}$, $Q_{Abr} = O_{Abr}/E_{Abr}$, and $Q_{Sbr} = O_{Sbr}/E_{Sr}$.

It is important to note that the average of the simulated O/E values (uncorrected for bias) is not necessarily exactly equal to the "face value" O/E. A small difference could still arise even if thousands of simulation were used; this is partly due to the statistical fact that the average of the ratios of two variables is not necessarily equal to the ratio of their averages.

(e). Confidence limits for O/E ratios

The frequency distribution of all the simulated O/E values for a particular BMWP index represents the degree of uncertainty in the true O/E value for that index for the site at the time(s) of sampling (either uncorrected or corrected for bias). This uncertainty can be summarised by the standard deviation of the simulated values. Additionally, 95% confidence limits for the true value are estimated as the lower and upper 2.5 percentiles of this frequency distribution (i.e. 2.5% of simulated O/E values were less than the lower limit and 2.5% were higher than the upper limit). When corrected for bias, the confidence limits tend to be higher and wider for O/E based on number of taxa and BMWP score than when bias is ignored, and slightly wider for ASPT. This is because of the extra degree of uncertainty introduced by estimating the bias for the sample. However, bias-corrected O/E values should, by definition, be correct, on average, and no longer have a tendency to underestimate the true quality at the site.

(f). Assignment to ecological quality bands

If quality band limits are provided for each BMWP O/E index, then each simulated sample can be classified into bands on the basis of its value for each individual O/E index. An overall band for the sample can be developed as the lower of the bands for the sample based on (say) number of taxa and ASPT. This classification can be done uncorrected for bias and, if available, corrected for bias. For each BMWP index and for the overall band scheme, the proportion of simulated O/E values falling in each band estimates the probabilities that the site at that time was of each ecological quality band.

(g). Face bands

The "observed" O/E ratios for the sample, namely O_T/E_T, O_A/E_A and O_S/E_S, are also classified to quality bands and given an overall band. These are the "observed" bandings which would be reported in the absence of any information on errors. They are termed the "face bands" uncorrected for bias. The "face band" corrected for bias is defined as the most probable band as estimated from the bias-corrected simulated samples.

   The "face band" uncorrected for bias will usually also be the most probable band uncorrected for bias. However, discrepancies may occur when the "observed" O/E ratio is very close to the boundary of a band, as the simulations may estimate the neighbouring quality band to be slightly more probable. Such differences will not have any major influence on tests for differences in O/E ratios in sample comparisons, or on probabilistic assessments of a change in quality band between two samples being compared.

(h). Assessing differences in O/E values and quality bands between two samples

This is done using an extension of the above simulation techniques for assessing individual samples. The first sample in a pair is known as sample 1 and the second as sample 2. In each simulation r, simulated O/E values are calculated for each of the two samples using the methods in *(a)–(d)* above.

   If the same values of the environmental variables were used to derive the expected values for both sample 1 and 2 in a comparison, the errors in expected values will probably be highly correlated for the two samples. In such cases, the same random deviates Z_{eTr} and Z_{eAr} in *(c)* are used to generate the errors in the two samples' expected values for any particular simulation; otherwise independent random deviates are used.

   For each simulation, the difference in the two simulated O/E values (sample 2 value minus sample 1 value) is calculated for each BMWP index (number of taxa, ASPT and BMWP score) to give D_{Tr}, D_{Ar} and D_{Sr} respectively when uncorrected for bias, and D_{Tbr}, D_{Abr} and D_{Sbr} respectively when corrected for bias.

   Each of the two samples is assigned to a quality band on the basis of its O/E values for that simulation. This is done to build up a two-way frequency (and hence probability) distribution that sample 1 belongs to band 'x' (say) and sample 2 belongs to band 'y'. From this two-way probability distribution, the probability that samples 1 and 2 are from the same quality band can be estimated, together with the probabilities that sample 2 is one band better than 1, one band worse, two or more bands better, or two or more bands worse.

   Confidence limits for the difference in O/E values are obtained from the frequency distribution of the differences, using the same approach as for single sample O/E values.

CHAPTER 4

Classification of the biological quality of rivers in England and Wales

BRIAN HEMSLEY-FLINT

Environment Agency, Northeast Region, Ridings Area, Phoenix House Global Avenue, Leeds, West Yorkshire, LS11 8PG, UK

Summary

Summarisation of complex biological information is crucial if it is to be utilised in river management strategies. In the past there has been a lack of standardised methodology for reporting biological data, and this has led to the under-utilisation of results. The 16th Report of the Royal Commission on Environmental Pollution recommended that a classification scheme for biological data should be produced for reporting river quality for 1995. The Environment Agency has acted on this recommendation and with the aid of RIVPACS has defined a scheme for categorising river sites into six quality grades, according to their macroinvertebrate communities. This scheme was developed by biologists within the Environment Agency, to be biologically meaningful and independent of, but complementary to, other classification schemes. It is intended that the classification scheme will be used not only for national quality reporting, but also for local river quality management. So far the scheme has been welcomed by staff throughout the Environment Agency and by others involved in river management.

Introduction

Before raw biological data can be used for river management purposes it must be converted into a form that is meaningful to river managers. This process generally relies on condensing complex data into a simpler form, but in so doing there is some loss of information content. For too long the biological component has been excluded from consideration in water management, simply because the message was too complex. Additionally, there was a lack of consistency in biological reporting across England and Wales.

Early history of biological classification schemes

There have been many attempts to summarise biological data into quality classes or grades. The National Water Council scheme of the 1970s incorporated a biological component such that the final quality grade, as determined chemically, could be amended to take account of the biological quality (NWC 1978). This scheme detailed the biological communities which would be expected in each of the four quality grades; however, these communities took no account of the differences in the macroinvertebrate fauna across the country, and the system soon became unworkable as biologists in different regions interpreted the scheme to suit their local needs.

In 1977, the Freshwater Biological Association (FBA) was commissioned by the Department of the Environment (DoE) and the Natural Environment Research Council to "type" rivers according to their biological communities, and to determine whether the macroinvertebrate fauna could be predicted from physical and chemical features. The resultant R&D eventually led to the development of the software package RIVPACS, described by Wright in Chapter 1.

In 1976 the Water Data Unit of the DoE convened a working party to provide a biological classification scheme for reporting the results of the 1980 National Biological Survey. The Biological Monitoring Working Party (BMWP) developed what is now termed the BMWP score system (Biological Monitoring Working Party 1978; National Water Council 1981), and whilst the raw score derived by this system was used to produce an annotated map, it was not adopted officially for reporting the 1980 survey. It has, however, been used by water industry biologists throughout the country for summarising the results of various biological surveys.

In some regions, water industry biologists developed their own means of condensing and reporting on biological data. Those in the Yorkshire Water Authority (1978) devised the Yorkshire Interpreted Index, which has been used successfully from the mid-1970s through to the present day for reporting the results of biological surveys to pollution control staff. This index remains unpublished, but in essence it uses knowledge of the rivers in Yorkshire to assess the faunal community to be expected in a river, and compares the fauna found during sampling with that expectation. The index is reliant on experienced biologists and is subject to debate; nevertheless, for more than 20 years the scheme has proved successful in highlighting problem areas and in achieving several successful prosecutions in court cases.

Anglian Water Authority developed and published the Lincoln Quality Index (Extence, Bates *et al.* 1987) using BMWP data, North West Water Authority (1982) developed their own quality classification scheme, and Severn-Trent Water Authority used the Trent Biotic Index (Woodiwiss 1964). This plethora of different systems led to confusion when attempting to compare biological reports around the country, and to competition for wider recognition of the individual schemes. Specific sampling methodologies associated with different indices and Water Authorities added to the problem of comparability.

When the water industry was privatised in 1989/90 and the National Rivers Authority (NRA) was created, there was for the first time one body responsible for reporting water quality. It was apparent to biologists within the NRA, with responsibilities for the collection and recording of biological data, that there had to be national consistency in sample collection, analysis and reporting. At this time RIVPACS II was made available to the NRA and with it came a requirement for a specific sampling regime. Agreement was reached amongst the regional biologists of the NRA that the RIVPACS methodology should be adopted for national sampling programmes, and for consistency some regions also adopted it in their regional methodology.

RIVPACS and a national reporting scheme for biological quality

The Institute of Freshwater Ecology (IFE) was commissioned by the NRA, as part of a larger R&D project, to develop a scheme to divide biological data into quality grades for use in reporting the results of the 1990 National Biological Survey. This was to utilise the results of RIVPACS analyses of the 1990 Biological Survey. A scheme (5M Grading system) was developed (Wright, Furse *et al.* 1991), but whilst it provided a nationally consistent presentation of biological quality, the resultant grades lacked the resolution required of an operational tool capable of helping to identify and prioritise expenditure by the newly privatised water companies and other industries discharging effluent into rivers. This lack of resolution was in part due to the limited number of quality grades (four), and in part due to omissions in the reference database of RIVPACS. Consequently the IFE was contracted to enlarge the database, assess the working of the software which comprised RIVPACS, and produce a revised system in time for reporting the 1995 National Biological Survey.

During 1992 the Royal Commission on Environmental Pollution published their 16th Report on Freshwater Quality. They concluded that biological assessment of water quality was an important part of water quality management and their first recommendation was *"that the regulatory authorities should endeavour to develop a general classification scheme based on biological assessment for use throughout the UK in the 1995 and subsequent surveys"*.

This recommendation was acted upon by the NRA, and during 1995-96 the Biological General Quality Assessment scheme (Biological GQA) was developed, utilising the revised RIVPACS III software and data collected during the 1990 and 1995 National Biological Surveys.

Early development of a biological general quality assessment scheme (GQA)

The concept of comparing the BMWP statistics for the macroinvertebrate fauna found in a sample with those predicted by RIVPACS, which was first used in the 1990 survey, was continued for the 1995 Biological GQA Survey. Use of the observed to expected (O/E) ratio, termed the Ecological Quality Index (EQI) for each BMWP index, offers a method for assessing the proportional similarity of the site to its unstressed state. EQIs can be calculated for each of the BMWP statistics of score, number of taxa (N-Taxa) and average score per taxon (ASPT). The results of R&D studies (Clarke *et al.* 1994) recommended that, for 1995 and subsequent reporting, ASPT and N-Taxa produced the most meaningful information from the data, and it was agreed by regional NRA biologists that these should be used together, to form the basis of the new biological classification scheme.

The development process was started by Tony Warn of Anglian Region, who produced a discussion paper for NRA water quality managers which proposed a classification system with six quality grades and distributions of river lengths in each grade proportionally similar to the Chemical GQA scheme, which was already established and used for reporting the chemical quality of rivers.

All regions of the NRA were asked to assess the proposals and comment on their applicability to local river systems. When the proposed classification scheme was applied to data from rivers of the Ridings Area of the Northeast Region, which reflect the whole spectrum of quality, it produced a distribution of results similar to the 1990 "5M" scheme and failed to adequately differentiate at the extremes of the quality scale (despite having two extra quality grades). A comparison of the results of the proposed scheme with the Yorkshire Interpreted Index, which is already accepted to be a reasonable representation of biological quality, indicated a lack of discrimination power in the new scheme at sites of very poor quality, indicating a need to amend the criteria for differentiating quality. Similarly, regions with very good quality rivers found that the proposed scheme was not adequately distinguishing the "very good" sites from those that are merely "good". It was therefore necessary to reassess the scheme in order to produce a system acceptable to all regions and covering all quality types.

Several meetings of NRA regional biologists were held to progress the development of the Biological GQA. It was agreed that the classification scheme should be biologically meaningful and that there should be no predetermined proportioning of river length per grade; criteria for the grades should be based on EQI ASPT, and EQI N-Taxa, considered together. A list of grade boundaries was proposed by Northeast Region but this was not readily acceptable to some regions, who proposed alternative grade boundaries (see Tables 4.1 and 4.2, p. 60). Some of these proposals worked on the principle that there should be "rounded" cut-off levels for simplicity and acceptability to outside users. Against this, it was argued that whilst the presentation of the GQA needed to be simple, the derivation required a certain level of complexity to achieve a biologically acceptable system. Since river ecology is extremely

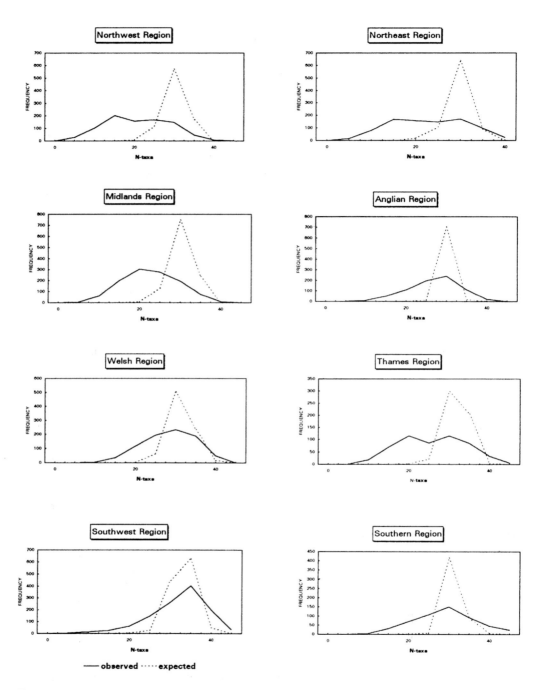

Figure 4.1. The regional distribution in England and Wales for the observed (solid lines) and expected (dotted lines) number of taxa (N-Taxa) of macroinvertebrates in rivers. Expected values were calculated using RIVPACS.

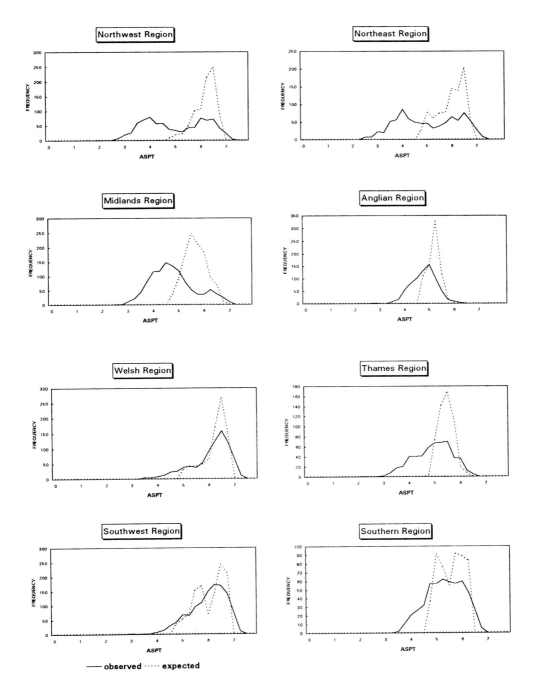

Figure 4.2. The regional distribution in England and Wales for the observed (solid lines) and expected (dotted lines) average score per taxon (ASPT) for macroinvertebrates in rivers. Expected values were calculated using RIVPACS.

complex, it follows that a simple system is unlikely to be able to produce a workable classification scheme.

Table 4.1. *Early proposals for the boundaries of six grades (a to f) based on EQI ASPT, for regions in England and Wales.*

Bold numbers indicate parts of the proposals that were finally utilised in the Biological GQA scheme (see the text).

Grade	Anglian	Anglian/Welsh	Midlands	Northeast	Final GQA
a	1.04	**1.00**	**1.00**	**1.00**	**1.00**
b	0.95	**0.90**	**0.90**	**0.90**	**0.90**
c	0.85	0.80	0.80	0.78	**0.77**
d	0.75	0.70	0.70	0.68	**0.65**
e	0.65	0.60	0.60	**0.50**	**0.50**
f	<0.65	<0.60	<0.60	**<0.50**	**<0.50**

Table 4.2. *Early proposals for the boundaries of six grades (a to f) based on EQI N-Taxa, for regions in England and Wales.*

Bold numbers indicate parts of the proposals that were finally utilised in the Biological GQA scheme (see the text).

Grade	Anglian	Anglian/Welsh	Midlands	Northeast	Final GQA
a	**0.85**	**0.85**	0.80	**0.85**	**0.85**
b	**0.70**	**0.70**	0.65	**0.70**	**0.70**
c	**0.55**	0.60	0.50	0.60	**0.55**
d	0.40	0.40	0.35	0.50	**0.45**
e	0.20	0.20	0.20	**0.30**	**0.30**
f	<0.20	<0.20	<0.20	**<0.30**	**<0.30**

At first it was difficult to understand why there were such differing views on what was acceptable as grade descriptors. It was only when the distribution of results across the country was examined that the differences became apparent.

Frequency distributions comparing observed and expected results from ASPT and N-Taxa

Plots of the frequency distributions of observed and expected BMWP scores, N-Taxa and ASPT, were made on a national and regional basis. For the last two parameters, regional plots are presented in Figures 4.1 and 4.2.

These text-figures revealed differences between the Environment Agency's eight regions, not only in the observed values but also in the expected values derived from RIVPACS. The expected differences were small but anticipated because rivers in different parts of the country have different faunal communities, and RIVPACS predictions will reflect this fact. Regional differences in the distribution of the observed data highlighted why there was no agreement in definition of "poor quality". Northwest, Northeast and Midlands Regions all had significant numbers of sites with large differences between observed and expected faunas, resulting in low EQIs, whilst Welsh and Southwest Regions had relatively few such sites.

The frequency distributions in Figures 4.1 and 4.2 showed that expected values of ASPT for Anglian Region were lower than those of, say, Welsh Region, whilst data for the Southwest and

were supported by training workshops for all Agency biologists.

Variability between sampling staff in the collection of biological and environmental data, across a range of river types and qualities, has been estimated in an R&D study (Furse, Clarke *et al.* 1995) and this information has contributed to the estimates of confidence we can now place on our data (see also Chapter 3). However, there is still further progress to be made on most of these topics.

Standards and targets for analytical performance

As it is not possible to construct standard samples for quality control purposes or to reliably re-analyse samples perfectly, it has been necessary to adopt a standard against which the Agency can measure its performance. The analytical quality of the team at the IFE, who undertake the audit, provides this standard, and the performance of our internal AQC analysts is measured against this. Although IFE staff are fallible, using their performance as our standard is realistic because it is also the standard to which the RIVPACS reference samples were analysed.

An R&D project undertaken by the Water Research Centre examined the early results of the audit and concluded that an average of no more than two missed taxa per sample was an achievable and recommendable target (Kinley & Ellis 1991). The throughput of samples within the Agency is not high enough to allow statistically meaningful measurements of the quality of analyses by individual biologists, so performance is measured at laboratory and regional level. Although the target (see van Dijk 1994) and the auditing procedures have been reviewed since they were first introduced, both remain substantially the same. Experience has shown that the target can be achieved by reasonably experienced analysts, without the need to spend excessive time on sorting and identification.

Sampling variability

Sampling is potentially a major source of variation and there is merit in attempting to improve precision for the national river quality surveys. Reducing the variability of the sampling process is one way in which this can be achieved. The methods currently specified for RIVPACS III are stricter than those in early versions, and in some cases are stricter than those used at some of the original reference sites. However, progressively more stringent criteria have been used for acceptance of reference sites in successive versions of RIVPACS.

The Agency's sampling handbook (Environment Agency 1997b) was written with close cooperation from the IFE, and represents the best practice for obtaining samples compatible with RIVPACS. It includes equipment specifications, site selection, sampling, the collection of environmental data (in the field and from maps), and procedures for macroinvertebrate sorting and enumeration. A second handbook (Environment Agency 1996) identifies a subset of procedures for national surveys, together with instructions for GQA site selection and data collation. A third handbook (Environment Agency 1999) will describe the quality assurance procedures used for the internal AQC and for the IFE audit.

To account for the variation which will inevitably remain after this standardisation of methods and careful training of operators, the IFE carried out a replicate sampling exercise at 16 sites which included the four major RIVPACS site groupings and also sites which ranged from good to poor biological quality. From this a set of error terms was developed, describing the average variation to be expected from the sampling process. The variability of the environmental data required for RIVPACS was also examined (see Furse, Clarke *et al.* 1995, and Chapter 3). These error terms, together with a facility for entering a measure of analytical performance for a given laboratory, have been incorporated into the latest version of the system (RIVPACS III+), and offer a procedure for grading rivers by their biological quality and attaching statements of confidence to a grade, and comparing paired datasets. These can be comparisons of two different sites or the same site on two different sampling occasions.

Local problems in introducing quality assurance

Initially, there was some resistance within the Agency (and its predecessor, the National Rivers Authority) to the adoption of standard, national protocols. This was partly a reaction to the formation of a single, national body from sections of ten separate Water Authorities. However, it also reflected the fact that individual laboratories had developed their own methods, over many years, in order to take account of the available resources, the characteristics of the watercourses in their area, and the type of operational work which they were asked to undertake. In most cases, the local procedures had proved to be appropriate over a long period. They were therefore reluctant to change their methods because the new protocol did not seem to help local operational work and because RIVPACS was rarely used in the water industry at that time, being still regarded as "Research and Development". Poor communication of ongoing developments between senior biologists on national steering groups and the operational staff managing the laboratories may have hindered the necessary changes, and this must be considered at an early stage when similar situations arise in the future.

Whether samples should be analysed after preservation or returned to the laboratory and analysed live is still a contentious issue within the Agency. At present, both procedures are acceptable and are described in the Agency procedures manual (Environment Agency 1997b).

The value of effective training

As part of the preparation for the 1995 GQA survey, training was given to *all* Agency biologists by means of practical workshops held in every region by two experienced staff, one from the IFE and one from the Agency. These workshops were vital in helping biologists to understand and adopt the new protocols, by means of practical demonstrations and explanations of the reasoning behind them. In many cases, this was the first time that operational biologists had direct involvement in the protocols.

The second and equally important aim of the training workshops was to tap into the wealth of practical experience in the regional biology teams. This proved to be especially valuable and they were able to make a substantial contribution to the further development of the protocols, ensuring that they dealt with the real problems faced by working biologists.

An earlier proposal for a central training session for key personnel who would then cascade the information in their own region was abandoned, and it is now apparent that the workshop approach had major advantages and played a large part in the effectiveness of the 1995 survey.

Developing good analytical performance

Inexperienced Agency staff undergo two phases of training, involving different levels of checking and supervision. Results produced by inexperienced staff are subject to the audit before being accepted for operational use.

Ensuring that staff receive suitable training is an important component of quality assurance, and full training records should be maintained. The Agency normally requires biologists to have a relevant degree or equivalent, but this is unlikely to have included detailed training in ecological survey or taxonomic analysis. The Natural History Museum offers a series of basic qualifications in identification (the IdQ exams) in order to promote high standards, but these are run on a commercial basis and no formal training is offered. Such qualifications make a statement about a person's ability at the time of the examination, but skills may decline through lack of use or failure to stay abreast of new taxonomy and methods. As part of its progressive implementation of quality assurance, the Agency may have to move towards more structured training to ensure that staff develop and maintain the necessary skills.

Audit

The practice of measuring errors in the sorting and identification of macroinvertebrates to BMWP family level was introduced in 1990, using the IFE to provide a standard against which to measure the analytical performance of Agency biologists. The IFE team have audited samples for the Environment Agency and equivalent organisations in Northern Ireland and Scotland since 1990, giving a high degree of consistency.

At BMWP family level, the majority of errors are the result of taxa being missed during sample sorting. These errors are termed "gains" by the auditors because they represent additions to the listing supplied by the Agency. "Losses", where the Agency analyst records a taxon which the auditors cannot find, are much less frequent and usually are the result of misidentification or errors in recording. The annual mean number of "gains" per sample is used to measure performance at laboratory and regional level. The precision of this mean is determined by the number of samples audited, rather than the proportion of samples audited and, after preliminary investigations, it was shown that the errors approximate to a Poisson distribution (Kinley & Ellis 1991). Hence, confidence limits can be calculated for the annual mean, and sixty samples per region each year gives an acceptably reliable estimate of performance.

An audit of the procedures for collecting macroinvertebrates was considered to be impractical. Instead, a training video was produced for the 1990 National Survey (National Rivers Authority 1990) and a revised draft of the sampling handbook (Environment Agency 1997b), accompanied by regional workshops, preceded the 1995 GQA survey.

The results of the audit over a period of seven years (Table 5.1) indicated that the quality of sample sorting and taxon identification varied substantially throughout the country, and in some cases was unacceptable. In the early years, some of the worst results were ascribed to sorting and identifying on the bank-side instead of following the recommended methods. It is unusual for a laboratory to have a combination of good and bad analysts, and although the ability of individuals varies, the overall standard generally reflects the "ethos" of the laboratory. Some laboratory teams, and especially their managers, take quality assurance more seriously than others. Changes in the number of "gains" are most noticeable when managers change their perception of what is acceptable.

Analytical quality control (AQC)

The audit provides a good estimate of the quality of the work done by each region. In addition, the auditors give details and information on those taxa involved in errors in each audited sample, and identify new taxa (i.e. "gains") to species. However, with a small team at the IFE doing the work, the small proportion of samples audited, and the fact that they are sent to the IFE in relatively large batches, there is inevitably a delay in receiving audit results. This means that if quality is falling it is generally too late to take action based on audit results. For this reason, an internal AQC scheme is also in operation within the Agency. The scheme is designed to provide rapid feedback to the analysts, allowing corrective action to be taken in good time. Whereas the audit simply measures quality, the AQC scheme allows the Agency to manage it. The AQC scheme was devised for the National Rivers Authority by the Water Research Centre (van Dijk 1994) and has been modified by the Agency in the light of experience (Environment Agency 1999). It is based on cusum statistics, as these are better at detecting small changes than the more common Shewhart chart approach (see, for example, BS 5700 1984). The same

Table 5.1. *Environment Agency audit results, showing mean numbers of taxa that were "gained" following audits of samples from each region in England and Wales (A – L) in successive years, from 1990 to 1996.*

Dashes (—) indicate gaps caused by the amalgamation of regions (from ten to eight in number).

Region	1990	1991	1992	1993	1994	1995	1996
A	3.55	1.40	2.70	2.38	1.73	2.25	1.85
B	3.32	1.12	0.71	0.65	—	—	—
C	—	—	—	0.80	1.48	1.52	1.38
D	1.40	1.18	1.12	—	—	—	—
E	4.39	3.68	2.77	2.30	2.54	2.51	2.62
F	3.75	1.88	2.10	2.48	1.83	1.84	2.20
G	1.90	1.28	1.77	1.37	1.13	1.33	1.95
H	1.90	1.08	1.53	1.32	1.13	—	—
I	—	—	—	—	—	1.53	1.13
J	3.66	1.73	1.88	2.28	2.38	—	—
K	2.74	1.98	2.20	2.07	2.42	2.05	2.03
L	2.37	1.48	2.08	1.95	1.30	1.98	1.88

procedures (i.e. re-sorting and determining the number of "gains") are used in the AQC as in the audit, except that one out of every batch of ten samples is selected for re-analysis. The re-analysis takes place within two weeks, and this provides the rapid feedback needed. The AQC analysts in each team are the most experienced biologists, who have proved their ability and consistency through previous audit results. An essential feature of the scheme is that it should be fair, and be seen to be fair. Random selection of samples, and the transfer of selected samples to fresh containers with coded labels, are just some of the procedures designed to ensure fairness.

The frequency with which AQC samples are selected is governed by the number of samples passing through the laboratory and the speed with which an indication of falling performance is required. The choice of one in ten was based on the throughput of an average laboratory. The statistics of the process indicate that if quality falls by an average of one missed taxon a warning will be given, on average, within ten AQC samples. Thus, if a laboratory analyses 20 samples per week, (i.e. 2 AQC samples), it will be five weeks before there is a warning of falling performance. The worse the performance, the more rapidly the alarm will sound. However, the need for a rapid alarm has to be balanced against the frequency of occurrence of false alarms, which are inevitable in any statistical scheme. The current scheme will only give a false alarm on average once in every 100 AQC samples, which equates to 1000 real samples.

The AQC scheme recognises three states.

(1). Accept, when the analytical quality is meeting the target of an average of no more than two "gains". In this state, no action need be taken.

(2). Defer, when it is unclear whether the analytical quality is acceptable or not (i.e. it may progress to the alarm state or it may move back to accept). In the defer state, no action should be taken as the process will often go back into accept.

(3). Alarm, when the quality is outside the target and remedial action is needed. In an alarm state, urgent action must be taken to return performance to the target level. This may involve the retraining of one or more staff members, allowing more time for analysis, cutting down on distractions (such as re-routing telephone calls) and many other possibilities.

Because of the effort involved in collecting the samples, an early decision was made that data from samples would not be discarded automatically due to AQC failures. This situation occurs in many analytical chemistry laboratories, and can result in the loss of data which may still be of some value despite being of lower quality. However, all original samples are retained when in defer mode so that they can be re-analysed if necessary.

For the AQC scheme to be effective, the internal AQC checking must be of the highest quality. Because "gains" are more frequent than "losses", errors in AQC checking almost always cause an underestimate of the number of errors in the original analysis. The AQC scheme therefore indicates that the laboratory's analytical quality is better than it actually is. Because of this, in 1995, some laboratories that failed to meet the quality target (as measured by the audit) had few, if any, alarms from their internal AQC scheme.

To resolve this issue, each laboratory target is now corrected to allow for the average number of taxa which their AQC analysts miss. By auditing samples which have been re-analysed for AQC, we determine the performance of the AQC analysts in each laboratory. This is subtracted from the national target of two missed taxa, to give a corrected target for that laboratory. This tactic provides an incentive for the AQC analysts to take care, because if they do not, their colleagues' target is lowered! It should be noted that for each audited sample, results are available for the original analysis and for the AQC re-analysis. Hence, the audit now serves two purposes: that of measuring overall quality, and also the performance of the AQC analysts.

Table 5.1 shows that, without exception, the performance of each region improved between 1990 and 1991, as displayed by a reduction in "gains". Region B, especially, took quality to heart, and made substantial improvements in performance by introducing its own internal AQC scheme. This was very effective, although it was considered to be too onerous for adoption nationally. In some regions there was, however, some later reduction in performance as experienced staff moved on and, perhaps, enthusiasm waned a little. Nevertheless, in general, quality assurance has been a success, although the national AQC scheme has yet to fully prove itself, as 1996 was the first year in which the revised scheme was run (the most significant change being from a random selection process, which sometimes failed to give an adequate number of AQC samples, to selection of one sample from each batch of ten).

The future: some practical issues

The quality assurance of work undertaken by outside contractors is a difficult but very important issue for the Agency. It is essential to ensure that all work, including that done by contractors, is of an acceptable and generally high quality. Contractors offering work of high quality may be undercut in price by others whose quality is poor. The Agency is therefore moving towards the requirement that all contracted work is subject to audit.

At present a number of problems remain.

(1). The Agency has no audit scheme for species-level analyses, for which identification errors are probably as important as sorting errors and the throughput of samples may be low.

(2). Similarly, the Agency has no criteria or methods for auditing estimates of abundance.

(3). If samples are audited after analysis there is sometimes doubt over whether the contractor has analysed and retained the entire sample.

(4). When using competitive tenders, cost is a major factor and the auditing of work undertaken by contractors increases overall costs.

(5). Agency experience indicates that there is no clear relation between the price a contractor charges and the quality of the work: some inexpensive contractors produce good quality work, and *vice-versa*!

(6). For a contractor to *guarantee* a certain level of quality is difficult (in effect, they have to insure themselves) and this introduces further costs.

(7). In practice, it is hard to include a penalty clause in a contract for failure to meet a quality specification, unless the quality assurance results clearly indicate unacceptable performance. Frequently there are too few samples for a statistically valid audit.

It is vital that the audit of contractors' work is undertaken under a separate contract to an independent company, or by Agency biologists. Contractors must never know which of their samples are to be audited.

There is a move within the Agency and other institutions to introduce laboratory accreditation issued by independent organisations. The Agency's analytical chemistry laboratories are accredited by the UK Accreditation Service but few biology laboratories have taken this route. Accreditation is primarily a paperwork audit trail, and concentrates on matters such as equipment maintenance and data handling. It is not specifically designed to solve the problems of analytical quality for ecological surveys.

Future developments within the Environment Agency will need to address outstanding methodological problems, such as deep-water sampling, improvement of structured training, and developing quality assurance for other biological techniques, including species-level macroinvertebrate analysis.

CHAPTER 6

The application of RIVPACS procedures in headwater streams – an extensive and important national resource

MIKE T. FURSE

Institute of Freshwater Ecology, River Laboratory, East Stoke, Wareham, Dorset, BH20 6BB, UK

Summary

Headwaters are defined as the first 2.5 km of a watercourse from its furthest upstream source. There are 146,853 mapped stream sources in Great Britain, and headwaters have an estimated collective length of up to 256,814 km. These small watercourses support many specialised taxa and contribute *ca* 20% of the total macroinvertebrate species richness in whole river catchments. However, by virtue of their size, they are very vulnerable to channel modification, agricultural pollution, acidification and drought.

Headwaters are an extensive national resource but one that is very under-represented in monitoring programmes and scientific studies. Trials using RIVPACS II to evaluate the quality of headwaters suggested that ASPT values could be predicted with reasonable accuracy, but the number of taxa to be expected was almost always over-predicted because RIVPACS lacked adequate reference sites.

The development and testing of a headwaters version of RIVPACS is described, based on the application of MDA to a TWINSPAN classification of the macroinvertebrate assemblages of 214 essentially unpolluted headwater sites. Problems of developing the system are considered in the wider context of the RIVPACS approach and options for the further development of the system are discussed.

Introduction

Definition of headwaters

The term "headwaters" is widely applied in ecological studies but its precise definition is rarely given. One early exception was provided by Carpenter (1928) in her zonation scheme for British rivers. She described headstreams (and highland brooks) as being small, often torrential watercourses, characterised by having low and relatively constant temperatures. A more empirical definition has been offered in the benchmark paper of Vannote, Minshall *et al.* (1980), who categorised headwaters as first to third order streams (*sensu* Strahler 1952, 1957). In subsequent publications by Vannote and his colleagues this definition was refined to first and second order streams only (Minshall, Petersen *et al.* 1983). Brown & Brussock (1991), Vuori *et al.* (1998) and Rheinhardt, Rheinhardt *et al.* (1998) have retained this latter definition. In contrast, Savage & Rabe (1979), in their classification of small streams, described first order streams as "the smallest headwater branches".

In most accounts, however, the term is more loosely applied and the authors' understanding of the word is left to be deduced through scrutiny of tabulated environmental data. For example, when investigating the impact of catchment disturbance on macroinvertebrate communities, Richards & Minshall (1992) described their five impact and five reference streams as "headwaters". However, their stream order varied from first to fifth and the stream catchment areas ranged from 2.9 to 298.8 km². Differences in interpretation of the term are hardly surprising, as the definition provided by the Shorter Oxford Dictionary (Little *et al.* 1959) is "the streams from the sources of a river" with no indication of the absolute length or size of watercourses so-classified. It is therefore essential that any reported study of headwaters clearly delimits the context in which the term is applied.

In a series of headwater studies upon which this account is based (Furse 1996, 1997, 1998; Furse, Winder *et al.* 1991, 1993; Furse, Symes *et al.* 1995), initial attempts to define headwaters compared the relative merits of the use of distance from source, stream order and discharge (Furse, Winder *et al.* 1991). As a result of the variation in stream size and distance from source associated with the use of stream orders to define headwaters, and in the absence of sufficiently detailed information on stream discharges, it was concluded that use of distance from source was the only reliable method of providing a precise, consistent and easily applied definition of headwaters. The inclusion of distance from source in the definition also requires that consistent cartographic sources are used in its application. Consequently, the definition of a headwater employed in this study is *"a watercourse within 2.5 kilometres of its furthest source, as marked by a blue line, on Ordnance Survey (OS) Landranger Series maps with a scale of 1:50,000".*

Number and length of headwaters

A detailed analysis of the distribution of freshwaters in Great Britain (Smith & Lyle 1979) indicated that there are 146,853 mapped first order streams in Great Britain. These are primary streams without tributaries. A further 36,534 second order streams, i.e. those formed by the merger of two first order watercourses (Strahler 1957), were identified (Smith & Lyle 1979). In total, first order streams represented *ca* 75% of the number of streams and rivers of all orders in Britain, and second order streams represented an additional 19%. No comparable figures are available for stream length but it has been estimated that the combined length of first and second order streams in England and Wales lies between 66,825 km and 125,964 km, or *ca* 70%, on average, of total watercourse length for the two countries (Furse 1997). If the same basis of estimation is extended to Scotland, then the total length of headwaters in Great Britain as a whole lies between 132,675 km and 256,814 km. When an attempt was made to quantify the relative lengths of small streams in the USA, Leopold *et al.* (1964) estimated that first to third order streams comprise *ca* 85% of the country's total stream length.

A detailed review of the conservation value of headwaters and the impact of environmental stress on headwater macroinvertebrate assemblages is provided by Furse (1998), and is summarised in the following sections.

The conservation value of headwaters

Despite their small size, headwaters make a major contribution to both the species richness of river catchments and the distribution of rare and threatened species. Where attention has been given to such watercourses, new or apparently rare species have been found. Examples include the blackfly *Metacnephia amphora* Ladle & Bass (Ladle & Bass 1975) and the rare mayfly *Paraleptophlebia werneri* Ulmer (Macan & Macan 1940). Both species are confined to intermittent headwaters of chalkstreams and would be greatly endangered by environmental degradation of their habitat. Similarly, many new records of the apparently rare caddisfly *Hydropsyche saxonica* McLachlan, have resulted from increased attention to the fauna of headwaters (Blackburn & Forest 1995). Due to their rarity, many taxa associated with headwaters, such as *P. werneri* and *H. saxonica*, have national or international conservation status (Bratton 1990; Wallace 1991).

Whilst headwaters often support rare species, many of which only occur in these small watercourses, their macroinvertebrate assemblages tend not to be characterised by high species richness. The relatively low species richness of headwaters is recognised in the River Continuum Concept (Vannote, Minshall *et al.* 1980; Minshall *et al.* 1985) which incorporates a theoretical pattern of relatively low richness in headwaters, rising to a maximum in middle reaches (fourth to sixth order) and then declining again further downstream. This pattern has been demonstrated practically in North American streams by Bruns, Minshall *et al.* (1982), Bruns & Minshall (1985), Bruns *et al.* (1987) and Crunkilton & Duchrow (1991), and also in two recent Irish studies which incorporated "headwater" reaches (Giller & Twomey 1993; Clenaghan, Giller *et al.* 1998).

In conservation terms, the significant feature of headwater macroinvertebrate assemblages is not their species richness but their overall structure and the rarity of some of their component species. Furthermore, other taxa may not necessarily be rare but simply exclusive to or largely confined to headwaters. In the Buffalo River, South Africa, twelve taxa were exclusive to a single headwater site (Palmer, Palmer *et al.* 1994). Thus, headwaters may make a significant contribution to overall species richness of river systems and play an important role in conserving individual species and overall catchment biodiversity.

The need to properly manage headwaters is a logical consequence of their conservation value. As a precursor to this, it is important to understand the environmental stresses operating on headwaters and to have reliable procedures for evaluating the impact of those stresses.

Environmental impacts on rural headwaters

The vast majority of headwaters are rural streams with few urban influences. Their catchments are used principally for farming. However, their rural context still leaves them vulnerable to a broad spectrum of environmental stresses. These stresses may be exacerbated by the small size and low discharge of these streams, which limit their capacity to buffer either physical or chemical impacts.

As a consequence of their size, rural headwaters are very vulnerable to the effects of channel dredging, straightening, culverting, loss of riparian vegetative strips or even relocation to improve land drainage or field size for farming (Howard-Williams *et al.* 1986; Iversen, Kronvang *et al.* 1993; Scott, White *et al.* 1994; Haapala & Muotka 1998). Access by livestock may cause physical damage (Quinn, Williamson *et al.* 1992) and headwaters are also vulnerable to point and non-point sources of pollution, such as slurry lagoons, dairy drainage, artificial fertilisers and a whole suite of agricultural chemicals (Department of the Environment and Welsh Office 1986; Sibley *et al.* 1991; Whiles & Wallace 1992; Zwick 1992; Rutt *et al.* 1993). In the uplands, forestry practices and acidification represent different forms of threat (e.g. United Kingdom Acid Waters Review Group 1989; Ahtiainen 1992; Smith 1992; Ormerod, Rundle *et al.* 1993; Harriman, Likens *et al.* 1994; Trayler & Davis 1998).

Drought also represents a serious problem in headwaters. As a result of their small size and discharge, headwaters are very vulnerable to climatic extremes which can cause severe reduction in flow or even complete drying up (Wright, Hiley *et al.* 1984; Giles *et al.* 1991). This situation is often exacerbated by improved land drainage (Vuori *et al.* 1998) or by the common practice of abstraction for irrigation (English Nature 1997).

Biological monitoring and evaluating the biological condition of headwaters

Headwaters represent about 70% of the total length of watercourses in Britain. However, from 8000 sites in the 1995 General Quality Assessment (GQA) of the condition of British watercourses, only 12% of sites were on headwaters. Even this was an improvement on the 1990 River Quality Survey (RQS) where just 11% of sites were on headwaters (Furse 1997).

There are obvious reasons for this poor representation. Larger streams contain the most important fisheries and are most likely to be subject to major industrial and urban pollution. They are also more often used as direct sources of drinking water. Where the National Rivers Authority (NRA), and subsequently the Environment Agency, have included headwaters in their national monitoring programmes, many of these are urban streams with well-known pollution problems (Furse 1997).

In their evaluation of the results of macroinvertebrate sampling programmes in the 1990 RQS (Sweeting, Lowson *et al.* 1992) and 1995 GQA (see Chapter 4), no distinction was made between the approaches used to evaluate the biological condition of headwaters and that of larger watercourses. RIVPACS II was the procedure applied to the 1990 RQS and RIVPACS III was used to evaluate the condition of sites in the 1995 GQA. All versions of RIVPACS operate on the basis of comparing (by analogy) the fauna of sites being evaluated with the fauna of substantially unstressed sites that have comparable environmental characteristics. If there are insufficient headwater sites in the reference dataset, then predictions for headwater sites may be inadequate.

RIVPACS II, the version used to analyse the 1990 RQS, contained only 33 headwater sites or 7.5% of the 438 reference sites. These were confined to a small number of end-groups and gave poor discrimination between the many different environmental types of headwaters which exist in Britain. Furthermore, the end-groups containing headwaters often contained other sites from slightly further downstream. This, in conjunction with the influence of other end-groups in the prediction process, led to a higher predicted richness for headwaters than is expected by current stream ecosystem theory (Vannote, Minshall *et al.* 1980). RIVPACS III provides a better proportional representation of headwaters, with 62 (10%) of the 614 sites meeting the definition of location within 2.5 km from source. However, even here, only nine of the 35 end-groups contained more than one headwater site. Only four groups (4, 5, 7 and 31) contained more headwaters than non-headwaters. Discrimination between different types of headwaters still remains poorer than for downstream reaches.

For evaluating the results of local small stream surveys, Welsh biologists developed two algorithms for defining the impact of acidification (Rutt *et al.* 1990) and agricultural pollution (Rutt *et al.* 1993). These were based upon TWINSPAN classifications of macroinvertebrate assemblages. For each source of stress, appropriate sites, of all conditions of quality, were classified to a small number of end-groups which were assigned different quality classes. One of these end-groups was the reference group for good ecological quality and the others represented varying degrees of loss of quality. Indicator taxa were used to key new sites, whose quality was being assessed, to one of these end-groups. The use of a multivariate classification and the role of the reference group thus provided some similarities to the RIVPACS procedures. However, these techniques were for particular types of sites in a limited geographic region. The biologists who developed them acknowledged that their effectiveness outside South Wales was unproven and unlikely to be universal.

Development of a headwaters version of RIVPACS

Awareness of the need

Early awareness of the limitations of RIVPACS for use with headwater streams arose during the analysis phase of Countryside Survey 1990 (Barr, Bunce *et al.* 1993). This survey was an extensive study on the state of the British landscape and the biological assemblages it supported. Landscape, land cover and ecological data were collected from 508 1-km squares throughout Britain.

In order to survey macroinvertebrate assemblages, one stream was sampled in each square containing a watercourse. Most squares contained only headwaters. Thus, of the 361 sites sampled, 254 were on headwaters. As an output of the survey, the biological condition of these sites needed to be assessed.

When RIVPACS II was applied, the environmental data for the large majority of headwater sites generated the in-built system warning that the site had little probability of lying within the scope of the system. When predictions for these sites were allowed to proceed, most of the headwaters were categorised as not being in good biological condition, as defined by the banding system then in use by the NRA. Banding was based on Ecological Quality Indices (EQIs) derived from ratios of observed (O) and expected (E) Biological Monitoring Working Party (BMWP) index values (Sweeting, Lowson *et al.* 1992; see also p. 57 in Chapter 4). However, in the light of the warnings given, the reliability of the banding was subject to considerable doubt.

The principal cause of the apparent loss of quality was the lower than expected taxon richness, as indicated by the low EQI values for the number of taxa (N-Taxa, i.e. BMWP families). Almost all sites had values less than unity for EQI N-Taxa. In view of the relatively small number of headwater sites in RIVPACS II, the expected numbers of taxa were largely based on the species richness of downstream sites. This may not be an accurate reflection of the lower intrinsic richness of headwaters (e.g. Vannote, Minshall *et al.* 1980).

In contrast, values for the expected average score per taxon (ASPT; i.e. BMWP score ÷ N-Taxa) resulted in many EQI values close to or in excess of unity and these may have been a more reliable indication of the true biological condition of the sites. This may be because ASPT values represent the average tolerance to organic pollution of the taxa present, irrespective of the richness of the fauna. If so, then values are less likely to vary between headwaters and sites a short distance further downstream.

As a consequence, EQIs for ASPT were the only values given when the findings of Countryside Survey 1990 were published (Barr, Bunce *et al.* 1993). However, in view of the shortage of analagous sites in RIVPACS II, even these were presented with reservation. Clearly a more appropriate form of RIVPACS was required for a reliable interpretation of the biological condition of headwaters.

Site selection

The considerations involved in site selection for the headwaters system are the same as those faced during the initial development of RIVPACS. In particular, what is the intrinsic potential of headwater streams? How does this potential vary between streams of different environmental characteristics and how does one determine which sites make good reference points against which to judge the quality of others? In order to meet the needs of the water industry, any new system must be based on reliable data of comparable quality from a relatively large number of sites. These sites must provide suitable reference standards and, in view of the potentially large number of headwaters which could be monitored, the system must be quick and convenient to use.

GROUP NUMBER	1A	2A	3A	4A	5A	6B	7B	8B	9B	10B	11C	12C	13C	14C	15C	16D	17D	18D	19E
ALTITUDE (m)	358.3	347.9	361.2	170.3	164.3	213.3	220.9	223.3	156.8	201.3	114.0	132.8	86.0	130.1	113.5	131.5	48.4	111.7	27.8
SLOPE (m km⁻¹)	42.8	65.1	78.8	75.7	71.3	64.5	44.2	67.8	40.6	25.4	44.5	31.5	36.6	37.6	36.6	33.8	4.9	18.7	4.4
DISCHARGE (cat)	1.0	1.0	1.2	1.0	1.0	1.0	1.1	1.4	1.2	1.3	1.0	1.0	1.1	1.0	1.0	1.0	1.2	1.0	1.0
DISTANCE (km)	0.9	0.9	1.2	0.8	0.8	1.1	1.2	1.1	1.5	1.5	0.5	1.2	1.4	0.8	0.8	1.3	1.0	1.1	1.5
WATER WIDTH (m)	1.0	1.0	2.4	1.2	1.3	1.4	1.4	2.1	2.0	2.3	1.0	1.3	1.4	0.8	0.9	1.4	2.1	1.8	1.7
MEAN DEPTH (cm)	21.1	12.9	13.3	7.9	8.8	10.2	9.6	13.4	15.5	23.4	6.8	9.7	9.7	7.1	14.9	11.6	15.6	27.6	29.2
BOULDERS/COBBLES (%)	33.0	44.1	61.3	49.4	40.9	69.8	37.6	45.5	64.3	55.2	11.2	30.8	22.3	9.3	4.2	33.4	9.0	31.8	0.0
PEBBLES/GRAVEL (%)	20.5	45.6	33.1	32.6	39.3	23.8	47.4	46.0	27.0	34.7	36.1	45.8	42.5	38.2	12.4	43.0	35.8	32.6	12.5
SAND (%)	17.1	8.8	4.1	11.1	8.9	2.3	6.0	4.5	5.9	9.0	18.0	10.3	12.2	8.4	6.8	9.7	14.1	7.2	2.5
SILT/CLAY (%)	29.5	1.5	1.5	6.8	10.9	4.0	9.0	4.0	2.8	1.2	34.7	13.2	23.3	44.1	76.6	13.9	41.2	28.5	85.0
MEAN AIR TEMP (°C)	8.60	8.85	8.77	9.52	9.21	9.21	9.70	8.84	8.98	9.08	9.80	9.37	9.95	10.27	9.40	9.86	10.30	8.65	10.16
AIR TEMP RANGE (°C)	11.08	11.71	11.23	11.45	10.73	11.38	12.15	10.60	11.04	10.36	12.21	12.03	11.45	11.86	10.49	11.86	12.62	10.60	12.98
LATITUDE (°N)	56.57	55.88	56.17	54.07	55.16	54.87	53.48	56.01	55.44	55.79	53.11	54.22	52.73	51.74	54.56	52.87	51.42	56.89	51.63
LONGITUDE (°W)	4.10	3.17	4.21	3.73	3.84	3.26	3.25	4.47	4.27	4.84	1.91	2.02	3.13	2.95	3.28	2.71	1.38	3.69	0.82
EXPECTED SCORE	90.4	92.9	98.1	103.6	98.0	104.9	114.0	97.4	97.6	101.8	91.4	101.0	106.0	94.0	95.0	105.0	95.8	96.5	91.4
EXPECTED N-TAXA	15.3	15.9	16.3	17.4	16.9	17.3	18.9	16.2	16.3	17.0	17.4	18.0	19.3	17.6	17.5	18.4	19.1	17.0	19.1
EXPECTED ASPT	5.89	5.85	6.00	5.91	5.77	6.07	6.00	5.97	5.98	5.99	5.23	5.61	5.46	5.32	5.43	5.67	4.99	5.70	4.78
OBSERVED SCORE	84.4	83.2	108.0	106.9	96.9	101.3	112.1	106.2	99.4	101.9	81.0	107.7	106.1	93.2	76.1	106.2	101.2	93.7	72.7
OBSERVED N-TAXA	13.4	13.9	16.7	17.4	15.8	15.5	18.4	16.6	16.0	16.4	15.0	18.4	18.7	17.0	14.6	18.3	20.8	16.9	16.2
OBSERVED ASPT	6.27	5.95	6.47	6.08	6.13	6.57	6.05	6.38	6.20	6.08	5.35	5.80	5.59	5.38	5.24	5.83	4.82	5.49	4.49

Figure 6.1. Mean values for 14 environmental characteristics in 19 end-groups of the headwaters site classification. Also shown are the mean expected (from RIVPACS II) and observed BMWP score, N-Taxa and ASPT. Five letters (A to E) in the group numbers indicate the five major groups of the classification (see Tables 6.1 and 6.2).

The IFE database used to develop the prototype "headwaters RIVPACS" contained almost 500 headwaters which offered the potential for selection as reference sites. From these, a subset of 357 sites were considered, all of which had four features in common. All sites were sampled using RIVPACS compatible methodologies, all were identified by IFE staff to a common level of precision, all had at least one sample collected in summer or early autumn and, with the exception of alkalinity, all sites had RIVPACS compatible environmental data available.

For two reasons, single samples from each headwater site were used to develop the system. Firstly, most sites in the IFE database, particularly those from Countryside Survey 1990, were sampled only once. Secondly, the use of single samples seemed to be more in keeping with the levels of staffing and financial resources that the water industry has available for monitoring the extensive network of headwaters in Britain. No advantage was seen in developing a system that had little possibility of practical application. In most cases the summer sample was selected for analysis, but it was sometimes necessary to use early autumn samples where no summer information was available.

The expected summer BMWP index values for each of the 357 sites in the dataset were then predicted using RIVPACS II. EQI N-Taxa and EQI ASPT were calculated and compared with the minimum values recommended by the IFE as representative of good biological condition (Band A) for single seasons (Clarke *et al.* 1994). All sites were eliminated which failed to obtain both minimum Band A values of 0.84 for EQI ASPT and 0.67 for EQI N-Taxa. The criterion for number of taxa was particularly rigorous as taxon richness tended to be over-predicted by RIVPACS II. However, the net effect was that only those sites with the best available overall standard were used in further analyses. In total, 214 sites were retained.

Structure and characteristics of the headwaters classification

As a prelude to creating a headwaters version of RIVPACS, the 214 selected sites were classified by TWINSPAN (Hill 1979a) into nineteen end-groups. Division of groups was stopped when any daughter-group of the division would have contained fewer than five sites. Group means were determined for several environmental variables and for observed and expected BMWP index values (Fig. 6.1). In this context, expected BMWP index values were derived using RIVPACS II. Group mean environmental values showed a gradual, somewhat discontinuous shift from Group 1 to Group 19, associated with declining altitude, slope, substratum particle size and latitude. This is more clearly demonstrated when the values are compared for the five principal groups of the classification (Table 6.1). Thus, mean altitude declined from 280.4 m in Group A to 27.8 m in Group E. Similarly, slope decreased from 66.7 m km^{-1} to just 4.4 m km^{-1}, and the proportion of the stream-bed covered by sand, silt and clay increased from 20.0% to 87.5%. There are some anomalies in this sequence, including the higher cover of fine particles (10.0%) in Group A, compared with 4.2% in Group B. This is accounted for by the presence of peat in upland, moorland streams.

Associated with change in altitude there is a geographic gradient, where the most northerly sites generally occur in the left-hand groups of Table 6.1 and the right-hand groups are mainly southern sites. A discontinuity in group-mean latitude in group D is due to one of its three component groups in the full classification. This particular group of ten sites (Group 18D in Fig. 6.1) included several in Scotland which probably had relatively high conductivities. Available alkalinity data indicate there is a conductivity gradient from low values in the left-hand groups to high values in the right-hand groups of Figure 6.1 and Table 6.1.

Headwaters RIVPACS thus mirrors the principal environmental gradient of the parent system, that of increasing conductivity and decreasing mean stream-bed particle size with decreasing altitude and slope (Wright, Moss *et al.* 1984). A gradient which is not shown in the

Table 6.1. *The mean environmental characteristics for the five major end-groups (A to E) of the headwaters site classification. Also given are the observed and expected (from RIVPACS II) BMWP scores (see p. 8, Chapter 1), and values for number of taxa (N-Taxa) and average score per taxon (ASPT).*

Variables	A	B	C	D	E
Environmental characteristics					
Number of sites	69	45	54	40	6
Altitude (m)	280.4	203.1	115.3	97.2	27.8
Slope (m km^{-1})	66.7	48.5	37.4	19.1	4.4
Discharge (categories)	1.0	1.2	1.0	1.1	1.0
Distance from source (km)	0.9	1.3	0.9	1.1	1.5
Water width (m)	1.4	1.9	1.1	1.8	1.7
Mean depth (cm)	12.8	14.4	9.6	18.3	29.2
Boulders/cobbles (%)	45.7	54.5	15.6	24.7	0.0
Pebbles/gravel(%)	34.2	35.8	35.0	37.1	12.5
Sand (%)	10.0	5.5	11.1	10.3	2.5
Silt/clay (%)	10.0	4.2	38.4	27.9	85.0
Mean air temperature (°C)	8.99	9.16	9.76	9.60	10.16
Air temperature range (°C)	11.24	11.11	11.61	11.69	12.98
Latitude (°N)	55.57	55.12	53.27	53.73	51.63
Longitude (°W)	3.81	4.02	2.66	2.59	0.82
BMWP indices					
Expected Score	96.6	103.1	97.5	99.1	91.4
Expected N-Taxa	16.4	17.1	18.0	18.2	19.1
Expected ASPT	5.88	6.00	5.41	5.45	4.78
Observed Score	95.9	104.2	92.8	100.4	72.7
Observed N-Taxa	15.4	16.6	16.7	18.7	16.2
Observed ASPT	6.18	6.26	5.47	5.38	4.49

headwaters RIVPACS is that of stream size. A comparison of the five major groups shows that mean distance from source only varies between 0.9 and 1.5 km, and mean width varies between 1.1 and 1.9 m.

Examination of the environmental characteristics of the nineteen headwaters classification groups demonstrates the broad range of stream types covered (Fig. 6.1). This means that the classification also has the potential to cover a wide range of optimal BMWP index values. This is most evident for ASPT. Typically, the highest values were in the upland sites, where stoneflies, mayflies and caddis dominate the fauna and non-insect taxa are comparatively few. The lowest values were in lowland streams where most stoneflies are absent but molluscs, leeches and crustaceans are commonplace. In this respect the headwaters classification showed the same sequence of rise and fall of values that is displayed in the full version of RIVPACS (Table 6.2). The five RIVPACS III groups used in this example are the same as the five referred to by Wright (Chapter 1), except that his lowland group has been subdivided to reflect the first two dichotomies of the TWINSPAN classification.

In RIVPACS III, there is also a pattern of relatively low mean number of BMWP families in the small and upland streams of major Groups A and B (Table 6.2). The mean number of BMWP families rises in the larger, higher discharge sites on the intermediate and lowland rivers of Groups C and D. The mean number of families is then slightly reduced in Group E which contains sites with, on average, the shallowest slope, lowest altitude, greatest depth and finest substratum of all five major groups.

Table 6.2. *A comparison of the mean values per site for the numbers of BMWP taxa (N-Taxa) and ASPT for the five major groups of sites in RIVPACS III (based on three seasons combined samples) and the headwaters site classification (based on a single season sample).*

The constituent end-groups of the RIVPACS III classification are:
1–9 (Group A), 10–17 (Group B), 18–24 (Group C), 25–32 (Group D) and 33–35 (Group E)
(see Chapter 1).

Index	Classification	Group A	Group B	Group C	Group D	Group E	Overall
N-Taxa	RIVPACS III	27.2	28.2	33.9	34.0	32.1	30.7
	Headwaters	15.4	16.6	16.7	18.7	16.2	16.6
ASPT	RIVPACS III	6.32	6.58	6.04	5.49	5.09	6.04
	Headwaters	6.18	6.26	5.47	5.38	4.49	5.82

The headwaters classification does not have the same inherent structure of developing stream size but it does retain the upland to lowland gradient. Thus there are the same elements of a rise in mean number of BMWP taxa (N-Taxa) from Group A to Group D and a subsequent decrease in Group E (Table 6.2). However, in comparison with RIVPACS III, the mean number of BMWP taxa per site and the variability of taxon numbers between sites are both lower in the headwaters classification. The average number of BMWP taxa per site in the headwaters classification is 16.6 (Table 6.2), compared with 20.4 for the summer samples only in RIVPACS III. Similarly, the single season coefficient of variation in the mean number of BMWP taxa in the 19 end-groups of the headwaters classification is 10.9%, and this compares with 14.5% for the 35 RIVPACS III combined seasons groups.

Scope of the headwaters classification

The inherent differences between the restricted richness of the macroinvertebrate fauna in headwater sites, and the more diverse faunal assemblages in RIVPACS III, has consequences for the scope of the headwaters classification. The stringent requirement that sites should attain a value of 0.67 for EQI N-Taxa sets a high standard for assessing faunal diversity for the majority of the sites located within the principal environmental gradient of the headwaters classification. However, it also tends to exclude sites at each extreme of that gradient, i.e upland, acidic streams and lowland, silty streams.

Many moorland streams are intrinsically acidic, frequently subject to spates (floods) and have relatively large stream-bed particle sizes, all of which contribute to a naturally low faunal diversity. In many cases the slight acidity of these streams has been enhanced by atmospheric precipitation and forestry practices (Stoner *et al.* 1984; Ormerod *et al.* 1989; Ventura & Harper 1996; Vuori & Joensuu 1996). The difficulty in setting up a headwaters version of RIVPACS, whose range of objectives might include the detection of acidification effects, is to determine the optimal species richness that moorland streams can support.

If the current, unsophisticated headwaters version of RIVPACS is to have operational value then it must be expanded to include a greater range of reference sites. Therefore the best available acid-water sites must be included in an extended version of the classification. These sites can then be used to evaluate new acid-water sites from targeted field programmes. As and when the newly sampled sites exceed the observed standards of the reference sites, improved classifications can be created in which the new sites are substituted for the existing ones.

This iterative process progressively raised the standards which accompanied the successive development of RIVPACS I, II and III (see Chapter 1). An inevitable consequence of this process, however, is the concomitant lowering of perceived quality of all sites that are judged by the new system. This may present particular management and political problems in its implementation.

The situation with upland, acidic streams is replicated in lowland headwaters. In the flat landscapes of eastern England, headwaters are likely to be naturally nutrient-rich, densely vegetated and silty. However, the high intensity of agricultural activity means that few if any of these streams can be free from the impacts of channel modification, organic enrichment and low flows. For example, in arable landscapes, which are the norm in the extreme lowlands, Barr, Bunce *et al.* (1993) and Furse, Symes *et al.* (1995) showed that 42% of headwater stream length was channelised, nitrate concentrations were three times those found in pastoral landscapes, and up to 45% of streams in some geographic areas ran dry in drought years.

Under these circumstances, it is unlikely that the small group of extreme lowland sites in the current headwaters classification includes the best possible reference cases. The iterative process of raising standards, indicated above for acidic streams, also applies to the flatland headwaters.

Linking biological and environmental data

Notwithstanding the difficulties of finding suitable reference sites for all stream types, the new headwaters classification provided an improved baseline against which the national distribution of headwater quality could be judged. The next stage was to use multiple discriminant analysis (MDA) to link environmental data to the biological classification. This provided the means for deriving the expected BMWP index values, against which the observed values could be assessed.

In the absence of alkalinity, and with distance from source and stream width providing little between-group discrimination, the most effective variables used in the MDA were altitude, slope, latitude, longitude, substratum composition and, to a lesser extent, stream depth. In a re-substitution test, a set of fourteen variables (Table 6.3) assigned 52% of the 214 sites to the same groups that they were assigned to in the 19-group biological classification shown in Figure 6.1. This was roughly equivalent to the results achieved for the prototype version of RIVPACS, where eleven physical and chemical variables successfully assigned 66% of the 268 sites to one of 15 groups (Moss, Furse *et al.* 1987).

Testing a headwaters version of RIVPACS

Application of the system

The preliminary headwaters version of RIVPACS was tested on a set of 131 rural sites selected at random from four river catchments with diverse geology, soil types, landscape characteristics and patterns of major land usage. These sites had been selected as part of a study of the impact of agricultural activity on headwater streams (Furse, Symes *et al.* 1995). An essential part of that research programme was to evaluate the biological condition of the sites as appraised through their macroinvertebrate assemblages.

For the purposes of the test, three environmental variables were eliminated from the MDA (prediction) process (Table 6.3). These were discharge, which offered almost no discrimination between headwater sites, and the two air temperature variables which could not be computed easily. Sites were evaluated using EQIs based on the observed BMWP index values for summer samples and the equivalent expected values, as predicted by headwaters RIVPACS.

The procedures adopted for categorising the biological condition of sites were similar to

Table 6.3. *Fourteen variables examined in a re-substitution test of the ability to use environmental data for predicting sites to their correct end-group in the national biological classification of headwaters.*

(1) Variables omitted from the prediction process for 131 sites used to study the impact of agricultural activities.

Variables (units)	Transformation
Water width (m)	Log_{10}
Water depth (cm)	Log_{10}
Boulders/cobbles (% cover)	Arcsine $\sqrt{}$
Pebbles/gravel (% cover)	Arcsine $\sqrt{}$
Sand (% cover)	Arcsine $\sqrt{}$
Silt/clay (% cover)	Arcsine $\sqrt{}$
Altitude (m)	Log_{10}
Slope (m km[-1])	Log_{10}
Distance from source (km)	Log_{10}
Discharge[1] (categories)	None
Latitude (°. mins)	None
Longitude (°. mins)	None
Mean air temperature[1] (°C)	None
Air temperature range[1] (°C)	None

those used in RIVPACS II (Wright, Furse *et al.* 1991) to interpret the 1990 River Quality Survey (Sweeting, Lowson *et al.* 1992) and were based on band widths for three seasons combined. EQI values were divided into four bands (A to D) representing "good", "fair", "poor" and "bad" biological condition respectively (Table 6.4). The lower Band A threshold for EQI ASPT was set at 0.89, which was the level attained by 95% of the sites in RIVPACS II when three seasons combined data were used. The same principle was adopted for values of EQI N-Taxa, with a lower threshold of 0.72. The latter threshold differs from that previously recommended for the 1990 survey where harsher targets were set by requiring Band A sites to meet the level attained by 90% of all RIVPACS sites. This modification to the contemporary RIVPACS practice was made to introduce similar rates of misclassification when banding by either N-Taxa or ASPT. The use of band widths based on samples for three seasons combined, set higher standards of discrimination than those attained with single season band widths, but did so at the expense of higher rates of misclassification.

Table 6.4. *Band ranges for values of EQI ASPT and EQI N-Taxa, used in the evaluation of headwater sites, based on identification of taxa to family level.*

Band	EQI ASPT	EQI N-Taxa
A	≥0.89	≥0.72
B	0.77–0.88	0.43–0.71
C	0.66–0.76	0.15–0.42
D	≤0.65	≤0.14

Evaluation of the results

When the 131 rural study sites were banded on the basis of their values for EQI ASPT, only 47% of sites were in good biological condition (Band A), 31% were fair, 15% poor and 6% bad (Furse, Symes *et al.* 1995). When EQI N-Taxa was considered, 49% of sites were good, 34%

fair and 18% poor. However, when each site was evaluated on the basis of the lower of its bands for either EQI ASPT or N-Taxa, only 40% of headwaters were considered to be in good biological condition, 31% were fair, 24% poor and 6% bad.

Direct comparisons were made between these results and those of the 1990 River Quality Survey, which was generally concerned with physically larger sites (Furse, Symes *et al.* 1995). Thus, when RIVPACS II was applied to just the English and Welsh summer samples from the 1990 survey, 57% of the sites were judged to be of good quality based on EQI ASPT, compared with 47% of headwaters (Table 6.5). For EQI N-Taxa, 59% were of good quality compared with only 49% of headwaters.

The results of the evaluations confirmed the anxieties expressed earlier in this chapter, concerning the condition of rural headwaters.

Table 6.5. *A comparison of the distribution (%) of bands of biological condition for 131 headwater sites and the full set of almost 6000 1990 River Quality Survey (RQS) summer samples from England and Wales, based on identification of taxa to family level.*

EQI index	Survey	Band A	Band D	Band C	Band D
ASPT	Headwaters	47.3	31.3	15.3	6.1
	1990 RQS	56.7	22.8	12.1	8.5
N-Taxa	Headwaters	48.9	33.6	17.6	0.0
	1990 RQS	58.6	28.9	11.7	0.8

The way forward

The principles underpinning RIVPACS are straightforward and the computer software needed to develop systems of this type is readily available. It is no surprise, therefore, to be able to establish the suitability of the method for evaluating the biological condition of headwater streams. In the current study, the value of the system has been shown in relation to a set of sites that were being evaluated for the impact of agricultural activities on their macroinvertebrate assemblages.

The results of the trial application of headwaters RIVPACS indicated that the biological condition of headwaters in general should represent a serious cause for concern, particularly in the light of the important contribution they make to total catchment biodiversity and the habitat they provide for rare taxa (Furse 1998). As a result of these findings, a new awareness has grown within the Environment Agency of the need to pay more attention to the condition of headwaters.

At present, headwaters RIVPACS has not been developed as a ready-to-use software package, but considerable merit is seen in adapting the existing information to fit into the standard RIVPACS shell, as used for RIVPACS III. However, several other steps may be required first to optimise its performance characteristics.

(1). It is important that effective reference sites are introduced to give better coverage for the extremes of the environmental gradients, represented by acidic upland sites and slow-flowing, nutrient-rich lowland streams. Here, the challenge is similar to that faced when setting up RIVPACS in countries where some types of unimpacted reference sites are rare or non-existent (see Chapter 14). Should it be conceded that, because of man's influence, certain streams will never achieve their full potential and, therefore, should the best available reference sites be used to set realistic standards? In practice this is the principle already accepted in the development of RIVPACS III. Alternatively, there may be other ways in which it is possible to extrapolate from the best known conditions in order to set higher targets (Chapter 20).

(2). Are BMWP indices the best measures for comparing the observed and expected condition? ASPT values do provide a gradient between upland and lowland headwater sites, but there is very little variation in the number of taxa expected in headwaters across most of the spectrum of environmental conditions. Additional and/or alternative approaches include goodness of fit (chi-squared) tests (Chapter 2) and the use of relative abundance data (e.g. the Q14 index; see Chapter 1, p. 19). Another approach might be to incorporate other complementary metrics such as trophic structure, biodiversity or measures of productivity, whilst the advantages of including other taxonomic groups, such as bryophytes, in the headwaters RIVPACS system might also be considered. The potential benefits of using a multimetric approach (Chapter 19) to complement RIVPACS are discussed in Chapter 24.

(3). Are single season samples adequate to assess site quality or are the uncertainties associated with single season sampling too great? Furse, Clarke *et al.* (1995) have demonstrated the greater variation associated with single season sampling and how this increases the difficulty of demonstrating statistically significant spatial and temporal differences in biological condition. However, in order to provide a realistic level of surveillance of small streams, reliance upon single season samples in a headwaters module of RIVPACS may be the only practical way to attain an adequate coverage of site types. This, and the other issues raised, remain to be resolved.

Acknowledgements

The studies upon which this chapter is based were jointly funded by the Natural Environment Research Council and the National Rivers Authority/Environment Agency. The author wishes to thank his many colleagues at the Institute of Freshwater Ecology who contributed so importantly to the research programme. The helpful comments of his fellow editors on the original text of this chapter have done much to improve it and are also gratefully acknowledged.

CHAPTER 7

The potential of RIVPACS for predicting the effects of environmental change

PATRICK D. ARMITAGE

*Institute of Freshwater Ecology, River Laboratory,
East Stoke, Wareham, Dorset, BH20 6BB, UK*

Summary

RIVPACS has been used successfully for biological assessment of river water quality but its potential in forecasting the effects of environmental change has not been investigated. This study has shown that it is possible to simulate faunal changes in response to environmental disturbance, provided that the disturbance directly involves the environmental variables used in RIVPACS predictions. These variables relate to channel shape, discharge and substratum. Many impacts, particularly those associated with pollution, will not affect these variables and therefore RIVPACS cannot simulate the effects of pollution. RIVPACS was sensitive only to major changes in substratum. It was concluded that, because of the static nature of RIVPACS, it cannot respond to the dynamic effects and processes associated with environmental disturbance. Thus RIVPACS, while showing direction of change and indicating sensitive taxa, cannot be used to predict or forecast the effects of environmental impacts.

Introduction

The "Rivers (Prevention of Pollution) Act 1951" set the scene for the beginning of the current monitoring and planning systems of the UK water industry. Since that time the assessment of environmental impacts on streams and rivers has been a prime concern of water resource managers. All national assessments of water quality before 1970 were based on chemical data, despite the existence of several biotic score systems. In part, this was due to the inability of these scores to be applied nationwide. However, even after the Biological Monitoring Working Party (BMWP) developed a nationally acceptable score system, there were difficulties associated with the high variability in achievable score in unpolluted sites over a wide range of physical conditions (Armitage *et al.* 1983). Other problems of score systems are dependency on sampling effort and the fact that they set the same target for all sites. The need to define a target community was the necessary precursor to the development of the River InVertebrate Prediction And Classification System (RIVPACS).

This system is founded on a large database of taxa lists and associated environmental features from unpolluted or best available quality sites throughout Great Britain. Selected environmental variables at a site are used to predict the probability of occurrence and relative abundance of taxa, and from this information, estimates of faunal parameters such as BMWP score, number of taxa, and average score per taxon (ASPT), are computed. The expected values of the faunal parameters are compared with those observed to provide an Ecological Quality Index (EQI) for the site (Chapter 4, p. 57). This is the most commonly used feature of

RIVPACS employed by the Environment Agency in its routine monitoring and Biological General Quality Assessment (Environment Agency 1996).

RIVPACS has other applications which make use of its ability to predict species. These predictions can be used to indicate baseline conditions before implementation of necessary management procedures. The predictions will indicate whether the site meets expectations or shows some form of stress. In "before and after" studies, RIVPACS can be used to monitor changing conditions. Close examination of predicted species/families occurrence and predicted abundance (for single season samples) can provide insights into the causative agents of change.

These applications have proved to be useful in assessing biological quality at the time of sampling (Armitage & Gunn 1996; Wright *et al.* 1994) but do not involve forecasting the future. However, it would be of considerable benefit for water managers to know what the precise effects of a given disturbance would be on the instream biota. Can RIVPACS be used in this way and if so under what circumstances? It is the objective of this chapter to examine the potential of RIVPACS to predict the effects of environmental stress.

Impacts

The main activities associated with river management are flow regulation, engineering works, and water treatment and disposal of effluents. However, disturbances in the catchment area due to agricultural practices, forestry work, quarrying, mining, construction activity and urbanisation, will also have a major influence on instream biota. These disturbances will have a variety of effects depending on their intensity, the type of river, and whether they are acting alone or with other impacting agents. Major disturbances and their primary effects are listed in Table 7.1, which shows that the disturbances relate to three main areas: flow regime, habitat and water chemistry. These in turn will have specific effects on the instream biota. For illustrative purposes, Table 7.2 presents a list of the families of macroinvertebrates found at East Stoke on the River Frome in Dorset, south-west England, together with the probable effects of specific disturbances on the occurrence of taxa, derived from published work.

Application of pesticides for agricultural purposes is often directed at insects. In this hypothetical example the effects of permethrin are shown to remove crustaceans and insects, and leave molluscs and annelids unaffected (Kingsbury 1986). Heavy metal pollution has a deleterious effect on molluscs and annelids (Hellawell 1986). Organic pollution results in the increasing loss of taxa as its severity is increased. Reduced flows favour deposit feeders at the expense of grazers, and increased flows have the reverse effect (Armitage 1987). Weed-cutting, depending on timing and extent, has little effect on the occurrence of any taxa although it may reduce abundance (Armitage, Blackburn *et al.* 1994). Construction work will generate silt and is likely to cause a reduction in taxa that require coarse substrata (Armitage & Gunn 1996).

As noted above, it is possible to theorise on the likely effects of particular impacts, based on information in the literature, but it would be preferable to simulate any given disturbance by altering environmental variables and observing the intensity and direction of the response of the instream community. Can RIVPACS be used for this purpose? Before this question can be answered it is necessary to consider which of the environmental variables used in RIVPACS will be affected by each of the possible impacts.

RIVPACS uses the following site descriptors to predict the faunal assemblages present at a site: national grid reference; altitude; distance from source; slope; alkalinity; discharge category; mean water width; mean water depth; substratum characteristics as percentage cover of boulders/cobbles, pebbles/gravel, sand, and silt/clay.

Of these descriptors, the first three cannot change (except in the most catastrophic of circumstances!). Slope could be affected by local channelisation activity but the RIVPACS

Table 7.1. *Major disturbances on rivers and their primary effects.*

Main activity	Impacts	Primary effects
Flow regulation	Increased flow	Substratum instability
	Reduced flow	Siltation
	Constant flow	Substratum stability
	Altered flow regime	Severe fluctuations in velocity
	Flood relief channel	No high flows
Engineering	Bridge construction	Substratum disturbance
	Channelisation	Channel shape
	Dredging	Substratum disturbance
	Dam construction	Flow regime
	Channel diversions	Flow regime
Water supply and disposal	Abstraction	Wetted area
	Transfer	Flow patterns
	Pollution from effluents	Increased nutrient load
Catchment activities	Agriculture	Nutrients/Pesticides
	Land clearance	Siltation
	Forestry	Siltation
	Quarrying and mining	Siltation/Pollution
	Construction work	Siltation
	Urbanisation	Pollution/Siltation
	Industry	Pollution

measure of slope is probably too crude to register change. Alkalinity is also unlikely to change unless there is a major pollution incident or the river is in receipt of transferred water with a different chemical composition. This leaves four variables that relate to channel shape, discharge and the substratum. Listed below are the likely effects of each impact (from Table 7.2) on the instream environment.

(1). Pollution. Five impacts are considered.
  (a). Pesticide: no RIVPACS variables will be affected.
  (b). Zinc: no obvious effects on variables recorded for RIVPACS.
  (c). Mild organic pollution: little effect on variables except possible algal growth on the substratum.
  (d). Severe organic pollution: increasing algal growth; no change to remaining variables.
  (e). Very severe organic pollution: growth of sewage fungus over the entire river bottom.

(2). Flow. Two impacts are considered.
  (a). Reduced flow: reduced width, depth, and discharge; increased siltation.
  (b). Increased flow: increased width, depth and discharge; removal of fines; concretion and formation of armoured layer.

(3). Weed-cutting. Reduced depth and width; increased velocity; redistribution of fines.

(4). Construction. Dredging and channelisation – engineering works. Increased sediment loads, altered slope, width, depth and substratum characteristics.

From the list above it is clear that RIVPACS could be used only to test those disturbances which are likely to affect wetted area and substratum characteristics. Organic and heavy metal

Table 7.2. *The possible effects of environmental disturbance on the occurrence of families of macroinvertebrates from an unstressed site on the River Frome, Dorset, south-west England, based on published work. Also shown are summary faunal parameters (number of taxa, BMWP score[1] and ASPT[2]) for pre-disturbance (natural, unstressed conditions) and post-disturbance at the site.*

(1) Total BMWP score for the site; (2) Average score per taxon = BMWP score ÷ number of taxa.

Score = BMWP score for individual sites; N = natural (unstressed); P = pesticide; HM = heavy metals; MO = mild organic; SO = severe organic, VSO = very severe organic pollution; Red = reduced flow; Inc = increased flow; Constr = construction (engineering works).

Taxa	Score	N	Pollution					River flow		Weed cutting	Constr
			P	HM	MO	SO	VSO	Red	Inc		
Neritidae	3	1	1	–	1	–	–	–	–	1	–
Valvatidae	3	1	1	–	1	–	–	–	–	1	–
Lymnaeidae	3	1	1	–	1	1	–	–	–	1	1
Physidae	3	1	1	–	1	–	–	–	–	1	–
Ancylidae	6	1	1	–	–	–	–	–	1	1	–
Sphaeriidae	3	1	1	–	1	–	–	1	–	1	–
Oligochaeta	1	1	1	–	1	1	1	1	1	1	–
Piscicolidae	4	1	1	–	–	–	1	–	–	1	–
Glossiphoniidae	3	1	1	1	1	1	–	–	1	1	1
Asellidae	3	1	–	1	1	1	–	1	–	1	1
Gammaridae	6	1	–	–	1	–	–	–	1	1	1
Baetidae	4	1	–	1	1	1	–	1	1	1	1
Heptageniidae	10	1	–	–	–	–	–	–	1	1	–
Ephemeridae	10	1	–	–	–	–	–	1	–	1	–
Leuctridae	10	1	–	1	–	–	–	–	1	1	–
Calopterygidae	8	1	–	–	1	–	–	1	–	1	–
Aphelocheiridae	10	1	–	–	–	–	–	–	–	1	–
Corixidae	5	1	–	–	1	–	–	1	–	1	1
Elmidae	5	1	–	–	1	–	–	–	1	1	–
Gyrinidae	5	1	–	1	1	1	–	1	–	1	–
Rhyacophilidae	7	1	–	1	–	–	–	–	1	1	–
Hydropsychidae	5	1	–	1	1	–	–	–	1	1	–
Leptoceridae	10	1	–	–	–	–	–	1	–	1	–
Hydroptilidae	6	1	–	–	1	–	–	–	–	1	–
Brachycentridae	10	1	–	–	–	–	–	–	–	1	–
Tipuliidae	5	1	–	1	1	1	–	1	1	1	1
Chironomidae	2	1	–	1	1	1	1	1	1	1	1
Simuliidae	5	1	–	1	1	–	–	–	1	1	–
Number of taxa:		28	9	10	19	8	2	11	13	28	8
Total BMWP score[1]:		155	29	49	78	26	3	56	69	155	31
ASPT[2]:		5.54	3.22	4.90	4.11	3.25	1.50	5.09	5.31	5.54	3.88

pollution will not affect the variables used in RIVPACS. Thus, although RIVPACS can be used to assess sites that are impacted by these factors, by comparing the observed faunal community with that predicted for a site with similar environmental conditions, it cannot be used to simulate the impacts of pollution. In contrast, disturbances which result in changes in channel characteristics and substratum composition may be amenable to simulation. These aspects will be addressed below.

Simulation of disturbance

An attempt to simulate disturbance with an early version of RIVPACS is reported by Armitage (1989). The substratum of a hypothetical upland site was changed from boulder/cobbles to silt, with all other variables kept constant, in order to examine the response of selected families and species (Fig. 7.1). Baetidae and Hydropsychidae are relatively insensitive to change, up to a mean phi value of 0 (sandy gravel), but as the substratum becomes finer these taxa (i.e. families) show a steep decrease in abundance. Nemouridae show an immediate reduction in response to decreasing particle size, in contrast to Sphaeriidae whose abundance increases. The species show similar fluctuations, but two, the stonefly *Leuctra geniculata* and the mayfly *Centroptilum luteolum*, are most abundant at mean phi values of 1 to 2. Knowledge of the habitat requirements of these taxa indicates that the predictions of abundance and occurrence make "ecological sense", and shows that there may be some potential in this technique for anticipating those organisms which are most likely to respond to increased siltation.

In a recent study (Armitage *et al.* 1997), attempts were made to simulate the effects of low flow by altering the environmental variables used in RIVPACS III predictions at three sites. Predictions were run for the summer season. Two of the sites, 200 m apart, are situated on the Mill Stream (a side channel of the River Frome, Dorset) and differ in channel shape and substratum (sites MH and MS). The third site (R) has physical features based on those of a typical chalk stream in its middle reaches. In all three sites the proportion of fine substratum was increased and width and depth decreased, to simulate the effects of reduced discharge (see Table 7.3). The results for these three sites are presented in Table 7.3, together with data from another two sites: an additional chalk stream middle reach (F), and an upland coarse-bottomed stretch of the South Tyne (ST) in Cumbria, northern England. Chalk stream sites dominate this selection because they show the most pronounced reaction to low flow stress (Armitage & Petts 1992). The upland site is included for comparative purposes. A further four sites on two small lowland streams, (Wool Stream and Swan Brook), where known substratum changes had taken place, were used to test the sensitivity of RIVPACS in detecting or highlighting change in the faunal assemblages (Table 7.3).

The full output from RIVPACS is voluminous and the results are presented in summary form only. For each site, observed environmental data were used to predict abundance and occurrence of invertebrate families. This was then considered as the control against which to measure the effects of simulation. The results are expressed as the difference between the control values and those derived from the most extreme simulation for each site. In most cases the combination of environmental variables used in the extreme simulation generated a warning notice from the RIVPACS program, indicating that a site with these physical characteristics had a low probability of belonging to any group in the dataset (Table 7.3). Only those families showing the greatest response are considered.

The effects of the simulations on occurrence are illustrated in Figures 7.2, 7.3 and 7.4, where positive values of percent difference indicate a reduction in the probability of occurrence of a taxon from the control to the simulated state. For example, if the probability of Ephemerellidae occurring at the control site is 50%, but this reduces to 30% for the extreme simulation, then the percent difference for control minus simulation gives a positive value of 20% for Ephemerellidae. The main points to note are the relatively small response in the Mill Stream sites (maximum difference <20% in Fig. 7.2) compared to a massive response in the South Tyne (over 90% in Fig. 7.4). Similar trends were observed for abundance (Fig. 7.5) but responses of individual families differed; for example, at site F, Rhyacophilidae showed the greatest response in occurrence (Fig. 7.3) but Ephemerellidae showed the largest change in abundance (Fig. 7.5). Similar results are seen at site R (cf. Figs 7.3 and 7.5).

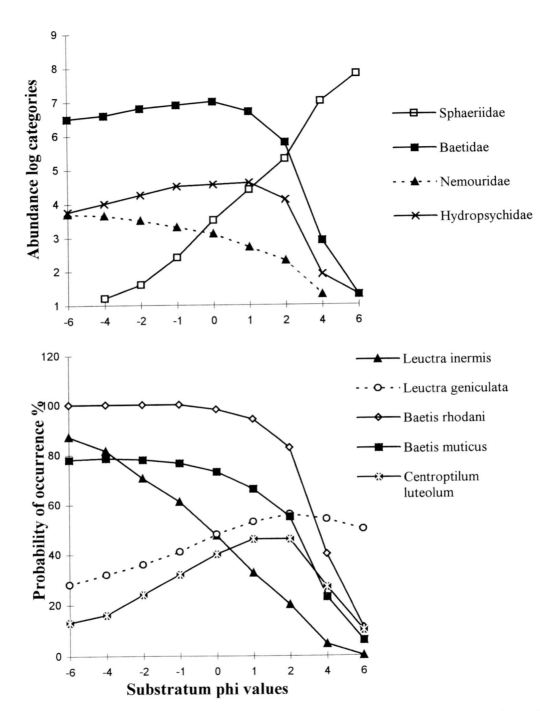

Figure 7.1. The effect of simulated change in mean substratum particle size on the predicted abundance of four macroinvertebrate families and the probability of occurrence of five species. (Predictions are based on three seasons).

Table 7.3. *The environmental parameters used in simulations for the Mill Stream sites (MH and MS), the middle reaches of a chalkstream (R and F), the South Tyne (ST), the Wool Stream (W3, W5) and Swan Brook (S4, S5).*

Discharge (m³ s⁻¹) is based on categories used in RIVPACS whereby <0.31 m³ s⁻¹ = 1, <0.62 = 2 etc.

Stream width is given in metres and stream depth in cm.

Values for substratum (bc = boulders and cobbles; pg = pebbles and gravel; sa = sand; sc = silt and clay) are percent cover, together with mean substratum particle size for each site in phi units.

Fit (final column) indicates the probability (%) of the site belonging to any group in the RIVPACS classification.

Site	Discharge	Width	Depth	Substratum (% cover) bc	pg	sa	sc	Mean size	Fit
MH Control	1.25	4.6	65	0	23	50	27	2.41	100
MH Test 1	0.62	4.3	50	0	10	60	30	3.28	100
MH Test 2	0.31	4	35	0	1	54	45	4.65	<5
MS Control	0.62	5	32	0	70	20	10	−1.08	100
MS Test 1	0.31	5	20	0	30	40	30	2.23	100
MS Test 2	0.31	5	15	0	5	35	60	5.34	<1
R Control	1.25	10	30	15	70	10	5	−2.84	100
R Test 1	0.62	5	15	1	10	29	60	4.98	100
R Test 2	0.31	5	5	1	4	10	85	6.79	<0.1
F Control	2.50	12	41	27	62	9	2	−3.77	100
F Test 1	1.25	9	30	15	40	30	15	−0.66	100
F Test 2	0.62	7	20	5	20	25	50	3.46	100
F Test 3	0.31	2	10	0	10	20	70	5.68	<5
ST Control	1.25	6	17	98	2	0	0	−7.66	100
ST Test 1	0.62	4	10	40	1	40	19	−0.81	100
ST Test 2	0.31	2	5	5	1	44	50	4.46	<0.1
ST Test 3	0.31	1	4	2	0	20	78	6.49	<0.1
W3 Control	0.31	2.6	16	2	55	37	6	−0.72	100
W3 Test 1	0.31	2.4	16	0	30	40	30	2.23	100
W3 Test 2	0.31	2.2	15	0	6	44	50	4.69	100
W3 Test 3	0.31	2	14	0	0	30	70	6.20	100
W5 Control	0.31	2.1	17	0	6	44	50	4.69	100
W5 Test 1	0.31	2.1	17	0	30	40	30	2.23	100
W5 Test 2	0.31	2.2	17	0	40	45	15	0.80	100
W5 Test 3	0.31	2.3	17	2	55	37	6	−0.72	100
S4 Control	0.31	3.3	21.6	25	60	10	5	−3.29	100
S4 Test 1	0.31	2.5	15	15	40	25	20	−0.36	100
S4 Test 2	0.31	1.5	10	10	20	20	50	2.98	100
S4 Test 3	0.31	1	5	5	5	15	75	5.75	<1
S5 Control	0.31	3.6	30.3	5	5	15	75	5.75	100
S5 Test 1	0.31	3.6	35	10	20	20	50	2.98	100
S5 Test 2	0.62	3.6	40	15	40	35	10	−0.96	100
S5 Test 3	0.62	3.6	50	25	60	10	5	−3.29	<5

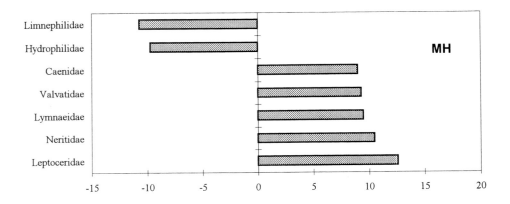

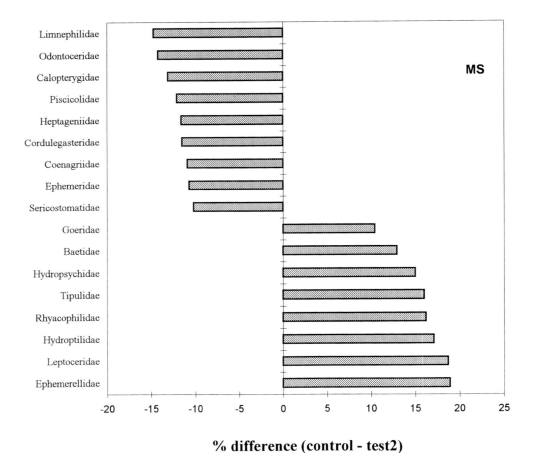

% difference (control - test2)

Figure 7.2. The difference between the probability of occurrence derived from control and extreme simulations for those families showing the greatest response at the Mill Head (MH) and Mill Stream (MS) sites, in lowland streams, Dorset, south-west England. Positive values of percent difference indicate a reduction in the predicted probability of occurrence of a taxon.

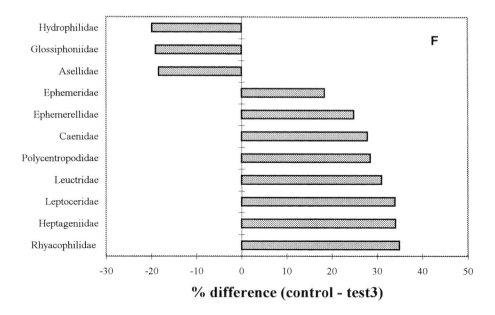

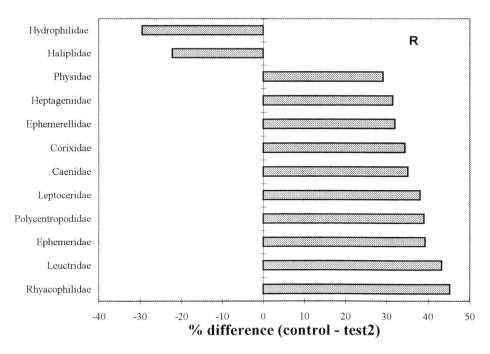

Figure 7.3. The difference between the probability of occurrence derived from control and extreme simulations for those families showing the greatest response at two chalk stream sites, F and R, in Dorset. Positive values of percent difference indicate a reduction in the predicted probability of occurrence of a taxon.

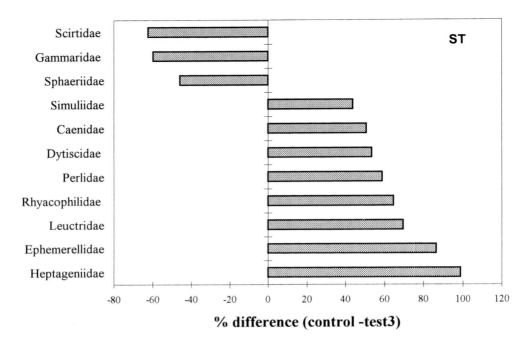

% difference (control -test3)

Figure 7.4. The difference between the probability of occurrence derived from control and extreme simulations for those families showing the greatest response at the South Tyne site near Alston in Cumbria, northern England. Positive values of percent difference indicate a reduction in the predicted probability of occurrence of a taxon.

Validation of prediction

The examples shown in Figures 7.2 to 7.5 illustrate how RIVPACS predictions respond to the effects of siltation in streams, but there is no validation of the prediction. In order to examine the "accuracy" of the RIVPACS simulation, two lowland streams are considered where known siltation has taken place.

The Wool Stream is a small spring-fed watercourse. In its lower reaches at site W5 it flows through pasture. It has been severely channelised and the banks have been poached by cattle. This, together with some constriction of flow through a culvert, has resulted in an increase in siltation. About 200 m upstream at site W3 there is no channelisation and the bottom is a sandy gravel. The question posed was: if the substratum of the upstream site (W3) is changed to that of the silted site (W5), will the predictions simulate the observed differences between sites?

The Swan Brook is a small lowland stream draining a hilly catchment and entering the sea at the town of Swanage, in Dorset. The town has been subject to severe floods and recently a relief channel has been constructed to divert all extreme flows. This has resulted in the siltation of the old channel downstream of the diversion (S5), since it no longer experiences flushing flows. A site above the diversion (S4) has a coarse substratum and reflects the pre-regulation situation. A similar question was posed: if S4 is silted-up to the level observed at S5, will the RIVPACS predictions simulate the observed differences between sites? Similarly, if silt is removed from S5, will the reverse hold true?

The results, based on predictions of occurrence, are shown in Figure 7.6. At the Wool Stream site (W3) it is clear that increase in the proportion of silt in the simulation had little effect on

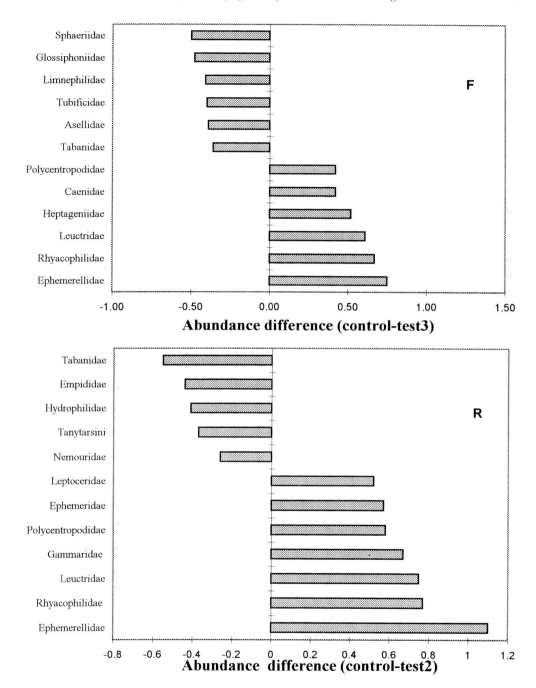

Figure 7.5. The difference between the predicted log$_{10}$ abundance values derived from control and extreme simulations for those families showing the greatest response at two chalk stream sites, F and R, in Dorset. Positive values of percent difference indicate a reduction in the predicted abundance of a taxon.

the predictions of faunal occurrence (percent difference <2.0%). In the Swan Brook, differences were greater (up to 30%) at both sites. At S4 the probability of occurrence of three families, Lymnaeidae, Nemouridae and Leptophlebiidae, increased with siltation, but a larger number (15) showed a reduced probability of occurrence. At S5 where the mean particle size was increased, the Leuctridae, Perlodidae, Hydropsychidae and Gammaridae showed an increase in their probability of occurrence.

In the Swan Brook, the tests are set up so that the most extreme simulation at S4 mimics the observed substratum at S5 and *vice versa*. Similarly, in the Wool Stream at W3 the most extreme simulation corresponds to the observed substratum at W5. The relationship between pairs of comparisons of observed and predicted abundances, and predicted probability of occurrence, was examined using the Spearman rank test. For probability of occurrence only predicted values could be compared, as observed values were either 100 or 0. The results from the matrix of comparisons are presented in Table 7.4. Values of the coefficients >0.359 and >0.329 are significant at the $p = 0.05$ level for the Swan Brook and Wool Stream respectively. The main conclusion from this analysis was that despite the changes in environmental parameters, the faunal characteristics of control and simulated predictions remained similar. Thus in the Swan Brook, the faunal abundances of the 24 test families predicted using the actual substratum variables, were close to those predicted when using the altered substratum variables (S4C/S4T, $r_s = 0.976$). The equivalent value for occurrence is 0.930. In the Wool Stream, similar relationships were noted between comparisons.

The particular comparisons that relate to the questions posed above are S4T/S5O, S5T/S4O, and W3T/W5O. The r_s values associated with these comparisons for abundances are respectively 0.515, 0.586 and 0.548. This indicates that a simulated reduction in mean substratum particle size at S4O results in predicted abundances similar to those observed at S5. Furthermore, the increase in the mean particle size of the substratum of S5O results in a fauna resembling that of S4O, and simulated reduction of particle size at W3O results in a fauna similar to that observed at W5O. However, association between other pairs of comparisons, as noted above, is much higher, and it is difficult to interpret these data. It appears that in streams of this type, simulations of environmental change do not result in major shifts in community composition.

Using faunal parameters

So far, the analyses have focused on family occurrence and abundance, but a more common treatment of survey data is to use faunal parameters to summarise the results. The observed and expected values of BMWP score, number of taxa and ASPT are listed in Table 7.5, for sites where simulations were tested. The effect of simulated change on the expected faunal parameters is presented in Figure 7.7, where the sites are ordered according to the amount of simulated substratum change (substratum difference). Thus the South Tyne (ST) ranged from a mean substratum of −7.66 (observed state) to 6.49 (extreme simulation) and the Mill Stream (MS) ranged from −1.08 to 5.34. In general there was a positive association between faunal difference and substratum difference but some sites, for example those on the Mill Stream, MS and MH, and at Wool 3, showed little response to changes in substratum.

The overall lack of response is shown in Figure 7.8, which depicts the situation in a hypothetical coarse-bottomed stream where the mean substratum particle size is reduced to 1.5 from a start value of −7.7. (This extreme change did not generate a warning notice from the RIVPACS program). It is clear that despite this reduction in mean substratum there is little change in the faunal parameter values. At present this is unexplained, but it may be related to the fact that changes in faunal composition are not always reflected by single parameter values.

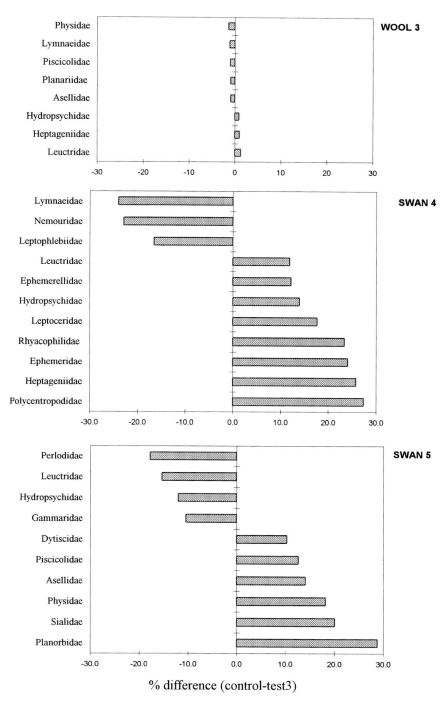

Figure 7.6. The difference between the probability of occurrence derived from control and extreme simulations for those families showing the greatest response at the Wool Stream site (W3) and at sites S4 and S5 on the Swan Brook, in Dorset. Positive values of percent difference indicate a reduction in the predicted probability of occurrence of a taxon.

Table 7.4. *Correlation (Spearmans, calculated from ranked values) between pairs of comparisons for Swan Brook sites S4 and S5, and Wool Stream sites W3 and W5, for observed (O), predicted control (C), and extreme simulations (T), based on predicted probability of occurrence and abundance.*

N = 24 for the Swan Brook and 28 for Wool Stream; * indicates invalid comparisons.

Further details are given in the text.

Swan Brook:	S4O	S4C	S4T	S5O	S5C
Abundance					
S4C	0.588				
S4T	0.546	0.976			
S5O	0.043	0.425	0.515		
S5C	0.511	0.927	0.966	0.591	
S5T	0.586	0.990	0.987	0.477	0.955
Occurrence					
S4C	*				
S4T	*	0.930			
S5O	*	*	*		
S5C	*	0.896	0.869	*	
S5T	*	0.992	0.936	*	0.907

Wool Stream:–	W3O	W3C	W3T	W5O	W5C
Abundance					
W3C	0.826				
W3T	0.827	0.997			
W5O	0.391	0.538	0.548		
W5C	0.824	0.998	0.999	0.547	
W5T	0.815	0.997	0.995	0.538	0.997
Occurrence					
W3C	*				
W3T	*	0.981			
W5O	*	*	*		
W5C	*	0.986	0.983	*	
W5T	*	0.997	0.980	*	0.991

That is to say, different combinations of environmental variables can result in the same BMWP score, ASPT or number of taxa. Another possibility is the starting point of the simulation. For instance a change from small cobble (phi –6) to fine gravel (phi –1), a difference of five substratum units, may generate greater differences in faunal parameters than a similar five units change, from coarse gravel (phi –3) to medium sand (phi 2). This requires testing on a wide range of examples.

Discussion

There is sometimes an expectation that RIVPACS has the ability to predict the effects of environmental change. However, this was never the objective and its main role has been in assessing environmental quality, by comparing observed faunal occurrence and abundance at a site with that predicted from environmental variables recorded at the same site. The ability to predict the effects of future impacts on a river system would be a valuable tool, and given the comprehensive database associated with RIVPACS, its potential as a predictor of the effects of

Table 7.5. *Observed values of three faunal parameters: BMWP score, number of taxa (N-Taxa) and average score per taxon (ASPT), with expected values from RIVPACS predictions for all control and test simulations.*

Site	Observed Score	N-Taxa	ASPT	Expected Score	N-Taxa	ASPT
MH Control	165	31	5.32	131.9	26.1	5.04
MH Test 1	165	31	5.32	129.4	25.7	5.03
MH Test 2	165	31	5.32	130.8	25.7	5.08
MS Control	190	33	5.76	139.2	26.4	5.25
MS Test 1	190	33	5.76	143.3	26.7	5.35
MS Test 2	190	33	5.76	140.2	26.4	5.29
R Control	122	23	5.3	147.2	26.8	5.48
R Test 1	122	23	5.3	140.9	26.2	5.36
R Test 2	122	23	5.3	105.5	21.8	4.81
F Control	137	25	5.48	144	25.7	5.6
F Test 1	137	25	5.48	144.6	26.3	5.49
F Test 2	137	25	5.48	146.8	26.7	5.48
F Test 3	137	25	5.48	119.6	23.4	5.08
ST Control	91	14	6.5	102.5	16.3	6.27
ST Test 1	91	14	6.5	109.3	17.7	6.17
ST Test 2	91	14	6.5	71.9	13.4	5.33
ST Test 3	91	14	6.5	64.5	12.4	5.16
W3 Control	133	26	5.12	112.8	23.5	4.79
W3 Test 1	133	26	5.12	112.6	23.5	4.78
W3 Test 2	133	26	5.12	112.5	23.5	4.78
W3 Test 3	133	26	5.12	112.5	23.5	4.78
W5 Control	56	14	4.0	112.7	23.5	4.78
W5 Test 1	56	14	4.0	112.9	23.5	4.79
W5 Test 2	56	14	4.0	113.2	23.5	4.8
W5 Test 3	56	14	4.0	113.7	23.5	4.83
S4 Control	100	19	5.26	136.3	24.6	5.53
S4 Test 1	100	19	5.26	136.4	24.8	5.48
S4 Test 2	100	19	5.26	131.5	24.3	5.41
S4 Test 3	100	19	5.26	111.8	21.6	5.15
S5 Control	63	17	3.71	139.9	26	5.37
S5 Test 1	63	17	3.71	145.3	26.5	5.48
S5 Test 2	63	17	3.71	140.9	25.6	5.5
S5 Test 3	63	17	3.71	137.1	24.9	5.5

environmental change required investigation. This preliminary study has shown that only those disturbances which involve changes to the variables currently used in RIVPACS can be considered. This restricts its possible use to changes involving channel characteristics, discharge and alkalinity (a surrogate for parent rock-type in the catchment).

The results indicate that it is possible to record faunal change by altering environmental variables to simulate potential impacts. However, the responses are relatively small and although the two validation tests carried out in this study indicate the possibility of simulating a real change, the process shows a lack of sensitivity except in the most extreme cases. The situation in the Wool Stream provides a good example of this insensitivity. Despite a change from a gravel substratum to one dominated by silt, the predicted family occurrence and

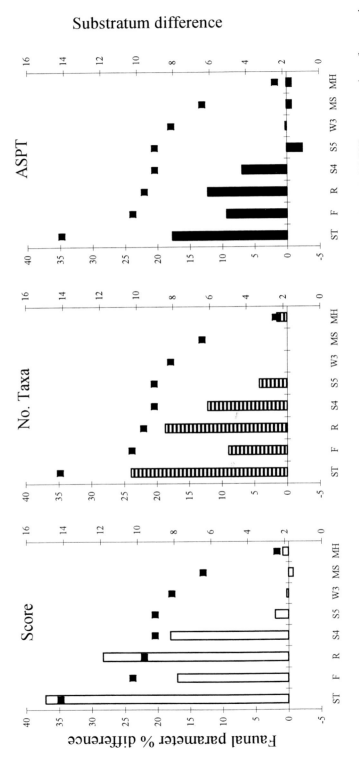

Figure 7.7. The effect of simulated substratum change (squares) on the prediction of three faunal parameters (columns): BMWP score, number of taxa and ASPT. The results are expressed as the percent difference between the control (unstressed) and most extreme test for each river. (ST = South Tyne; F and R = chalk stream middle section; S4 and S5 = Swan Brook; W3 = Wool Stream; MH = Mill Head, MS = Mill Stream). Also shown is the difference between substratum values of control and extreme tests – thus a simulated change from a mean substratum value of phi –4 to phi +5 represents a change of 9 units.

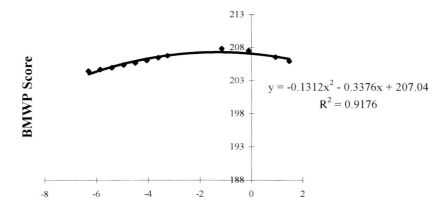

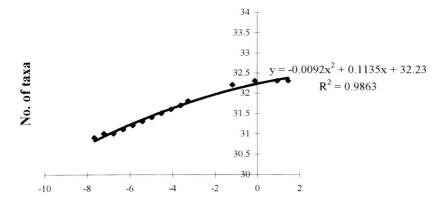

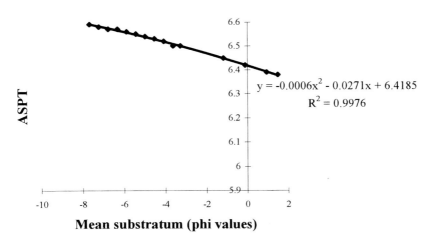

Mean substratum (phi values)

Figure 7.8. The effect of simulated increase in siltation on predictions of three faunal parameters: BMWP score, number of taxa and ASPT. Points represent the mean substratum values entered in the simulations, and their distribution is described by the fitted polynomial.

abundance did not alter. Even the most extreme simulation did not generate a warning notice from the program, and the predicted group membership did not change. The observed environmental conditions placed the site in RIVPACS III group 31 with a probability of 97.8%, and the most extreme simulation placed it in the same group with a probability of 99.9%. This group contains small lowland streams with a high alkalinity, and it is these properties which define the group, despite a wide range of substratum conditions. This feature makes RIVPACS insensitive to substratum changes in streams of this type. In addition, extreme simulations are frequently unsuitable for RIVPACS, and the program provides a warning when the particular combination of environmental variables has a low probability of occurrence in the dataset. These reasons alone show that RIVPACS probably does not have much potential to predict the possible effects of environmental disturbance or stress.

Another possible reason for the lack of sensitivity may be the RIVPACS sample itself, which includes all available habitats. This means that if some prime habitat is much reduced it will still be sampled, and it is highly likely that the species will occur in the sample. The use of abundance data will improve matters but there will be cases where animals are concentrated into a small area, and when this is sampled, abundance will seem to be relatively high. An example is seen when chalk stream systems are subject to low flow, where Rhyacophilidae will be concentrated in areas of fast flow channelled between weed-beds.

It is clear that most stresses/disturbances on the lotic system involve changes, either directly or indirectly, to instream habitat. For example, dredging and channel engineering will affect the distribution of substratum particles and alter channel dimensions (Brooks 1994). Flow regulation below reservoirs may result in modifications to the substratum (Simons 1979; Gore 1994) and the removal or addition of water (transfers and abstractions) may radically alter the wetted area in a stream and hence the availability and quality of habitat (Armitage & Petts 1992). The patchwork of habitats or mesohabitats, observed from the bank of a river, possess characteristic faunal assemblages (Armitage *et al.* 1995; Pardo & Armitage 1997) and disturbances will affect their distribution and extent. In RIVPACS, all available habitats are sampled roughly in proportion to their occurrence but are combined, so there is no habitat-specific data. An ideal system for forecasting the effects of environmental change on macroinvertebrate assemblages will require habitat-specific sampling, and knowledge of the area or percentage cover of the habitat patches constituting the area of investigation. The effects of particular disturbances and management regimes on instream habitat will provide a necessary first step towards modelling and forecasting the effects of changes and disturbances to the environment.

RIVPACS is a static model and cannot validly be used as a forecasting system. Such a system will need separate development and will require different types of data. Predictive models are particularly well developed with respect to the effects of nutrient enrichment in lake ecosystems (Vollenweider 1975; Aldenberg & Peters 1990; Reynolds 1996; Reynolds & Irish 1997) and in rivers (Dauta 1986; Reynolds & Glaister 1993), and are frequently based on detailed information on the response of algal populations to changing environmental conditions. Alternatively, historical data may be used to forecast ecological succession (Bravard *et al.* 1986). Such information is not a part of RIVPACS.

Where next? The modification of RIVPACS to include polluted sites may offer the possibility of classifying pollution responses in a wide range of river types. However, prediction of change would still be impossible because of several complicating factors, such as synergistic effects of variables, differing rates of recovery from pollution, and recolonisation processes. An alternative approach would be to build on knowledge of the processes involved in environmental disturbance. To forecast or predict the effects of environmental change we need to know what happens when disturbances take place, how long the effects will take to develop, and their duration. A series of case-histories in different river types may provide suitable data on the physical changes that accompany disturbance. This, in conjunction with more detailed information on geomorphology, hydraulics and siltation relationships, will contribute to the development of a system which could predict future impacts. When this is linked to information on the effects of a suite of pollutants under different flow conditions, at different concentrations and in different seasons, we would have the ingredients for an expert system. Such a system should enable the manager of a river to forecast the likely effects of an environmental disturbance. This is a long way in the future, and depends on the investment of the water resource organisations in acquiring knowledge of the processes associated with specific disturbances. At present it must be concluded that RIVPACS, while showing direction of change and indicating sensitive taxa, cannot be used to predict or forecast the effects of environmental impacts.

Acknowledgements

This work has been supported financially by the Natural Environment Research Council. I am grateful to Ralph Clarke, Kay Symes, Lucy Crowhurst and Dave Bradley at the Institute of Freshwater Ecology for their help, and Paul Wood (University of Huddersfield) for his comments on the typescript.

CHAPTER 8

Development of a national river bioassessment system (AUSRIVAS) in Australia

PETER E. DAVIES

Land and Water Resources R&D Corporation, 95 Northbourne Ave, Canberra ACT 2601, AUSTRALIA, and Department of Zoology, University of Tasmania, GPO Box 252C-5, Hobart, Tasmania 7001, AUSTRALIA

Summary

The history and development of the new Australian national river bioassessment system is described. The AUStralian RIVer Assessment Scheme (AUSRIVAS), contains a river bioassessment system largely based on the British RIVPACS. It has been developed in a cooperative effort between federal and state government agencies, and a variety of researchers. Despite the maintenance of state and territory boundaries in developing a national river bioassessment framework, uniformity of sampling, modelling and reporting was sought. The encapsulation of the reference condition within a bioassessment system was also seen as important. The RIVPACS framework was selected for adaptation to Australian conditions under the nationally-managed Monitoring River Health Initiative (MRHI), and over 1500 reference sites were sampled over a 2-year period for invertebrates and environmental variables, under a common protocol. The political, managerial and environmental context of Australia markedly shaped the manner in which RIVPACS was adopted. The 48 RIVPACS-type models developed under the MRHI are run behind a common software platform, accessible over the internet. Differences between RIVPACS and AUSRIVAS are described. AUSRIVAS is being used to conduct the first national assessment of river health, and is becoming integrated into a variety of policy and regulatory mechanisms. Problems associated with developing and maintaining integrated, evolving systems like RIVPACS at a national level are described, including the recent wave of changes to the public sector.

Introduction

The occurrence of a persistent and extensive blue-green algal bloom in the Darling River, in 1991, brought the condition of Australia's river ecosystems to national attention (Wasson, Banens *et al.* 1996). Following this, in 1992, a Prime Ministerial Statement on the Environment was issued, which provided funding for a national initiative to assess and report on the ecological condition of Australia's rivers – the Monitoring River Health Initiative (MRHI). Following a protracted period in which funding calls were made under this and related initiatives, the MRHI was combined with several other programs under a common banner – the National River Health Program (NRHP).

The MRHI became focussed on establishing a national river bioassessment system using invertebrates and based on the River InVertebrate Prediction And Classification System (RIVPACS). The major initial thrust for the development of the bioassessment system was to assess impacts of water quality on biota, although the general concept of ecological condition or "health" was also promoted. Two primary aims of the MRHI became: (1) to develop and enhance techniques to monitor and assess the health of Australia's rivers, and (2) to establish a national approach to monitoring and assessing the health of Australia's rivers. Priorities within the MRHI were informed by commissioned reviews on bioassessment indicators (Norris *et al.* 1993) and on biomonitoring research needs (Arthington, Hart *et al.* 1993).

"Ecological health", though criticised within the context of its original conception (Suter 1993), and for its rapid unthinking uptake in management culture, was still seen as a useful concept for framing some of the thinking within the MRHI. A working definition of river health was adopted under the MRHI (markedly modified from that of Karr & Dudley 1991) as follows: *"The ability of the aquatic ecosystem to support and maintain key ecological processes and a community of organisms with a species composition, diversity and functional organisation as comparable as possible to that of natural habitats within a region".*

Early consideration within the MRHI rejected the concept of basing a national bioassessment system on simplistic indicators or metrics of biological condition (Metcalfe 1989; Plafkin, Barbour *et al.* 1989). These were thought to be based on concepts of community structure, function or response which were either not readily transferable to Australia or poorly conceived. A framework was sought which incorporated the concept of reference conditions, with the potential for regional definition of the reference conditions, against which "test" sites could be benchmarked. RIVPACS, with its predictive approach, was seen as the best initial option.

Development in the Australian context

The development of any bioassessment system at a regional, national or continental scale is inevitably shaped by the political, managerial and environmental context in which it is placed.

Political and resource management context

Australia has a federal system of government modelled on the UK Westminster system, but with six states and two territories. The federal (national) government has no jurisdiction over natural resource management except as it affects a specific national agenda. Water resource management is not a direct responsibility of the federal government, and national coordination and leadership in environmental management have been provided through two primary mechanisms: national funding programs focussed on water and environmental issues, and by the establishment of management agencies and authorities responsible for specific issues or cross-sectoral agency coordination. An example of the first mechanism is the Murray–Darling Basin Commission, responsible for managing land and water resources in "The Basin", which covers around 20% of Australia's land area. The second mechanism is typified by the attempt to vertically integrate the structure of environment protection agencies at state and federal levels. The primary effect of this federal–state split is that national programs such as the MRHI must provide incentives for the involvement of state and territory governments, particularly when new environmental management frameworks are being promoted.

Another important contextual issue for the MRHI is that there has been very little investment in aquatic ecological R&D or biological monitoring by government. This is despite over 50 years of investment in water resource infrastructural development, 30 to 40 years of effort aimed at quantifying water resources through establishing state and national river gauging networks, and 20 years of massive investment in water quality monitoring programs and the development of a large, accredited water chemical analytical industry (Environmental Protection Agency 1995).

This lack of previous agency focus on the incorporation of environmental objectives in water resource management or bioassessment was seen as a key opportunity for the MRHI. It should of course be emphasised that Australia has maintained a substantial and enthusiastic freshwater ecological research effort, though almost exclusively through academic institutions and through the efforts of a small group of key individuals. The NRHP was able to capitalise on this tranche of expertise in its attempts to "transfer" an aquatic ecological ethos into water management.

Environmental context

Australia is recognised as one of the world's most arid continents. It does have substantial water resources, but these are concentrated largely around the northern, eastern and southern coastal fringes. The Western Plateau, covering 32% of the continent, produces almost no runoff, while an additional 17% never drains to the ocean (Wasson, Banens *et al.* 1996). Rainfall is both spatially and temporally variable, at a range of scales. Australian rivers are recognised as having particularly high variability per unit runoff (McMahon, Finlayson *et al.* 1992), comparable only to southern Africa, and highly dissimilar to northern-hemisphere continents in which river bioassessment has been developed.

Australia has five broad climatic/hydrological regions (Fig. 8.1; also see Fig. 10.1 p. 146), overlying a number of broad landform types. Dominant features include the Great Dividing Range in the east, which is the source of much of the continent's runoff and ground water, as well as being a core component of the Murray–Darling River catchments.

Impacts from industrial discharges and urban runoff in Australian rivers are limited, as most human settlements are on the coasts. Much of the continent has been (and continues to be) cleared of native vegetation, and riverine environmental problems are dominated by changes in flow regimes due to regulation, abstraction and land clearance, by increased salinity, nutrients and sediment transport, and by degraded riparian conditions, all related to rural development.

Major declines in riverine condition, typified by degraded water quality and loss of native biodiversity and ecosystem structural complexity, have occurred throughout the eastern, south-eastern and south-western parts of the continent. Threats to river condition are now increasing in the north and semi-arid interior.

Key issues for bioassessment in Australia

Following on from the context described above, several issues were seen as key constraints with regard to the development of a national bioassessment framework. Operational issues included the level of funding available, the availability of biological expertise, and the potential for adoption of bioassessment in water resource management.

Technical constraints included the need to standardise sampling, data analysis and modelling at a national level, ensure quality control/assurance at key steps in the RIVPACS process, and use an adequate number of sampling events for the characterisation of macroinvertebrate community structure at each site. Further considerations included the spatial density of reference sites, the availability and representativeness of the reference condition, temporal variability in community composition, and the status of taxonomic knowledge and resources (e.g. identification keys, voucher collections, specialists available).

Standardisation and quality control

As with any large multicomponent system, standardisation and quality control are major issues. There was a need to standardise all aspects of site selection, sampling, sample processing, environmental variables, data analysis and modelling. Quality control was required for key components – sample processing, identification and enumeration.

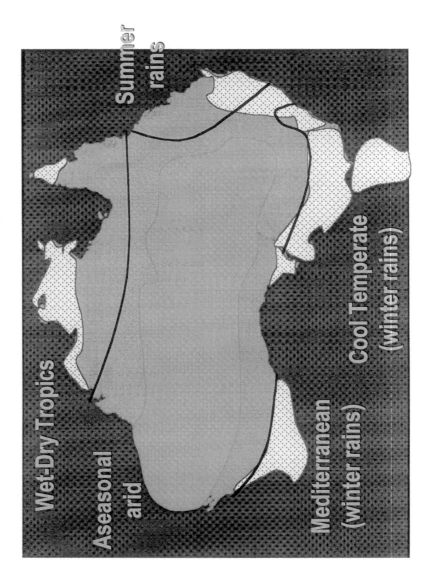

Figure 8.1. The major climatic regions of Australia.

Temporal variability

Temporal variability in rainfall, hydrology and hence aquatic biological community composition, was seen as a potential limitation or barrier to the adoption of the RIVPACS approach in Australia. Alternatives, such as the use of before-after-control-impact (BACI)-type designs and their variants (see Underwood 1997), although ideal, were seen as impracticable for a bioassessment system designed to work at regional, state and national levels. Consequently, an understanding of temporal variability, its influence on invertebrate community persistence, and its implications for the use of a RIVPACS-type system in Australia, was a high priority under the MRHI. This issue has been addressed by Humphrey *et al.* in Chapter 10.

Taxonomic and ecological knowledge base

For a bioassessment program working at a national level, lack of taxonomic resources, as well as autecological knowledge, was also a potential problem for bioassessment using any group of aquatic biota, and particularly invertebrates.

Reference condition

It was recognised early that the adequate definition, availability and sampling density (in time and space) of the reference condition is critical to the success of a RIVPACS-type bioassessment system. It was also recognised that the use of the reference concept was in part subjective (i.e. socially derived) and incremental in development. The number and spatial pattern of reference sites that was to develop under the MRHI was therefore influenced largely by pragmatism.

The Monitoring River Health Initiative (MRHI): Phase 1

Phase 1 of the MRHI (1994–1998) had three main activities: development of the RIVPACS-type bioassessment system in all major river basins in Australia, and all states and territories; support for an integrated R&D program to facilitate its development; and implementation of a range of communication activities aimed at introducing and establishing riverine bioassessment into water and environmental management frameworks.

Development of the river bioassessment system

A RIVPACS-type model was to be adopted, based on the UK approach (Wright 1995), and then adapted for Australia. It was developed by: (1) a preliminary evaluation of the RIVPACS approach by a Technical Working Group which recommended modifications to be adopted under the Australian MRHI; (2) writing a single bioassessment manual which described the process of developing a RIVPACS-type model, with a number of amendments agreed on for Australian conditions (Davies 1994); (3) contracting one government agency in each of the eight states and territories to develop RIVPACS-type models using that manual; (4) contracting a research organisation (the Cooperative Research Centre for Freshwater Ecology, CRCFE) to assist the eight contracted agencies with statistical training and analysis, and to develop the final models and software platform; (5) continual review of key issues by a Technical Advisory Committee, overseen by a program Management Committee.

Key decisions made during the development of the Australian river bioassessment system are summarised below.

Sampling and sample processing. It was decided to sample habitats within river reaches separately and to develop discrete RIVPACS-type models for each habitat. Five habitats were initially identified, of which between three and four were sampled by the agencies at reference sites, and two were selected for modelling. Samples were taken twice a year in either spring/autumn (for southern, south-eastern and western Australia), or late dry/early dry (for northern Australia). 250 mm-mesh kicknets were used for all sampling, and a standard area of each habitat type was sampled. Samples were processed in one of two ways; by live-picking or by laboratory sorting of preserved subsamples. Invertebrates were identified to family level only, with several exceptions, and it was decided to use a standard minimum set of environmental variables for model development.

Model development. It was decided to use unweighted pair-group mean arithmetic averaging (UPGMA) cluster analysis for all reference site classification, with hybrid multi-dimensional scaling (HMDS) ordination and TWINSPAN as supplementary aids in identifying groups (Davies 1994). All "infrequently occurring taxa" are removed from the datasets prior to classification and modelling – typically those taxa which occurred at 10% or less of reference sites in the classification. A 30% re-classification criterion is used for the discriminant function analysis. Two forms of output were adopted: observed/expected (O/E) for number of taxa, and O/E SIGNAL, where the latter is a ratio of the observed to expected SIGNAL score for a site. SIGNAL is an Australian analogue of average score per taxon (ASPT), based on scores analogous to the UK Biological Monitoring Working Party (BMWP) score system of taxon susceptibility to water pollution (Chessman 1995). Further details on model development are given by Simpson and Norris in Chapter 9.

Use of models. A single platform was used for all models derived from the MRHI state/territory bioassessment effort. A total of 48 models have been developed to date, consisting of separate models for each combination of two habitats, two seasons plus combined seasons, and eight states and territories. While details of the datasets and protocols behind the eight sets of models may differ slightly, it was considered vital to the national focus of the program to have a single modelling and software platform, and reporting framework. To support this, we have incorporated internet access from a central server as the primary way in which models can be accessed (via passwords) and run. It also enables models to be updated and made available with minimal delays.

Reference sites and samples

The MRHI bioassessment manual (Davies 1994) stipulated an initial process for the contracted state and territory government agencies to identify reference sites, defined as those "least disturbed" within a region. The agencies sampled over 1500 reference sites nationally (Fig. 8.2) on four occasions between 1994 and 1997, typically once in two seasons per year over two consecutive years. A second year of sampling was specified in order to provide the opportunity to incorporate multi-year sampling into models if desired and also to evaluate inter-annual differences in model performance. Some 200 additional reference sites have been sampled between 1997 and 1999.

All samples were processed and identified, and the biological and site environmental data were entered into databases. All agencies conducted the UPGMA and ordination analyses, and selected the final classifications used in the models. This involved some culling of reference site data, where sites were identified as outliers and/or impacted *post hoc.* All models had been successfully developed by mid-1997, with the exception of those for the Northern Territory whose sampling had started significantly later. This "beta" set of models was subject to preliminary testing (see Chapter 9). A final "alpha" set of tested, refined models is to be developed by mid-1999.

Figure 8.2. The locations of *ca* 1500 reference sites sampled for AUSRIVAS bioassessment model development during the first phase of the Monitoring River Health Initiative (MRHI).

The Australian River Assessment Scheme (AUSRIVAS)

Late in 1996, the Australian RIVPACS-type model was given an official name – AUSRIVAS (the AUStralian RIVer Assessment Scheme). The processes of developing and using AUSRIVAS are illustrated in Figure 8.3 and are essentially similar to RIVPACS. Although the RIVPACS approach still formed the kernel of the bioassessment system, sufficient differences existed to warrant a change in name. In addition, it was planned to increase the breadth of the system's capabilities to include habitat assessment and protocols for other structural and process indicators of aquatic ecosystem health.

Research and development under MRHI Phase 1

The development of the national AUSRIVAS bioassessment system, under Phase 1 of the MRHI, was paralleled with contracted research and activities aimed at providing support through: (1) performing external quality control on taxonomic identification and enumeration, and on sample processing (see Chapter 10), and developing a Quality Assurance/Quality Control (QA/QC) framework for the bioassessment system; (2) development of supporting

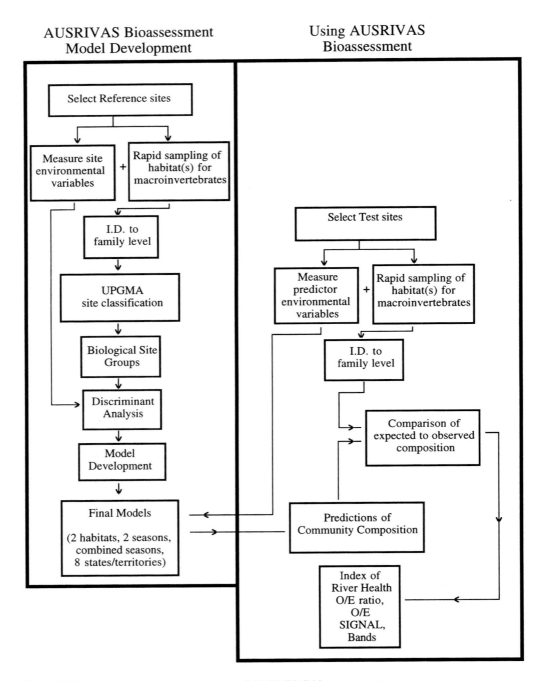

Figure 8.3. Steps in the development and use of AUSRIVAS bioassessment.

taxonomic aids and tools; (3) evaluating and developing the form of outputs of the bioassessment system best suited to water resource managers; (4) development of the modelling platform for AUSRIVAS (see Chapter 9).

In addition, R&D projects were funded to test and develop bioassessment for other riverine biota, notably fish, benthic diatoms, macrophytes and phytoplankton, and for benthic metabolism. Several projects focussed on identifying macroinvertebrate responses to specific water quality characteristics as a diagnostic aid for AUSRIVAS bioassessment. Further development and testing of the modelling framework on which AUSRIVAS is based was seen as essential, and an evaluation of an ordination-based approach to predictive modelling from reference site data was also funded. Assessing the degree of temporal variability in macroinvertebrate community composition at reference sites, and how temporal variability may be built into the bioassessment framework, was seen as important, especially in the Australian context and given concerns raised about the need for monitoring program designs that incorporate temporal variability (e.g. Underwood 1997; and Chapter 10). Projects were also funded to evaluate several issues related to quality assurance, including how compositional data from the prescribed sampling methods compared with quantitative sampling methods, and the optimum area of habitat to be sampled.

Significant R&D was also being performed by academics not directly funded by the program, answering some key questions for the development of AUSRIVAS (see Marchant 1990; Chessman 1995; Growns, Chessman *et al.* 1995; Marchant *et al.* 1995; Norris & Norris 1995) and adding considerably to the cooperative nature of the national effort.

Though much of the R&D effort associated with AUSRIVAS bioassessment is currently still underway, key early results are available for the following issues (*a – e*).

(a). QA/QC. Problems have occurred with taxonomic QA/QC even at family level (remediable by training), although these were less significant than some problems which could occur with sample processing (Chapter 10) and environmental data (Chapter 9).

(b). Temporal variability. This is a significant issue for those parts of Australia with high hydrological variability, and can be dealt with in a number of ways (Chapter 10).

(c). Reference sites. Issues of identification and representativeness of reference sites will be ongoing (particularly for lowland and inland semi-arid streams), and will require a move away from assumptions of natural biological distributions within the reference site dataset, as well as a willingness to think at a range of spatial scales.

(d). Taxonomic coding. Adoption of a standard taxonomic coding system, and its use within new keys for identification, was a major aid.

(e). Sample sizes. The size of the sampled area for all modelled habitats was adequate to describe the dominant community of the habitats that were modelled.

Early results from using the preliminary AUSRIVAS models indicate that they are sufficiently robust to detect at least major impacts. The scores and bands derived from different habitats at the same site could differ, however, raising questions about the differential sensitivity of models and/or of the fauna in each habitat. Results from Queensland indicate that the influence of a major drought was significant in depressing both test and reference site scores.

The Monitoring River Health Initiative (MRHI): Phase 2

In 1996, with a change of federal government, a new environmental funding framework was established under the National Heritage Trust. Fortunately, this provided a further stimulus to the MRHI, and some 7 million Australian dollars were pledged for further work in this area, of which 5 million have actually been made available. The priorities of what has become MRHI Phase 2 are: (1) to conduct a First National Assessment of River Health (FNARH) using the current AUSRIVAS protocols and platform; (2) to further refine and develop AUSRIVAS and its capability; (3) to complete the "technology transfer" of AUSRIVAS to state water and environment agencies, industry and community groups.

The FNARH consists of a single national survey – being conducted between 1997 and 1999 – of some 4000 to 6000 river sites around Australia. Sampling at all sites is being conducted with the AUSRIVAS sampling protocols. The data will be assessed using a final ("alpha") version of each of the AUSRIVAS models, which will have been refined by adding more or higher quality reference site data.

Adoption of AUSRIVAS

It was recognised early in the program that instability at all levels in the public sector, due to continuing downsizing, deskilling, repetitive restructuring and the general policy push for outsourcing and the "purchaser-provider" split (see Jones 1996), was a major risk for the long-term stability (even survival) of an integrated bioassessment system operating at a national level. It was therefore decided to attempt to "hook" AUSRIVAS into a number of key federal and state regulatory, policy and other processes, to ensure both its continuance and adoption.

AUSRIVAS is to be advocated as a key tool in the Australian national water quality guidelines, first published in 1992 (ANZECC 1992) and currently being revised. It is also accepted as a major reporting tool for both federal and state "State of the Environment" (SOE) reporting, with the FNARH set to provide a major data layer on "river health" in the year 2000 national SOE report. In addition, it has been accepted as a major datasource for the first National Land and Water Audit, currently being prepared, as well as being a key indicator of "Catchment Health".

At the state level, AUSRIVAS is already seen as a key provider of data for "State of the Rivers" reporting, for providing data relevant to environmental flow allocation (e.g. in Queensland), and for incorporation into catchment planning and state environment policies. It is envisaged that adoption into state water and environmental policy and regulatory frameworks will continue.

International links

The development of AUSRIVAS bioassessment has involved substantial international cooperation, facilitated by an active policy within the MRHI to fund exchanges and visits with both the IFE and the NRA (now Environment Agency) in the UK, the input from whom has been substantial. In addition, there have been multiple discussions and exchanges with managers and researchers in this field in South Africa, Canada and the USA.

Future developments and issues

The AUSRIVAS "package"

AUSRIVAS is set to develop into an integrated river assessment "package" incorporating both bioassessment and physico-chemical assessment of river condition. A new R&D effort will be expended in the area of standardised physico-chemical assessment, with a sound geomorphological underpinning. An AUSRIVAS Resources Package will be developed by mid-2000, with the following elements (*a – f*).

(*a*). *Primer booklet.* This will consist of an introduction to AUSRIVAS, its history, components, uses, how the models work, what is needed to conduct an AUSRIVAS assessment, site and model access, password.

(*b*). *Biological sampling protocols.* For macroinvertebrates, this will include site selection, timing and frequency of sampling, sampling methods, sample processing, identification and data entry, with appropriate QA/QC procedures. Additional sampling protocols will be available for algae, fish and measurement of rates of benthic metabolism. These will include site selection, timing and frequency of sampling, sampling methods, sample processing and identification, and pointers to analytical techniques.

(*c*). *Invertebrate taxonomic keys and coding system.* Produced on CD-ROM, www and in printed form.

(*d*). *Habitat assessment protocol.* This will include a new site survey protocol, measurement and ranking protocols, data entry and introduction to relevant software.

(*e*). *Software manual.* A manual will be made available on the www site.

(*f*). *Training and accreditation materials.* Video, training manuals and accreditation procedures for AUSRIVAS.

Additional technical challenges are yet to be met. These include a potential change in modelling technique to a more ordination-based approach (Chapter 9), the incorporation of temporal variability into the bioassessment process (Chapter 10), and the ability to develop predictive bioassessment for the highly unpredictable streams of the semi-arid and arid regions of the continent.

Issues for the future

Several issues are prominent with regard to the future development, adoption and stability of a national bioassessment framework like AUSRIVAS. There is a need for a stable "custodial" environment for such an integrated, incremental and evolving approach. The success of RIVPACS in the UK is a testament to the role of both the IFE and NRA (now the Environment Agency) in its management. Public sector instability and fragmentation, as well as the privatisation of the water industry in Australia, are major problems in this regard.

Another parallel push to "outsource" environmental management to "the community", through a variety of community and catchment management groups with a wide range of capabilities, skills and stability, is a potent destabilising influence in natural resource management in Australia. It may or may not enhance the quality of environmental management and hence provide an environment which finds AUSRIVAS useful. Much depends on the ability of non-professional biologists to utilise such an approach, and the ability of remaining government natural resource agencies to support quality management processes.

There is also, largely as a result of priorities developing under the new National Heritage Trust, an atmosphere largely antithetical to research in the Australian public sector (see Beckman 1996). This makes it difficult to sustain research and development in the area of aquatic ecosystem science and management, and provide effective technical support.

On the other hand, the provision of a nationally applicable system such as AUSRIVAS, with broad applicability, can result in overenthusiastic adoption by agencies, with a tendency to want to use rapid bioassessment in a wide variety of situations, some of which it was not designed for. Coupled with this is a valuable and potent process of independent academic criticism, already being voiced over the use of AUSRIVAS.

Ready adoption of AUSRIVAS bioassessment by water and environmental agencies, at both national and state level, is already occurring. There is strong support for its use in a wide variety of agency activities. Future developments should see the broader adoption of AUSRIVAS bioassessment, in a wide variety of environmental management settings, by government, community and industry, frequently coupled with quantitative bioassessment protocols and water quality assessment.

Acknowledgements

John Wright and an anonymous reviewer are thanked for comments on the manuscript. Thanks are owed to the UK and Australian agencies (Environment Agency, Institute of Freshwater Ecology, Environment Australia, Land and Water Resources R&D Corporation) for support and assistance with organising the Oxford conference, and supporting the presence of the Australian delegates, and particularly to Roger Sweeting (Environment Agency, and now Chief Executive of the Freshwater Biological Association, UK).

CHAPTER 9

Biological assessment of river quality: development of AUSRIVAS models and outputs

JUSTEN C. SIMPSON AND RICHARD H. NORRIS

Cooperative Research Centre for Freshwater Ecology,
University of Canberra, Canberra 2601, AUSTRALIA

Summary

Biological assessment is rapidly emerging as a standard river quality assessment tool to be used in conjunction with more traditional physical and chemical methods. AUSRIVAS is based largely on techniques developed in Britain, where RIVPACS has been employed for a number of years, successfully using aquatic macroinvertebrates to provide assessments of river health. However, there are several important differences between AUSRIVAS and RIVPACS. Australia is much larger and has a more varied landscape than Britain. Australia's size required, initially, development of 48 models for individual states or distinct geographic areas, in order to achieve better resolution for assessing sites within a particular region. In Australia, habitats are sampled separately, allowing both single and multiple habitat assessments. Rules have been developed for combining the assessments obtained from different habitats as well as assessments from different seasons. Extensive testing is still required to ensure confidence in these "combined" assessments. Separate classifications and sets of predictor variables are used for each of the 48 AUSRIVAS models currently being developed, but latitude, longitude and alkalinity were common to two-thirds of them. Only those taxa having ≥50% probability of occurrence are used in the AUSRIVAS models for calculating the expected number of taxa and SIGNAL index at a site. Large numbers of models, and the proposed extensive number of users, led to the development of AUSRIVAS as an internet-based program. The First National Assessment of River Health in Australia, for which sampling is being undertaken in 1997–1999, will be the first large-scale test of AUSRIVAS in providing useful information on the ecological condition of Australia's rivers and streams.

Introduction

In Australia there has been increased pressure on water managers and the government to maintain ecological values (Norris & Norris 1995). Consequently, the National River Health Program (NRHP) was formed by the federal government to provide a means of assessing the ecological condition of Australia's river systems. Central to the NRHP was the development of predictive models, similar to the British RIVPACS models (Wright 1995), which predict the biological condition of a site in the absence of environmental stress. The NRHP involves the major environment agency in each state and territory, and is administered by Environment Australia and the Land and Water Resources Research and Development Corporation (LWRRDC). The Cooperative Research Centre for Freshwater Ecology developed the predictive software called AUStralian RIVer Assessment System (AUSRIVAS). Currently,

AUSRIVAS has been developed to a level where it can be accessed and run by authorised users via the internet (Simpson, Norris *et al.* 1997). So far, 40 AUSRIVAS models are available, covering all states and territories with the exception of the Northern Territory. In addition to model building and software development, there also has been comprehensive agency training in the use of AUSRIVAS.

The development of AUSRIVAS has required some innovative changes to RIVPACS. There are some fundamental differences in sampling strategy, geographic coverage of models, taxa selected, model construction, model running, outputs and supply of supporting information. Some of these differences took advantage of advances in computer and statistical techniques, while others were necessary because of Australia's unique environment. These differences have resulted in AUSRIVAS looking and operating in a very different way from RIVPACS.

AUSRIVAS is now being used in Australia's First National Assessment of River Health (FNARH), for which about 6000 sites are being sampled over three years (LWRRDC 1997). Results from FNARH will provide valuable information for testing the effectiveness of the techniques chosen for AUSRIVAS in providing useful assessments of river condition for both managers and researchers alike.

This chapter describes what has been achieved in the NRHP thus far and considers the implications of differences in approach between AUSRIVAS and RIVPACS.

Methods

Field sampling

Over 1500 minimally disturbed sites were sampled across Australia to establish a reference site database from which to build the AUSRIVAS models. Each controlling state/territory agency was responsible for site selection and sampling, mainly within their administrative borders. Sites were normally visited in autumn and spring for two consecutive years. The two most common aquatic habitats in each state/territory, from a choice of riffle, edge, main channel, macrophytes and pool rocks, were selected for model construction.

Habitat assessment. A large number of habitat variables, including physical, chemical and map measurements (Simpson, Norris *et al.* 1997), were taken to characterise each site. Some of these variables may also provide an indication of potential pollutants for test sites. A standard set of habitat variables was collected by all agencies (Davies 1994); however, extra variables were collected by individual states as required to suit geographic conditions. The variables measured were similar to those reported by Wright, Moss *et al.* (1984) and Moss, Furse *et al.* (1987), but also included the addition of the invertebrate habitat assessment estimates of the US Environmental Protection Agency (Plafkin, Barbour *et al.* 1989).

Invertebrate sampling. At each site, invertebrates were collected separately from the chosen habitats in each region. Triangular or D-framed kicknets with a 300–350 mm base and 250 mm-mesh were used to sample a 10 m transect of each habitat. Four states/territories (Australian Capital Territory, Northern Territory, Tasmania and South Australia) preserved the entire invertebrate sample in the field and used laboratory subsampling, while three states (New South Wales, Queensland and Victoria) live-picked in the field for a timed period to obtain a subsample. Western Australia used a combination of both subsampling techniques. A subsample size of 200 animals was desired for both field and laboratory subsampling.

Identification. Invertebrates were identified to family level with the exceptions of Oligochaeta (Class), Acarina (Order), Collembola (Order), Turbellaria (Order), and Chironomidae (Subfamily). Invertebrate data were also converted to presence/absence form before analysis because the AUSRIVAS models only predict the occurrence of taxa and not their expected abundance. A nationally adopted coding system was used to assign a specific code to each taxon (Trueman, Lee *et al.* 1996). These codes facilitated sorting and other data management requirements for building and running the AUSRIVAS models.

Analyses

Many Australian taxa have sparse distributions, occurring at few sites (Faith & Norris 1989; Marchant, Hirst *et al.* 1997). Such taxa were removed from further analyses to reduce unexplained variability caused by their patchy occurrence (Gauch 1982; Norris & Georges 1993). In the development of AUSRIVAS, rare taxa were defined as those that occurred at less than 10% of sites for datasets of up to 100 sites, or that occurred at less than 10 sites for datasets of more than 100 sites. All taxa collected are used when constructing RIVPACS models (Wright, Moss *et al.* 1984).

Classification analysis. The first step in building an AUSRIVAS model was to classify the reference sites based on invertebrate composition, using the agglomerative clustering technique, flexible unweighted pair-group mean arithmetic averaging (UPGMA), as recommended by Belbin & McDonald (1993) after their extensive testing of classification procedures. The Bray–Curtis association measure was used on the recommendation of Faith *et al.* (1987) as a robust measure of association for cluster analysis. Classifications were then visually inspected as dendrograms to identify groupings of sites.

Wright *et al.* (1993) recommended that classification groups should contain not less than five sites. Groups containing less than five sites can result from poor representation of a particular habitat type, problems with the initial sampling, or degradation of sites in some manner, resulting in loss of taxa indicative of reference conditions. Small classification groups were either deleted from further analysis, or those sites were amalgamated with another group of appropriate reference sites after review (Simpson, Norris *et al.* 1997).

Discriminant function analysis. Like RIVPACS, AUSRIVAS models use habitat features that are little affected by human activities to predict which taxa should occur at a site in the absence of environmental stress (Wright, Moss *et al.* 1984; Moss, Furse *et al.* 1987). Stepwise multiple discriminant function analysis (MDFA) is used to select the predictor variables best able to discriminate among the invertebrate classification groups.

Subsets of habitat variables from the Stepwise MDFA were then tested in an MDFA to predict the probabilities of group membership for each reference site. Biased discriminations were avoided by using the cross-validation option that predicts group membership of each site separately (SAS Institute 1995). A subset of habitat variables that produced the lowest error in predicting the membership of reference sites to the invertebrate classification groups was obtained from this procedure. The invertebrate and habitat data from the reference sites were then used to construct the AUSRIVAS models, following methods described by Wright, Moss *et al.* (1984) and Moss, Furse *et al.* (1987).

The AUSRIVAS models currently available have been constructed from data collected from only two seasons. In the near future, data collected from a further two sampling occasions will be incorporated into the existing models. The exception is the Australian Capital Territory (ACT), the models for which incorporate data from four sampling occasions. Separate models were constructed for each habitat, in both seasons and for each habitat, using combined season data. Thus, each region has six AUSRIVAS models from which to choose.

Predicted, expected and observed numbers of taxa

Unlike the RIVPACS models, which use all of the taxa predicted to occur (Moss, Furse *et al.* 1987), the AUSRIVAS models only consider families that were calculated to have 50% or greater probability of occurring at a test site (Simpson, Norris *et al.* 1997). The total number of taxa listed with a predicted probability of occurrence ≥50% represents the number of "predicted" taxa. In contrast, the sum of the probabilities of occurrence for taxa predicted with a ≥50% chance of occurrence gives the number of taxa "expected" (E) to be found at a test site. The "observed" (O) number of taxa is the total number of taxa with ≥50% chance of occurrence that is actually found at a site.

SIGNAL scores

In addition to calculating the expected number of taxa at a test site, AUSRIVAS also calculates the expected SIGNAL (Stream Invertebrate Grade Number Average Level) score for a site. The SIGNAL index (Chessman 1995) is similar to the British average score per taxon (ASPT) (Wright *et al.* 1993), summing the scores for each taxon occurring at a site and then dividing by the number of scoring taxa. As with ASPT (Wright *et al.* 1993), SIGNAL allocates pollution-sensitive taxa to high grades and pollution-tolerant taxa to low grades on a scale from 10 to 1 (Chessman 1995).

Expected SIGNAL scores are calculated by multiplying a taxon's SIGNAL grade by the probability of occurrence for that taxon, if it is ≥0.5, summing all grades and dividing by the number of predicted taxa. Observed SIGNAL scores are the sum of the SIGNAL grades for the predicted taxa (≥50% chance of occurrence) that were found at the site, divided by the number of scoring families. AUSRIVAS then compares both the expected number of taxa and the expected SIGNAL score against the taxa that were actually observed at a test site. This provides two O/E ratios (O/E Taxa and O/E SIGNAL) that provide a measure of biological impairment at a test site.

Internal and external testing

Initially, a number of reference sites (usually 10% of the total) were set aside when the AUSRIVAS models were built, and then run through the completed models to ensure that the models would correctly assess them as suitable reference sites. The models were then rebuilt including these sites. A number of sites with known impacts were also sampled in conjunction with the reference sites. These were also run through the models to test for predictive accuracy.

As an internal check of predictive accuracy and also as a validation of reference site condition, the reference sites used to build an AUSRIVAS model were run through that model. Sites that produced O/E ratios below 0.75, i.e. 25% of their expected taxa were missing, were reviewed and discarded if it was deemed they were unsuitable to use as reference sites. Undersampling, unusual habitat conditions, extreme flow events before sampling, and unexpected pollution impacts, are some of the factors investigated when reviewing failed reference sites. Some reference sites appeared to fail because the habitat type found at those sites was under-represented, a problem that can only be rectified when additional reference sites from future sampling occasions are added to the models.

Outputs

To simplify interpretation and to aid management decisions, AUSRIVAS presents both O/E Taxa and O/E SIGNAL as bands representing different levels of biological condition (Table

Table 9.1. *Division of AUSRIVAS indices, O/E Taxa (families) and O/E SIGNAL, into five bands for reporting the biological condition of Australian rivers. Labels (**in bold**) for each band refer to the relationship of the index values to the reference condition (Band A), followed by brief explantion of each band. Possible interpretations are also given for each observed/expected (O/E) index.*

Band	Label	O/E Taxa (families)	O/E SIGNAL
X	**Richer than reference**	More families found than expected.	Greater SIGNAL value than expected.
	O/E greater than 90th percentile of reference sites	Potential biodiversity "hot spot".	Potential biodiversity "hot spot".
		Mild organic enrichment.	Differential loss of pollution-tolerant taxa (potential impact unrelated to water quality).
		Continuous irrigation flow in a normally intermittent stream.	
A	**Reference**	Expected number of families within the range found at 80% of the reference sites.	Index value within range of central 80% of reference sites.
	O/E within range of central 80% of reference sites.		
B	**Below reference**	Fewer families than expected.	Lower SIGNAL value than expected.
	O/E below 10th percentile of reference sites. Same width as Band A.	Potential impact on water and/or habitat, resulting in loss of families.	Differential loss of pollution-sensitive families. Potential impact on water quality.
C	**Well below reference**	Many fewer families than expected.	Much lower SIGNAL value than expected.
	O/E below Band B. Same width as Band A.	Loss of families from substantial impairment of expected biota caused by water and/or by habitat quality.	Most expected families that are sensitive to pollution have been lost. Substantial impact on water quality.
D	**Impoverished**	Few of the expected families remain.	Very low SIGNAL value.
	O/E below Band C to zero.	Severe impairment.	Remaining families, if any, hardy and pollution-tolerant.

9.1). The width of the AUSRIVAS bands are based on the distribution of the O/E values for the reference sites in a particular model (Fig. 9.1).

Sites that fall within the central 80% of reference O/E values about the mean (i.e., 10th to 90th percentiles) are considered equivalent to reference (Band A). The next two bands (B and C) have the same width as Band A, but the width of Band D will vary, depending on the variability of the reference O/E values (Table 9.1). A site with O/E values below the lower boundary of Band A (i.e., the index value is smaller than the 10th percentile of the reference sites) is judged to have fewer families or a lower SIGNAL score than expected, and is allocated to one of the lower bands according to its value. A test site O/E value that exceeds the upper bounds of Band A (i.e., the O/E value is greater than the 90th percentile of the reference sites) is judged to be richer than the reference condition, and is allocated to Band X (Table 9.1).

Separate habitat and seasonal AUSRIVAS models may produce different assessments. A set of rules which standardise the procedures to be followed in cases where a site receives conflicting assessments, are provided in the AUSRIVAS manual (Simpson, Norris *et al.* 1997). If each assessment is valid, the site is assigned to the band furthest from Band A. Allocation to Band X, richer than reference, should result in further assessment to determine whether the site naturally has a high diversity or an impact such as mild nutrient enrichment.

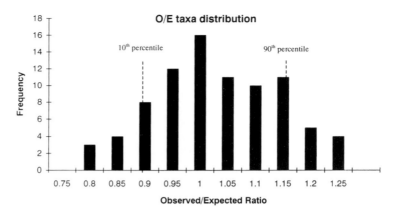

Figure 9.1. Distribution of O/E taxa values for 88 reference sites from the ACT spring riffle habitat model.

AUSRIVAS

A "stand alone" software package for distribution to individual users was deemed impractical because of the large number of AUSRIVAS models and potentially large number of users. However, state/territory agencies stipulated that a central agency to which data would be sent for assessment was unacceptable. These circumstances were met by developing AUSRIVAS to be managed from a central site and accessed by users via the internet. When an authorised user accesses AUSRIVAS, the latest version of a model is downloaded to their computer to be run "on site" by agency personnel. After the user enters test site data and chooses a model, the program accesses the relevant model data files from the central site and completes the analysis. At this stage any test sites with no appropriate reference group for comparison are identified and highlighted as "beyond the experience of the model". This test is identical to the chi-squared test described by Clark, Furse *et al.* (1996). A centrally-accessed program greatly simplifies trouble-shooting, management of daily use, and user access. Such a system also facilitates the ease of performing and distributing upgrades to the program, models and manual. The website also allows incorporation of sound and video into the manual, to clarify methods.

First National Assessment of River Health: Australian Capital Territory

The First National Assessment of River Health (FNARH) is an extension of the NRHP, involving the sampling of about 6000 sites across Australia over three years (LWRRDC 1997). The majority of these sites will be test sites for the assessment of river condition, with a component of reference site sampling to fill gaps in the present reference site database (LWRRDC 1997).

The Australian Capital Territory (ACT) component of FNARH initially consisted of 65 sites with potential impacts and 10 reference sites, covering the Cooma, ACT and Yass regions upstream of Burrinjuck Dam (Fig. 9.2). Sites were visited during autumn 1997, with riffle and edge habitats sampled at each site where they were present. All invertebrate samples were subsampled in the laboratory and identified mostly to family level, as described previously. Invertebrate and habitat data from the sites were then run through the appropriate ACT edge or riffle autumn model.

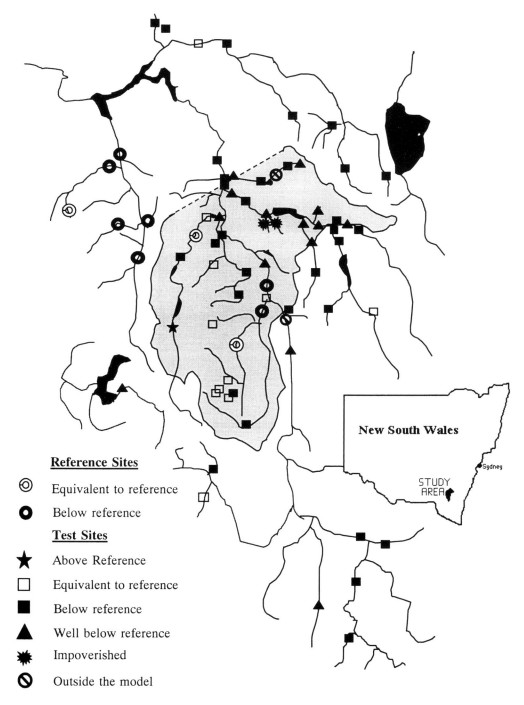

Figure 9.2. Location of test and reference sites, with their AUSRIVAS assessments, for the Australian Capital Territory component (shaded area) of the First National Assessment of River Health (FNARH).

Table 9.2. List of completed AUSRIVAS models, including the number of reference sites used for each model, misclassification error, number of reference site groups and O/E Taxa bands. Western Australia "dry" and "wet" models refer to the seasons when sites were sampled. Western Australia "B" models use two years of data. Mean classification error for all models is 31.1%. Note that the Canberra and ACT models are synonymous.

Model/No. of Reference Sites	Misclassification error (crossvalidation)	Number of reference site groups	Band X	Band A	Band B	Band C	Band D
					Bands for Taxa O/E		
Canberra autumn edge / 78	13.6	4	>1.13	1.13 - 0.88	0.87 - 0.61	0.60 - 0.34	0.33 - 0
Canberra autumn riffle / 88	22.4	6	>1.12	1.12 - 0.89	0.88 - 0.65	0.64 - 0.41	0.40 - 0
Canberra spring edge / 91	39.9	5	>1.13	1.13 - 0.88	0.87 - 0.62	0.61 - 0.36	0.35 - 0
Canberra spring riffle / 88	33.8	4	>1.12	1.12 - 0.89	0.88 - 0.65	0.64 - 0.41	0.40 - 0
Canberra autumn+spring edge / 85	36.4	5	>1.10	1.1 - 0.91	0.90 - 0.71	0.70 - 0.51	0.50 - 0
Canberra autumn+spring riffle / 76	29.8	4	>1.11	1.11 - 0.90	0.89 - 0.68	0.67 - 0.46	0.45 - 0
New South Wales autumn edge / 174	28.2	5	>1.20	1.20 - 0.81	0.80 - 0.41	0.40 - 0.01	0
New South Wales autumn riffle / 117	40.4	5	>1.17	1.17 - 0.84	0.83 - 0.50	0.49 - 0.16	0.15 - 0
New South Wales spring edge / 169	34.8	8	>1.19	1.19 - 0.82	0.81 - 0.44	0.43 - 0.06	0.05 - 0
New South Wales spring riffle / 117	30.6	5	>1.19	1.19 - 0.82	0.81 - 0.44	0.43 - 0.06	0.05 - 0
New South Wales autumn+spring edge / 191	23.2	8	>1.19	1.19 - 0.82	0.81 - 0.44	0.43 - 0.06	0.05 - 0
New South Wales autumn+spring riffle / 118	40.2	6	>1.11	1.11 - 0.90	0.89 - 0.67	0.66 - 0.44	0.43 - 0
Queensland autumn bed / 121	26.6	4	>1.21	1.21 - 0.80	0.79 - 0.37	0.36 - 0.01	0
Queensland autumn edge / 127	40.7	4	>1.21	1.21 - 0.80	0.79 - 0.38	0.37 - 0.01	0
Queensland spring bed / 127	33.1	4	>1.19	1.19 - 0.82	0.81 - 0.44	0.43 - 0.06	0.05 - 0
Queensland spring edge / 110	39.8	4	>1.19	1.19 - 0.82	0.81 - 0.45	0.44 - 0.08	0.07 - 0
South Australia autumn edge / 59	35.0	4	>1.19	1.19 - 0.82	0.81 - 0.44	0.43 - 0.06	0.05 - 0
South Australia autumn riffle / 44	25.7	3	>1.12	1.12 - 0.89	0.88 - 0.65	0.64 - 0.41	0.40 - 0
South Australia spring edge / 74	45.0	6	>1.17	1.17 - 0.84	0.83 - 0.49	0.48 - 0.14	0.13 - 0
South Australia spring riffle / 46	24.1	4	>1.18	1.18 - 0.83	0.82 - 0.46	0.45 - 0.09	0.08 - 0
South Australia autumn+spring edge / 54	33.7	5	>1.18	1.18 - 0.83	0.82 - 0.46	0.45 - 0.09	0.08 - 0
South Australia autumn+spring riffle / 37	10.3	3	>1.18	1.18 - 0.83	0.82 - 0.47	0.46 - 0.11	0.10 - 0
Tasmania autumn edge / 81	35.7	3	>1.13	1.13 - 0.88	0.87 - 0.62	0.61 - 0.36	0.35 - 0
Tasmania autumn riffle / 84	34.8	3	>1.14	1.14 - 0.87	0.86 - 0.58	0.57 - 0.29	0.28 - 0
Tasmania spring edge / 88	43.4	3	>1.14	1.14 - 0.87	0.86 - 0.59	0.58 - 0.31	0.30 - 0
Tasmania spring riffle / 88	38.0	4	>1.11	1.11 - 0.90	0.89 - 0.67	0.66 - 0.44	0.43 - 0
Tasmania autumn+spring edge / 87	49.9	5	>1.11	1.11 - 0.90	0.89 - 0.68	0.67 - 0.46	0.45 - 0
Tasmania autumn+spring riffle / 82	31.4	3	>1.10	1.10 - 0.91	0.90 - 0.72	0.71 - 0.53	0.52 - 0
Victoria autumn edge / 170	31.9	5	>1.16	1.16 - 0.85	0.84 - 0.54	0.53 - 0.23	0.22 - 0
Victoria autumn riffle / 116	30.5	5	>1.17	1.17 - 0.84	0.83 - 0.50	0.49 - 0.16	0.15 - 0
Victoria spring edge / 173	44.2	7	>1.17	1.17 - 0.84	0.83 - 0.49	0.48 - 0.14	0.13 - 0
Victoria spring riffle / 129	56.1	6	>1.18	1.18 - 0.83	0.82 - 0.47	0.46 - 0.11	0.10 - 0
Victoria autumn+spring edge / 189	38.8	5	>1.15	1.15 - 0.86	0.85 - 0.56	0.55 - 0.26	0.25 - 0
Victoria autumn+spring riffle / 138	31.9	6	>1.18	1.18 - 0.83	0.82 - 0.46	0.45 - 0.09	0.08 - 0
Western Australia dry channel / 90	18.4	5	>1.19	1.19 - 0.82	0.81 - 0.45	0.44 - 0.08	0.07 - 0
Western Australia dry macrophyte / 56	12.8	3	>1.23	1.23 - 0.78	0.77 - 0.31	0.30 - 0.01	0
Western Australia wet channel / 132	22.3	5	>1.15	1.15 - 0.86	0.85 - 0.57	0.56 - 0.28	0.27 - 0
Western Australia wet macrophyte / 75	19.6	5	>1.17	1.17 - 0.84	0.83 - 0.51	0.50 - 0.18	0.17 - 0
Western Australia wet channelB / 101	17.5	5	>1.13	1.13 - 0.88	0.87 - 0.61	0.60 - 0.34	0.33 - 0
Western Australia wet macrophyteB / 50	0.0	4	>1.16	1.16 - 0.85	0.84 - 0.52	0.51 - 0.19	0.18 - 0

Results

National River Health Program (NRHP)

Forty of the 48 AUSRIVAS models planned for Australia have been completed and are available for use (Table. 9.2). As yet there is no AUSRIVAS coverage for the Northern Territory, and combined season models for the edge and main channel habitats are yet to be completed for Queensland. Misclassification errors for the completed models were generally low, ranging from 0 to 56.1% with a mean of 31.1% (Table. 9.2). This compares with a mean misclassification error of 44% for RIVPACS II (438 sites in 25 classification groups), where the less rigorous re-substitution method was used for testing (Wright, Furse *et al.* 1991). The distribution of reference site O/E values, represented by the assessment bands (Table 9.2), provides a good measure of model resolution. Models with narrow bands, such as Tasmania autumn + spring riffle, are considered to have good resolution because only a few taxa can be lost before an impairment will be detected. Models with wider bands, such as Queensland autumn edge, have poorer resolution because more taxa have to be lost for an impairment to be detected.

The frequency with which certain predictor variables were used by the AUSRIVAS models could be roughly grouped at three spatial scales. First, broad-scale variables describing geographic position, such as latitude and longitude, were the most common predictors used to relate a site to invertebrate composition (Table 9.3). Alkalinity, which probably describes catchment geology, was also a commonly chosen predictor variable. Second, variables that described stream size and flow conditions, such as distance from source and catchment size upstream of the site, were the next most frequently chosen predictors. Third, small-scale, habitat-specific features at a site provided the greatest range of possible predictors from which to choose, and thus individual variables were often restricted to a small number of models. Of the site-specific variables, those that described characteristics of the riparian vegetation and substratum composition appear to be important predictors; e.g. width of riparian zone and percent composition of substratum (Table 9.3).

Table 9.3. *List of commonly used predictor variables for AUSRIVAS models.*

(1) The number of models using each variable as a predictor; total number of models = 40.

(2) Variables used by up to six models in Victoria only.

Variable	No. of models[1]	Variable	No. of models[1]
Longitude	31	Macrophyte taxa[2]	6
Latitude	28	Flow pattern	5
Alkalinity	28	Macrophyte cover	5
Altitude	21	Shading	5
Distance from source	15	Bedrock	5
Catchment area	12	Stream width	4
Conductivity	9	Riffle depth	4
Stream slope	8	Pebble	4
Riparian width	8	Edge/bank vegetation	4
Cobble	8	Vegetation category[2]	4
Boulder	7	Range, mean annual air temperature[2]	4
Stream order	7	Gravel	3
Discharge	7	Silt	3
Sand	6	Clay	2

Table 9.4. *The mean numbers of all taxa collected, the mean numbers of taxa collected with a ≥50% chance*
of occurring (observed taxa), the mean numbers of predicted taxa and mean numbers
expected with ≥50% chance of occurring at reference sites for each of the six
Australian Capital Territory models (four single season and two combined seasons).

See Table 9.2 for the number of reference sites in each model.

Model	No. of taxa collected	No. of observed taxa	No. of predicted taxa	No. of expected taxa
Autumn edge	22	14	18	14.2
Autumn riffle	20	15	18	14.8
Combined edge	27	19	23	18.7
Combined riffle	25	21	25	20.6
Spring edge	19	11	14	11.6
Spring riffle	18	14	17	13.5

Table 9.5. *Comparison of mean O/E Taxa with mean O/E SIGNAL from test sites for the ACT AUSRIVAS models.*

The twenty test sites were sampled concurrently with reference site sampling in spring and autumn 1994 and 1995.

Model	Mean O/E Taxa	Mean O/E SIGNAL
Autumn edge	0.69	0.87
Autumn riffle	0.73	0.91
Autumn + spring edge	0.79	0.92
Autumn + spring riffle	0.73	0.95
Spring edge	0.79	0.88
Spring riffle	0.78	0.91
Grand mean	0.75	0.91

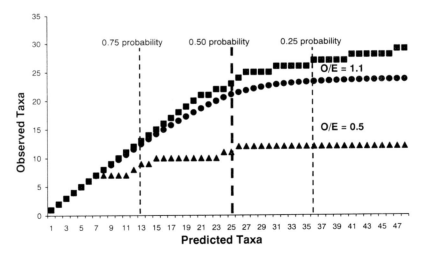

Figure 9.3. Taxa accretion curves for a predicted reference site (circles), an actual reference site (squares) and an impaired site (triangles). Taxa below the 0.5 probability of occurrence cut-off provide little information that is useful for making an assessment of biological condition at a site. The data are from the Canberra (ACT) autumn + spring riffle model.

Data from autumn and spring were combined to produce models with larger taxa lists for each site, reducing the influence of sampling variation (Table 9.4). Combined season models also predicted more taxa to occur than single season models, providing more taxa from which to make an assessment of river condition (Table 9.4). The riffle habitat in all cases had fewer taxa collected at a site but more taxa predicted to occur than the edge habitat (Table 9.4).

The O/E Taxa ratio was consistently lower than the O/E SIGNAL ratio for impacted sites for all models in the initial ACT sampling (Table 9.5). Similar trends were observed in the state agency data; however, these data were unavailable for publication.

The decision to use only those taxa that were predicted to occur at a site with ≥0.5 probability was supported by plotting the expected occurrence against actual occurrence for three sites. The taxa accretion curves (based on combined season data) for a predicted reference site, an actual reference site and an impaired site, all within the ACT, clearly demonstrate that taxa with probabilities of occurrence <50% contribute little information that is useful for assessing site condition (Fig. 9.3).

First National Assessment of River Health: Australian Capital Territory component

Sampling for the First National Assessment of River Health (FNARH) has been completed for the ACT (Canberra) component. 21 test sites and 10 reference sites were assessed using the ACT autumn riffle AUSRIVAS model, and 65 test sites and 10 reference sites were assessed using the ACT autumn edge AUSRIVAS model (Tables 9.6 and 9.7).

At the time of sampling the study area was in drought. It appears that the resulting low flow conditions had caused a regional reduction in biological condition, with four of eight riffle and five of ten edge reference sites assessed as below reference. Using the combined assessment rules, i.e. take the lowest score of the two habitats and of the two O/E ratios, the majority of rural sites were found to be mildly impaired, commonly falling into Band B. Based on the assessment of reference sites, approximately half of the test sites falling into Band B could be expected to be equivalent to reference in the absence of drought. Urban sites were more severely stressed, mainly falling into Band C, and two large urban drainages were assessed as Band D.

The assessments for the FNARH samples from the autumn riffle model, using O/E Taxa, classed two test sites as impoverished, one as well below reference, seven below reference and eight as equivalent to reference (Table 9.6). Three test sites were beyond the experience of the model and no assessment could be made. Four reference sites were classed as below reference, four as equivalent to reference, and two sites were beyond the experience of the model (Table 9.6).

Assessment of the test sites using O/E SIGNAL from the riffle model, classed two sites as impoverished, two as well below reference, four as below reference and ten as equivalent to reference (Table 9.6). All reference sites, with the exception of those outside the experience of the model, were classed as equivalent to reference (Table 9.6). Consistent with previous test site results (Table 9.5), assessments for the riffle habitat from FNARH sampling also produced an average O/E Taxa value lower than average O/E SIGNAL (Table 9.6).

Assessments for the FNARH samples from the autumn edge model, using O/E Taxa, classed one test site as impoverished, 13 as well below reference, 33 as below reference, 15 as equivalent to reference and one site as above reference condition (Table 9.7). Two test sites were classed as beyond the experience of the model and no assessment could be made. Five reference sites were classed as below reference and five as equivalent to reference (Table 9.7).

Table 9.6. *AUSRIVAS outputs for autumn **riffle habitat** samples from the Australian Capital Territory (ACT) component of the First National Assessment of River Health (FNARH).*

The combined index site assessment is the lower band value of O/E Taxa or O/E SIGNAL for each site.

Site	No. of Taxa predicted	No. of Taxa expected	No. of Taxa observed	O/E Taxa	Band	Expected SIGNAL	Observed SIGNAL	O/E SIGNAL	Band
Riffle habitat									
Test sites:									
4102172	18	14.22	10	0.7	B	5.96	5.6	0.94	A
4102189	20	16.35	2	0.12	D	6.25	2.5	0.4	D
4102191	19	15.45	10	0.65	B	6.13	4.9	0.8	C
4102198	20	16.75	4	0.24	D	6.25	3.25	0.52	D
4102201	10	9	9	1	A	5.13	5.22	1.02	A
4102202	20	16.69	11	0.66	B	6.23	5.36	0.86	B
4102204	20	16.7	13	0.78	B	6.23	5.85	0.94	A
4102206	20	16.88	9	0.53	C	6.24	5.11	0.82	C
4102208	17	14.76	12	0.81	B	6.61	5.92	0.89	B
4102211	18	14.27	14	0.98	A	6.23	6.14	0.99	A
4102214	18	14.52	12	0.83	B	5.6	5.58	1	A
4102218	18	14.73	13	0.88	A	6.01	5.54	0.92	B
4102222		This site is outside the experience of the model							
4102230		This site is outside the experience of the model							
4102233		This site is outside the experience of the model							
4102234	20	16.9	16	0.95	A	6.24	6.44	1.03	A
4102238	20	16.88	15	0.89	A	6.24	6.2	0.99	A
4102240	20	15.17	16	1.05	A	6.41	6.38	0.99	A
4102243	18	14.47	13	0.9	A	6	5.85	0.98	A
4102251	20	15.99	14	0.88	B	6.65	6.07	0.91	B
4102255	18	14.74	14	0.95	A	6.6	6.64	1.01	A
Mean O/E values for 21 test sites:				0.77				0.89	
Reference sites:									
4102003		This site is outside the experience of the model							
4102019	20	15.82	12	0.76	B	6.34	6.25	0.99	A
4102028	18	14.78	14	0.95	A	6.34	6.36	1	A
4102041	10	9	9	1	A	5.13	5	0.97	A
4102129		This site is outside the experience of the model							
4102130	20	16.92	14	0.83	B	6.25	6.29	1.01	A
4102133	20	15.93	17	1.07	A	6.22	6.06	0.97	A
4102136	20	16.71	13	0.78	B	6.25	6.38	1.02	A
4102138	19	15.33	13	0.85	B	6.25	6.31	1.01	A
4102139	17	14.68	13	0.89	A	6.62	6.54	0.99	A

Assessment of the test sites using O/E SIGNAL from the edge model, classed three sites as well below reference, 24 as below reference and 36 as equivalent to reference (Table 9.7). All reference sites were classed as equivalent to reference (Table 9.7). Consistent with previous test site results (Table 9.5), assessments of the edge habitat from FNARH sampling also produced an average O/E Taxa value lower than average O/E SIGNAL (Table 9.7).

Table 9.7. *AUSRIVAS outputs for autumn **edge habitat** samples from the ACT component of the FNARH.*
The combined index site assessment is the lower band value of O/E Taxa or O/E SIGNAL for each site.

Site	No. of Taxa predicted	No. of Taxa expected	No. of Taxa observed	O/E Taxa	Band	Expected SIGNAL	Observed SIGNAL	O/E SIGNAL	Band
Edge habitat									
Test sites:									
4102089	15	12.45	10	0.8	B	5.91	5.6	0.95	A
4102115	21	15.71	12	0.76	B	5.16	5	0.97	A
4102172	21	15.7	14	0.89	A	5.16	4.93	0.95	A
4102187	15	12.51	5	0.4	C	5.93	4	0.67	C
4102188	21	15.63	7	0.45	C	5.17	3.71	0.72	B
4102189	15	12.46	3	0.24	D	5.92	3	0.51	C
4102190	14	11.76	10	0.85	B	5.78	5.5	0.95	A
4102191	14	11.31	8	0.71	B	5.73	5.13	0.89	B
4102192	21	15.71	8	0.51	C	5.16	3.88	0.75	B
4102193	14	11.11	5	0.45	C	5.52	4	0.72	B
4102194	21	15.71	10	0.64	B	5.16	3.9	0.76	B
4102195		This site is outside the experience of the model							
4102196	21	15.71	10	0.64	B	5.16	4.2	0.81	B
4102197	14	11.86	8	0.67	B	5.8	4.63	0.8	B
4102198	17	13.74	7	0.51	C	5.49	3.86	0.7	B
4102201	17	13.87	8	0.58	C	5.45	4.5	0.83	B
4102202	17	13.65	10	0.73	B	5.51	5.2	0.94	A
4102203	21	15.71	14	0.89	A	5.16	5.21	1.01	A
4102204	21	15.65	14	0.89	A	5.16	5.29	1.02	A
4102205	14	11.67	10	0.86	B	5.77	5.4	0.94	A
4102206	15	11.91	10	0.84	B	5.86	5.6	0.96	A
4102208	17	12.96	13	1	A	6.24	6	0.96	A
4102209	21	15.7	8	0.51	C	5.16	4.13	0.8	B
4102210	15	12.34	9	0.73	B	5.92	5.22	0.88	B
4102211	16	12.8	12	0.94	A	5.59	6.08	1.09	A
4102214	18	13.83	11	0.8	B	5.4	4.91	0.91	A
4102215	21	15.7	9	0.57	C	5.16	4.56	0.88	B
4102216	21	15.61	11	0.7	B	5.17	5	0.97	A
4102218	21	15.71	12	0.76	B	5.16	5.08	0.98	A
4102219	16	12.74	10	0.79	B	5.16	4.8	0.93	A
4102000		This site is outside the experience of the model							
4102222	17	13.85	10	0.72	B	5.46	5.6	1.03	A
4102223	17	13.77	10	0.73	B	5.48	4.8	0.88	B
4102225	21	15.71	10	0.64	B	5.16	4.9	0.95	A
4102227	15	12.53	8	0.64	B	5.93	5.25	0.89	B
4102228	19	14.54	11	0.76	B	5.28	4.64	0.88	B
4102229	16	12.83	11	0.86	B	5.59	5	0.89	B
4102230	13	10.91	11	1.01	A	5.2	5.18	1	A
4102231	21	15.67	13	0.83	B	5.16	5.15	1	A
4102232	21	15.65	10	0.64	B	5.16	4.7	0.91	A
4102233	17	13.83	9	0.65	B	5.46	4.78	0.87	B
4102234	15	11.87	11	0.93	A	5.84	5.82	1	A
4102235	15	12.42	8	0.64	B	5.91	4.63	0.78	B
4102236	13	10.79	5	0.46	C	5.33	4.6	0.86	B
4102237	17	13.68	8	0.58	C	5.5	4.13	0.75	B

(Table 9.7 is continued overleaf)

(Table 9.7 continued)

Site	No. of Taxa predicted	No. of Taxa expected	No. of Taxa observed	O/E Taxa	Band	Expected SIGNAL	Observed SIGNAL	O/E SIGNAL	Band
Edge habitat									
Test sites (continued):									
4102238	15	12.43	12	0.97	A	5.91	6.08	1.03	A
4102240	16	12.16	15	1.23	X	5.96	6.27	1.05	A
4102241	17	13.29	9	0.68	B	5.39	5.11	0.95	A
4102242	21	15.71	11	0.7	B	5.16	4.45	0.86	B
4102243	15	12.44	11	0.88	A	5.92	6.18	1.04	A
4102244	15	12.53	8	0.64	B	5.93	4.63	0.78	B
4102246	19	14.52	5	0.34	C	5.28	3.4	0.64	C
4102247	14	11.86	6	0.51	C	5.8	4	0.69	B
4102248	15	12.53	8	0.64	B	5.93	5.5	0.93	A
4102250	21	15.7	10	0.64	B	5.16	5.3	1.03	A
4102251	17	13.59	15	1.1	A	5.49	5.6	1.02	A
4102252	17	12.88	11	0.85	B	6	5.73	0.95	A
4102253	15	12.52	9	0.72	B	5.93	5.67	0.96	A
4102254	15	12.47	12	0.96	A	5.93	6.08	1.03	A
4102255	15	11.69	13	1.11	A	5.9	6.31	1.07	A
4102256	18	13.63	15	1.1	A	6.38	6.4	1	A
4102257	16	12.42	14	1.13	A	6.13	6.14	1	A
4102258	19	13.84	12	0.87	B	6.13	6.42	1.05	A
4102259	17	13.52	8	0.59	C	5.54	4.63	0.83	B
4102260	16	12.25	12	0.98	A	5.98	6.25	1.05	A
Mean O/E values for 65 test sites:				0.74				0.90	
Reference sites:									
4102003	15	12.49	12	0.96	A	5.93	5.92	1	A
4102019	15	11.64	11	0.95	A	5.68	5.82	1.02	A
4102028	15	12.53	12	0.96	A	5.93	6.08	1.03	A
4102041	15	12.47	10	0.8	B	5.92	5.6	0.95	A
4102129	14	11.81	9	0.76	B	5.79	5.44	0.94	A
4102130	17	13.87	11	0.79	B	5.45	6	1.1	A
4102133	14	11.53	10	0.87	B	5.29	5.5	1.04	A
4102136	17	13.51	12	0.89	A	5.55	6.08	1.1	A
4102138	15	12.53	10	0.8	B	5.93	6.4	1.08	A
4102139	16	12.47	13	1.04	A	6.14	6.15	1	A

Discussion

The AUSRIVAS models

The development of AUSRIVAS began in 1993 as a research tool at the University of Canberra (Norris 1994). The present level of development has resulted largely from the National River Health Program and the Cooperative Research Centre for Freshwater Ecology's commitment to developing a nationally accessed and standardised river quality assessment tool.

The large size of the Australian continent, with its varied physiography, states and territories, has dictated the need to regionalise model coverage. Additionally, it was envisaged that the models would be widely available. Thus, discrete habitat models, temporal and spatial variability, and the wide availability of models, laid the foundations for an internet application (Simpson, Norris *et al.* 1997). An internet-based application also facilitates model updates as new data are collected.

AUSRIVAS and RIVPACS

Habitat sampling. In Britain, RIVPACS sampling requires that all the habitats at a site are sampled in proportion to their occurrence, with the collected invertebrates combined into a single bulk sample (Furse, Wright *et al.* 1981). Several authors (e.g. Jenkins *et al.* 1984; Rutt *et al.* 1989; Pettigrove 1990; Parsons & Norris 1996) have shown that the composition of invertebrate assemblages collected from a habitat, for example the edge, are more similar to assemblages from the same habitat at other sites than they are to those found in different habitats at the same site. Thus, proportionally greater sampling effort in a spatially dominant habitat may bias a combined habitat sample towards edge taxa at one site and riffle taxa at another, when in reality the taxa found at each site are similar. Taxa predicted by a model using combined habitat data (e.g. a RIVPACS model) may then be an indication of habitat type rather than condition of water quality (Parsons & Norris 1996). The AUSRIVAS models avoid this potential problem by habitat-specific sampling. It is necessary, however, to sample sufficient habitats to ensure that all likely test sites will have at least one of the habitats represented. In Australia, sampling two habitats in each state and territory has been sufficient to provide good site coverage.

Number of taxa. One argument for combining invertebrate samples from all habitats at a site is to increase the robustness of the RIVPACS models by providing a larger list of taxa from which to obtain predictions (Wright, Moss *et al.* 1984). In Australia, the view was taken that lists of taxa could be increased by combining seasonal data, while still keeping individual habitat data separate. Combining seasonal data increases the taxa encountered at a site in two ways. First, as with any increased sampling effort, more habitat is sampled and therefore more taxa are collected. Second, because of the turnover of taxa throughout the year (Hynes 1970), some taxa could be collected later at a site though absent at an earlier time of sampling.

Larger taxa lists provide more taxa for predictions (Table 9.4), making the models more robust to small sampling variations in collected taxa. For example, if 10 taxa were predicted to occur at a site and one was missed by chance, that missing taxon appears more significant than if 20 taxa were predicted and the same taxon was missed. Ormerod (1987) reported that macroinvertebrate assemblages were categorised best by combining seasonal data. A larger list of taxa also increases the chance of detecting an impact because a larger range of taxa will provide a wider range of responses to more types of pollutants. Interestingly, even though the edge habitat consistently produced more taxa for sites sampled in the ACT (Table 9.4), the riffle habitat had higher numbers of predicted taxa for all models (Table 9.4). This occurred because the edges had more taxa that had lower probabilities of occurrence in the predictive models. Therefore, site assessments using riffle samples are more robust, suggesting that this should be the habitat used if only a single habitat can be sampled.

Sampling from multiple habitats can provide more confidence in a site assessment if similar results are obtained from each habitat. However, if there is a disparity between the results from the habitats sampled at a site, the overall assessment becomes more complicated. Were either of the habitats undersampled or oversampled; were there any unusual habitat conditions that might result in low or high numbers of taxa; were there any small tributaries upstream that may have provided extra taxa through drift; were there any unusual flow conditions before sampling; does the impact preferentially affect a particular habitat? These are all questions that must be investigated when disparate results are obtained from different habitats at a site. If, after investigation, all habitat results are accepted as valid, the site should be classed at the level of the lowest quality habitat. This ensures that any impact at a site will be noted even if the majority of the site is assessed as healthy.

Predictor variables. Both RIVPACS II and RIVPACS III use one classification for Great Britain, based on species-level data (RIVPACS II) or species-level data plus family-level logarithm-category data (RIVPACS III), even when family-level assessments are being made (Wright 1995; Wright, Moss *et al.* 1997). When the AUSRIVAS models were built, it was decided to use separate classifications for the six models in each of the eight regions presently covered. This was done to improve the resolution of the models by relating the habitat characteristics found at a site to the invertebrates collected at the time of sampling, rather than to a single all-encompassing invertebrate classification. This resulted in a separate list of predictor variables for each model. Therefore, while RIVPACS uses variations of the same twelve habitat variables for predictions (Wright 1995), the options for AUSRIVAS models are much greater. At present there are about 100 potential predictor variables in any combination, although in practice only 28 have been commonly used (Table 9.3).

Results from the AUSRIVAS Stepwise MDFAs generally had low misclassification errors (Table 9.2) when compared with those obtained by RIVPACS, although the AUSRIVAS models also contain less sites and groups than RIVPACS. The lower MDFA errors indicate that the predictive relationship between the reference site groups and habitat variables was improved by using region-specific invertebrate classifications. At present the regions covered by each classification have political boundaries. It is assumed that using more appropriate ecological boundaries for future sampling (e.g. biogeographic regions) will further improve the predictive power of the AUSRIVAS models.

Seven sites in the ACT FNARH sampling, however, were assessed as being outside the experience of a model (Tables 9.6 and 9.7), including two reference sites that had been assessed successfully in earlier studies using the predictive models (Simpson 1995; Williams 1996). Some of the test sites (4102222, 4102230 and 4102233) had characteristics (e.g. large upstream catchment areas and distance from source) that indicated an under-representation of reference sites of that type in the model. Assessment of these test sites will only be possible by enlarging the reference site database to include reference sites with similar habitat features. Reference sites 4102003 and 4102129, however, appear to be failing because of extreme values for predictor variables that are measured subjectively, such as percent cobbles. This was clearly demonstrated by sites that were accepted by the edge model but could not be assessed by the ACT riffle model (Tables 9.6 and 9.7). It is possible that these variables are not as robust as was first thought, and vary more than expected or in a manner independent of temporal influences. In either case the solution lies in selecting more robust variables that vary across seasons in a consistent manner and are less susceptible to operator interpretation. The selection of predictor variables can be done by more careful selection from the range of variables already measured, or by adopting less subjective methods for their measurement.

Taxa probabilities. When taxa are predicted to occur at a new test site, both RIVPACS and AUSRIVAS assign each taxon a probability of being collected. However, RIVPACS offers a range of probability limit options (0.1% or more) to produce the list of predicted taxa, whereas AUSRIVAS uses only the single $\geq 50\%$ probability level for all models. In theory, using the $\geq 0.1\%$ probability means it is possible to have an O/E Taxa ratio close to unity even though few taxa with high probabilities are present, if these taxa are replaced by several of those taxa predicted with a low probability (Wright, Furse *et al.* 1991).

The possibility of low probability taxa biasing an assessment has been acknowledged and tested in RIVPACS II and RIVPACS III, where all reference sites were examined for this possibility as a test of the predictive system (Wright, Furse *et al.* 1991; Wright, Furse *et al.* 1995). Wright, Furse *et al.* (1991) identified 12 sites, from a set of 65 generally high quality sites, which had significant differences (p <0.05) between observed and expected taxa.

Although most of these sites were being poorly predicted by RIVPACS because they appeared to be outside the limits of the reference dataset, the potential influence of taxa with low probabilities of occurrence should be cause for concern. Impacts that produce shifts in community composition could be missed if the shift favours taxa with a low probability of occurrence. RIVPACS provides lists of unexpected absences (not captured but probability of occurrence >50%) and unexpected presences (captured but probability of occurrence <50%) to highlight this potential problem for users. Further testing of this issue is required for AUSRIVAS models, but initially it was decided to reduce the likelihood of the problem by using only those taxa with ≥50% chance of occurrence.

Taxa with a low probability of occurrence also have the potential to bias a site assessment because, even though they contribute little to the expected number of taxa, their occurrence at a site carries the same weight in the list of observed taxa as those with a high probability of occurrence. This potential bias highlights the need to include enough taxa in the models to make them resilient to sampling variability, while trying to include only taxa that will provide meaningful information about a site. It appears that taxa predicted at and above the 50% probability of occurrence level provide a suitable compromise to meet the above requirements (Fig. 9.3).

Bands of impairment. Both the RIVPACS and AUSRIVAS bands were derived using the reference site O/E distribution. However, the widths of the RIVPACS bands are measured from the 10th percentile to unity (5th percentile for ASPT) in contrast to AUSRIVAS, which uses the 10th to 90th percentile interval to set band widths. The RIVPACS method could be interpreted as being slightly biased because the distribution of reference site O/E values fall either side of the mean value of 1.0. Thus, a reference site has as much chance of falling above unity as it does below and this should be accounted for in the calculation of the band widths. There is also cause to include a band representing sites that fall above the 90th percentile of O/E ratios (Band X in AUSRIVAS). These sites may be naturally taxon-rich and therefore of significant conservation value, or they could be experiencing an impact (e.g. from mild organic enrichment). Bands B, C, and D for a RIVPACS model will also be narrower than those for an AUSRIVAS model with an equivalent reference site O/E value distribution, because only the lower half of the reference site O/E distribution is used to set their width. While both banding systems are largely arbitrary, the AUSRIVAS models include the whole range of reference conditions, and not just the lower half of the distribution.

Because of the large numbers of AUSRIVAS models, a major consideration when deciding upon the assessment bands was how to automate their creation and still maintain ecological meaning. The present banding scheme effectively represents a percentage taxon loss at a site, weighted by the variability of invertebrate assemblages at reference sites. This banding method appears to be an acceptable combination of a biologist's ecological interpretation of what taxon loss represents and the need for an objective banding scheme essential for an automated software system.

As part of testing RIVPACS, the variability of the three indices (O/E BMWP, O/E Taxa and O/E ASPT) from the reference dataset was investigated. O/E ASPT, which is similar to O/E SIGNAL, was found to be the least variable measure and as such produced the tightest distribution of reference site O/E values (Wright, Furse *et al.* 1991; Wright, Furse *et al.* 1995). The tight distribution of reference site O/E ASPT values was interpreted as O/E ASPT having greater predictive accuracy because it was more robust to sampling variation. Rather than interpreting this as predictive accuracy, in Australia the tight distribution of SIGNAL O/E ratios has been interpreted as SIGNAL being insensitive to small changes in invertebrate assemblages. This interpretation is supported by the original assessment of test sites with known impacts, where O/E SIGNAL was consistently higher than O/E Taxa (Table 9.5). Further evidence is provided by the ACT FNARH site assessments using the bands of biological condition. O/E SIGNAL bands are set using the same criteria as those used for O/E Taxa, i.e. both banding schemes are related to the reference site O/E distribution. This distribution accounts for the variability in both indices, therefore removing any difference between the banding schemes that might have arisen because of sampling variability. Even so, O/E SIGNAL bands still generally rated FNARH sites as having a higher biological quality than when assessed using O/E Taxa (Table 9.6). If O/E SIGNAL bands were set using the 5th percentile, as is done in Britain, the bands become even less sensitive, with all impaired sites – except the two sites classed as impoverished – moving up to the next band. This insensitivity appears to be related to SIGNAL being an average score, so more taxa have to be lost to produce a shift in the SIGNAL O/E ratio than for O/E Taxa. In fact, if taxa with SIGNAL grades close to the mean SIGNAL score for a site are lost in the future, no shift in the SIGNAL O/E ratio may occur. The O/E SIGNAL score still provides valuable ecological information about a site, but in the light of results to date, greater emphasis should be placed on O/E Taxa.

Conclusion

AUSRIVAS has a number of innovative differences from the British RIVPACS. The sampling of individual habitats removes the potential for habitat-related sampling biases. Multiple habitat assessments for a site may also provide more complete site assessments, as well as allowing cost savings if only a single habitat sample is required. The decision to produce models for distinct regional areas, relating the local invertebrates to predictor variables specific to that region, was made to increase the predictive accuracy of the models. Problems arising from unexpected variation in some variables, and the subjective nature of others, has meant that further investigation is required to select more robust predictor variables. The large number of AUSRIVAS models has led to the development of an internet-distributed software and support system. Using the internet has greatly simplified day-to-day management and distribution of model updates. The internet also provides many advantages and opportunities for the development and expansion of AUSRIVAS that would be impossible for a more traditionally-distributed package.

Acknowledgements

We thank the Land and Water Resources Research and Development Corporation and Environment Australia for funding; each state/territory agency involved with the National River Health Program for use of their data and interaction with analyses; the CRC for Freshwater Ecology and the University of Canberra for facilities and technical support; Paul Blackman for programming. Advice on model development was provided by Ralph Clarke and John Wright (Institute of Freshwater Ecology, UK) and also Dorian Moss and Ruth Cox (Institute of Terrestrial Ecology, UK).

CHAPTER 10

AUSRIVAS:
operator sample processing errors and temporal variability – implications for model sensitivity

CHRIS L. HUMPHREY[1], ANDREW W. STOREY[2] AND LISA THURTELL[1]

[1]*Environmental Research Institute of the Supervising Scientist,
Locked Bag 2, Jabiru, NT 0886, AUSTRALIA*
[2]*Department of Zoology, The University of Western Australia,
Nedlands, WA 6907, AUSTRALIA*

Summary

At the onset of AUSRIVAS, it was recognised that any serious compromise to the sensitivity of derived models was most likely to arise from errors in field live-sorting procedures and from temporal variability of macroinvertebrate communities. Sorting error and the degree of temporal variability have been quantified using family-level presence/absence data, to assess the implications for the development of models.

External Quality Assurance/Quality Control (QA/QC) audits of state/territory sample processing procedures (laboratory subsampling and sorting of preserved samples, and field live-sorting procedures) have confirmed the potential of the live-sort procedure to result in high error rates, particularly as the result of a poor recovery of small and cryptic taxa. Many of these missed taxa are common in samples. Temporal variability of macroinvertebrate communities has been shown to be high for much of Australia, at least on a seasonal basis. This is attributable largely to the vicissitudes of the Australian climate. For the most part, current operator sorting errors and temporal variability are unlikely to prevent successful model development, but either in isolation or combination could lead to increased frequency of misclassification and inaccurate model predictions. This conclusion is supported by simulations based on actual errors recorded by QA/QC audits. Refinements are currently being made to live-sorting protocols, to reduce sample processing errors. Combined seasons models, together with concurrent repeated sampling of selected reference sites to adjust models, may offer the only suitable solutions to temporal variability. Our results are consistent with the promotion of AUSRIVAS as a coarse, broad-scale screening tool for biological monitoring in Australia.

Introduction

In 1993, the Australian Government funded the National River Health Program (NRHP) to assess and monitor the health of the nation's rivers (Schofield & Davies 1996). Part of this program is the Monitoring River Health Initiative (MRHI), involving government agencies from all Australian states and territories in a national program to develop a standardised, and coordinated, rapid assessment approach to biological monitoring of Australia's rivers and streams. The River InVertebrate Prediction And Classification System (RIVPACS; Wright 1995) was adopted as a national framework for the Australian program. Models were to be based on family-level identifications of macroinvertebrates collected by habitat-specific kick-sweep sampling, at an initial 1400 reference sites across Australia in representative seasons (Schofield & Davies 1996). A full description of AUSRIVAS (AUStralian RIVer Assessment Scheme), as developed to 1997, is provided in Chapter 8.

It was recognised early in the development of the MRHI that sample processing error due to live-sorting of samples in the field, together with temporal variability in community composition and structure in a country of climatic extremes such as Australia, would probably pose the most serious risks to the development of sensitive, predictive models for biological monitoring. These issues and possible implications to successful model development are the subject of this chapter. Progress to date has focused on quantification of errors and variability, with only preliminary steps being taken to determine how some of the results might affect model development and output. Full implications of errors and variability will be the subject of more detailed R&D to be commissioned under the second phase of the program (Chapter 8).

An assumption of predictive modelling is that macroinvertebrate community composition is reasonably constant over time. While seasonal variability has been factored into development of RIVPACS, all reference sites being sampled in each of spring, summer and autumn, inter-annual variability has received little attention. Clarke, Furse *et al.* (1996) considered temporal variability as a factor when identifying the sources of uncertainty for RIVPACS, but only as a potential source of error for the observed fauna and not the expected fauna. This is despite the fact that the reference site database for RIVPACS has accumulated through the addition of data for different sites over time (1977 to 1995) (Wright 1995). The degree of possible variability arising from natural changes in macroinvertebrate community composition over this period and the effect of this, if any, upon model construction, has not been reported.

Whilst the degree of environmental variation can affect persistence, i.e. the tendency for community composition or structure to remain unchanged (see the review by Hildrew & Giller 1994), studies conducted by a number of British workers indicate that the degree of temporal variability evident in long-term macroinvertebrate data from UK streams would probably be too slight to adversely affect development of predictive models, based on the concordance of site classification (Townsend *et al.* 1987; Weatherley & Ormerod 1990). Wright (1995), however, cautioned that temporal variability of macroinvertebrate communities of small temporary streams in the UK might be sufficient to be of concern in this respect.

One of two objectives of this chapter is to describe results of a broad-scale program to quantify the degree of temporal variability evident in long-term datasets from representative streams across Australia. Where lack of persistence is observed, a longer-term aim is to explore the implications of this result for model sensitivity, by assessing the degree of fidelity of long-term data in groups derived from current AUSRIVAS classifications. Some possible ways to account for temporal variability are also raised for discussion.

AUSRIVAS has adopted a standardised approach for sample collection, i.e. 10 m kick-sweep of each dominant habitat at each site using a 250 µm-mesh dipnet. However, agencies have opted for one of two approaches for sample processing: 30-min live-sort of each sample in the field, or field preservation of samples and subsequent laboratory-based subsampling and sorting.

A second objective of this chapter is to describe the results of an external Quality Assurance/Quality Control program (QA/QC) conducted to assess the adequacy of agency sample processing procedures. QA/QC is recognised as an essential component of any large project involving many different parties. Its purpose is to ensure that methods for data collection are standardised, that data are of a consistent and high quality, and that this quality is maintained throughout the project. Equivalent biological monitoring programs using rapid assessment protocols in the UK (Wright 1995), and the USA (Plafkin, Barbour *et al.* 1989; Cuffney *et al.* 1993a (cited by Cuffney *et al.* 1993b)), have associated QA/QC programs, described by van Dijk (1994) and Dines & Murray-Bligh (see Chapter 5) for the UK, and by Cuffney *et al.* (1993b) for the USA.

The nature and degree of error arising in agency sample processing procedures have been quantified, and the implications of high error rates for model sensitivity are explored by way of preliminary simulations. Lastly, revisions to current protocols are described and further information needs identified for future funding rounds of the MRHI program.

Features of the Australian climate and stream hydrology

Any discussion of temporal variability of macroinvertebrate communities of Australian streams needs to be prefaced by a description of the main features of the Australian climate and stream hydrology. A review of these issues is provided by Lake (1995). Much of Australia straddles the subtropical, high-pressure belt of the Southern Hemisphere. The tropical north is relatively well-watered, receiving its rain in the southern summer, whereas the well-watered south-west and south-east portions of the continent derive much of their rain in winter or year-round (Fig. 10.1). However, rainfall across two-thirds of the continent is low (<500 mm rainfall per year) and variable. By world standards, Australian streams have low discharges and considerable variability in flow. Thus, many of Australia's streams are intermittent, flowing seasonally or unpredictably. Average values of the coefficient of variation of annual stream flow for different continents or regions, from lowest to highest variability, are: South Pacific, 0.25; Europe, 0.28; North America, 0.29; Asia, 0.35; northern Africa, 0.37; South America, 0.52; Australia, 0.69; southern Africa, 0.79 (Peel 1998).

Part of flow variability is linked to El Niño–Southern Oscillation (ENSO) events. Droughts and major floods are associated closely with marked deviations in the Southern Oscillation Index. On the Australian continent, the northern and particularly eastern portions are most severely affected by El Niño–related drought. In the period 1950 to the present, eight such drought periods have affected Australia (three in the 1990s), the median period of duration being 11 months (Bureau of Meteorology: http://www.bom.gov.au). Drought- and flood-dominated periods can be recognised in most long-term stream hydrographs in Australia. Rain depressions arising from tropical cyclones in summer contribute to episodic and heavy flooding of large parts of Australia, extending well into arid inland regions. The greatest occurrences and influences of cyclones for mainland Australia are along the north-west (Western Australia) and north-east (Queensland) coasts; on average, six cyclones cross the Australian coastline per year (Crowder 1995).

Methods: temporal variability

Source of long-term datasets

Data from a number of researchers across Australia were compiled to quantify the temporal variability of stream macroinvertebrate communities (Humphrey *et al.* 1997). Ten geographical regions, 13 catchments and 38 individual sites were represented (Fig. 10.1). The average duration of the datasets was *ca* 6 years, with some datasets extending to 10 years. Sites were located in streams of permanent and seasonal flow. The main shortcoming of the study was the dominance of data from riffle habitat, with only one dataset providing information for pools and macrophyte habitat.

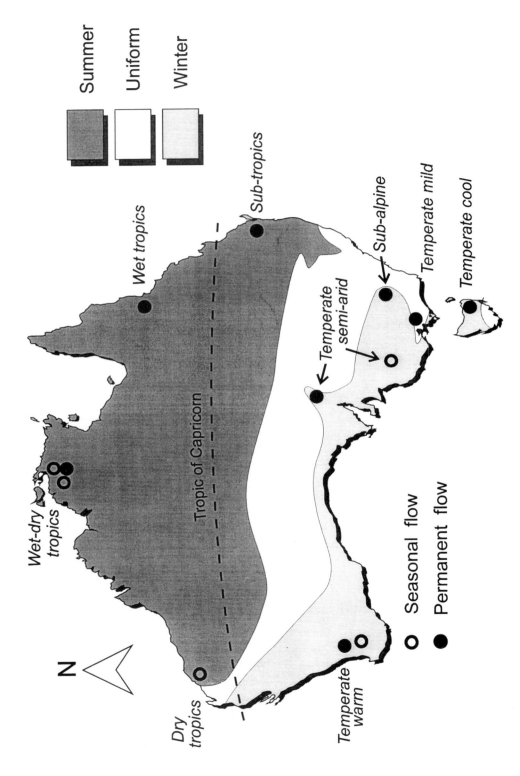

Figure 10.1. Map of Australia showing the geographical regions and catchments from which long-term macroinvertebrate community data were derived, in relation to zones of major seasonal rainfall patterns and climate, and flow status of streams.

Quantifying temporal variability

Temporal variability was expressed in terms of an "Inconstancy Index", determined for each site and season as the proportion of inter-annual comparisons of community composition (presence/absence) and structure (relative abundance) for which community dissimilarity measures (family-level identifications) exceeded pre-determined thresholds. The Bray–Curtis dissimilarity measure was used to describe the degree of (dis)similarity between inter-annual samples. As this measure is the basis of unweighted pair-group mean arithmetic averaging (UPGMA) classification of MRHI data for model development, it was potentially best suited for quantifying the degree of temporal variability inherent in a dataset. Similarly, the concept of threshold "exceedances" was useful in determining the implications of high variability for model development. This concept best reflects the dichotomous nature of classifications and the notion of misclassification between groups that would occur with high error rates or variability.

For each site and season, analysis of community data from amongst years was conducted using the top 50 and 90% of taxa, as assessed by average relative abundance of taxa across years. These proportional cut-offs were made in order to standardise across regions of naturally varying taxa richness. The top 90% cut-off was used for compositional (presence/absence) data, this value being relevant to MRHI datasets used for modelling where taxa occurring at 10% or less of sites for a given regional dataset are excluded from analyses (see Chapter 9, p. 127). Dissimilarity measures based on community structure (relative or rank abundance) data are less sensitive to proportional taxa number as defined here. Humphrey *et al.* (1997) found that the measures for a given dataset were virtually the same whether the basis of comparison was the top 50 or 90%. A "top 50%" cut-off was applied to relative abundance data. For relative abundance analysis, raw abundance data for all taxa occurring at each site and year of sampling were divided by the abundance value of the numerically dominant taxon in that site and year, resulting in a list of taxa on a scale of 0 to 1, ranging from the least abundant taxon (in this case absent) to the most abundant taxon.

Threshold exceedances for dissimilarity values, calculated for every possible pairwise inter-annual comparison of community data, were set at 0.35 for compositional data and 0.5 for relative abundance data. The threshold of 0.35 was selected as the value separating groups in an UPGMA classification, the basis of an AUSRIVAS model using laboratory subsampled and sorted data (Storey & Humphrey 1997). This was regarded as a conservative value of allowable error or variability in a model arising from a single source. The threshold dissimilarity value of 0.5 was set for relative abundance data on the simple assumption that, on a scale of 0 to 1, exceedance of 0.5 would probably indicate a real decrease in affinity in community structure between two samples. Thus values of the Inconstancy Index (INI) were calculated for each season and site for compositional data as "% dissimilarities >0.35 for top 90% of taxa", and for relative abundance data as "% dissimilarities >0.5 for top 50% of taxa".

Possible implications of high temporal variability for model construction

One of the ultimate tests of the extent to which high temporal variability presents problems for predictive modelling is whether long-term data for a site classify together in large, regional datasets and give a similar result in predictive model outputs. This exercise was partially carried out for data from the Top End of the Northern Territory (NT), by classifying long-term data from two adjacent streams (South Alligator River and Magela Creek) in an UPGMA classification of NT macroinvertebrate samples from riffle habitat that were gathered from the late dry seasons (October–December) of 1994 and 1995. Humphrey *et al.* (1997) reported a switch in macroinvertebrate community structure and, to a lesser extent, composition, in the

South Alligator River in response to changes in the baseflow of the river, from a high to a low flow state over the period 1987 to 1997.

Methods: sample processing errors

Results of external QA/QC of MRHI agencies indicated very low errors associated with taxonomic identifications (Hawking & O'Connor 1997) and relatively low errors associated with laboratory subsampling and sorting of preserved samples (Humphrey & Thurtell 1997). Moreover, these samples are usually stored and hence there is potential to retrieve lost information. Conversely, there was always some concern over the efficacy of live-sorting, particularly as sample residues are usually discarded after sorting. This was confirmed by Humphrey & Thurtell (1997) who demonstrated that the highest error rates were observed for the live-sorting method. Hence, the focus of study here was on live-sorting error and possible implications for model development and sensitivity.

Deriving criteria for assessing the quality of live-sort data

The aim in live-sorting is to maximise taxa recovery (Davies 1994). To determine how well agency staff met this objective, taxa richness, and community composition and/or structure in a random selection of live-sort samples, were compared with the same community summaries of corresponding residues retained after live-sorting. Specifically, residues were processed to obtain a proportional Whole Sample Estimate (WSE), i.e. an estimate of the community composition and/or structure present in the original sample if the same number of animals as those that were live-sorted had been derived from laboratory subsampling and sorting. WSE data were estimated from addition of taxa information derived from (1) subsampling and sorting the residue, and (2) subsampling, to a similar proportion, the live-sort component. A proportional scaling-down of the combined fractions was then made to achieve the same sample size as the live-sort component. Samples were also scaled to a sample size of 100 animals for live-sort samples which contained <100 animals. The standardisations and scalings involved in deriving WSE are described in Humphrey & Thurtell (1997); the taxa number estimates derived after scaling-down compare well with the results from rarefaction equations cited in the literature (Heck *et al.* 1975).

Live-sort (LS) and WSE data were compared firstly for taxa number, using a ratio of the numbers of taxa recovered by the live-sort and the whole-sample estimate procedures, LS/WSE, (hereafter termed the "taxa number ratio"), and secondly for community composition (presence/absence) using the Bray–Curtis dissimilarity measure. If one sorting method was less efficient than another and resulted in recovery of fewer taxa, then taxa number ratio and dissimilarity measure would both be useful assessment criteria. However, live-sorted data may be biased for, as well as against, certain taxa. A consistent bias might not necessarily present a problem for classification and modelling if all samples for model-building and subsequent testing of sites used the same procedure. It does, however, complicate the use of the Bray–Curtis dissimilarity measure to compare live-sort and WSE data. As we show below, failure to remove common taxa is a serious error associated with live-sorting and hence the taxa number ratio is regarded as the better assessment criterion for detecting this problem. Therefore, it is the measure of performance used hereafter.

Possible implications of high sample processing errors for model construction

To determine possible consequences to model construction and performance of the biases in taxa recovery arising from live-sorting, a simulation study was undertaken. This addressed the consequences of missed common taxa for (a) UPGMA classification (the initial stage in model construction used to define site groupings), and (b) accuracy in model outputs. For this, the commonly-occurring taxa in an AUSRIVAS dataset (i.e. an Australian Capital Territory (ACT) agency dataset of 96 sites, derived from laboratory-processed samples) were altered to match the bias observed in live-sort data. Two sets of live-sort data were used in the simulations, one representing data from one of the poorer performing agencies (New South Wales (NSW)), and another for the average bias observed across eastern states of Queensland (QLD), NSW, Victoria (VIC) and Tasmania (TAS). These data were derived from Figure 10.5 (see later), plus data for Corbiculidae and Sphaeriidae, provided in Humphrey & Thurtell (1997). The average bias was not as severe as that for the single agency. Deletion of taxa was performed at random from actual occurrences in the original ACT dataset, until the occurrences matched that of the bias represented in the two datasets. The deletions involved 16 out of a total of 39 taxa. Ten separate simulations and classifications were then run for each of the single agency and average agency datasets.

In addition, a functioning model based on the original ACT data was constructed, following the established AUSRIVAS protocols for model construction (see Chapter 9). The original data and the data derived from the ten simulations of the single agency and average agency were run through the model, and the resulting output bandings were recorded, where Band X = more taxa than predicted (possibly indicating slight nutrient enrichment), Band A = equivalent number of taxa to the reference condition, Band B = slightly impacted, Band C = moderately impacted and Band D = severely impacted. The percentage of samples in each model banding was recorded and outputs from each dataset were compared.

Methods: data analysis

Multivariate analyses were performed using the PATN software package (Belbin 1992). For numerical site classifications, Bray–Curtis dissimilarity measures were calculated on the presence or absence of families after eliminating taxa present at 10% or less of samples, as in the standard approach to preparation of MRHI data for construction of predictive models (Chapter 9, p. 127). Classifications were derived using flexible UPGMA in the FUSE option in PATN, with the beta (dilation) parameter set at the default (–0.1). Procedures for developing the predictive model used in this study are described in Chapter 9.

Results: temporal variability

Degree and extent of temporal variability: relative abundance data

For half of the catchments studied, over 30% of inter-annual comparisons exceeded a Bray–Curtis dissimilarity value of 0.5 (Table 10.1). Only for a relatively small portion of southern Australia, for which inter-annual variability of stream discharge is low (i.e. Tasmania, south-west Western Australia, and possibly parts of Victoria) would there appear to be potential for development of AUSRIVAS models based upon relative or rank abundance data. Given this restriction and the fact that current AUSRIVAS models use compositional data, the focus is now on results using presence/absence data.

Degree and extent of temporal variability: presence/absence data

In seven of the ten regions studied for which two seasons of data were available, inter-annual variation was greatest following seasonal flooding (Humphrey *et al.* 1997). For two northern Australian streams, inter-annual variation was greatest at the end of the dry season, attributable to changes in community composition as a result of low flow conditions and drought. The distribution of the Inconstancy Index for the most variable season was very broad, ranging from 0 to 93 (Humphrey *et al.* 1997).

A combined seasons index was derived by averaging the Inconstancy Index (INI) across seasons for presence/absence data. The magnitude of this index for different catchments is shown in Table 10.1, in relation to climatic regions, stream flow and latitude. Regression analysis was used to seek relationships between dependent INI and independent environmental variables. The best predictive relationship was a bivariate equation derived between the INI variable and two independent variables: the coefficient of variation (CV) of annual stream flow, and flow status (FS). This relationship is described by:

$$\log_{10} \text{INI} = 0.62 + 0.704 \text{ CV} + 0.265 \text{ FS}; \ (R^2 = 0.73, \text{ p} < 0.001)$$

where INI = inconstancy index (% dissimilarity >0.35 for top 90% of taxa), CV = coefficient of variation of annual flow (or mean of any range in values), and FS = flow status, using a dummy variable, 0 = permanent flow, 1 = seasonal flow. The two independent variables were significant at p = 0.001 (CV) and p <0.05 (FS). Latitude was found to be only weakly (and negatively) correlated with INI (p = 0.24 for this variable in the best of the derived regression equations).

Table 10.1. *Temporal variability of stream macroinvertebrate communities from riffle habitat across different regions of Australia, based upon family-level, presence/absence (PA) or relative abundance (RA) data. Flow status is permanent (P) or seasonal (S), with coefficient of variation (CV) for annual flow. Inconstancy indices (INI) are averaged across seasons for PA (% dissimilarity >0.35) and RA (% dissimilarity >0.5). Latitude is given as degrees.decimal minutes.*

(1) Data gathered using a sample processing method inappropriate for recovering relative abundance data.

(2) MH = macrophyte habitat.

Region	Flow status	INI for PA	INI for RA	Flow CV	Latitude
Temperate (VIC-Latrobe)	P	4.5	68.0[1]	0.32	38.0
Temperate (SW WA)	P	6.5	3.5	0.49 – 0.73	32.3
Temperate (TAS)	P	7.5	5.5	0.47	41.3
Wet-dry tropical (SAR, NT)	P	13.5	40.5	0.58	13.35
Wet tropical (NE QLD)	P	15.0	33.5	0.50	18.1
Wet-dry tropical (RMC, NT)	S	17.0	0	0.58	13.35
Subtropical (SE QLD)	P	19.0	52.5	1.04 – 1.07	26.3
Temperate-dry (VIC-Wimmera)	S	19.5	41.5	0.58 – 0.98	36.3
Wet-dry tropical (Magela, NT)	S	21.0	36.0	0.56	12.4
Temperate (SW WA)	S	24.0	15.0	0.49 – 0.73	32.3
Temp. semi-arid (Flinders, SA)	P (Riffle)	25.0	6.0	1.25	31.1
Subalpine (NSW)	P	27.5	37.5	0.50 – 0.75	36.3
Temp. semi-arid (Flinders, SA)	P (MH[2], pool)	51.7	16.5	1.25	31.1
Dry tropics (NW, WA)	S	93.0	27.0	1.40	21.3

Several points emerge from the results presented in Table 10.1 and from regression analysis. (The term "persistence", the converse of "inconstancy", is used to describe the degree of similarity in community composition over time).

1(a). A high negative correlation is observed between persistence and inter-annual variation of stream discharge.

1(b). Persistence of macroinvertebrate communities is significantly higher in streams of permanent flow than in streams of seasonal flow. (For seasonally-flowing streams that dry out, lower persistence may be related to the stochastic nature of recolonisation following re-wetting).

1(c). There is a tendency for macroinvertebrate communities of permanent streams in temperate Australia to be more persistent than those in tropical regions. (Given the greater seasonal extremes in discharge and warmer waters, invertebrates in tropical streams tend to have shorter life cycles).

2. For the limited data available, macroinvertebrate communities from riffle habitat appear to be more persistent than those from other habitats, even at the same sites of permanent flow (cf. data for Flinders Ranges streams, Table 10.1); see also Weatherley & Ormerod (1990).

3. Measures of temporal variability used in this study (family-level presence/absence data), and averaged across the seasons, indicate relatively high persistence of macroinvertebrate communities for all but one or two of the regions represented. For regions exhibiting high INI values, cyclonic disturbance and flooding (Robe R, north-west WA) and drought in 1995 (Barker-Barambah Creeks, south-east QLD) were attributed as the cause (Humphrey *et al.* 1997). The Robe R site lies in the most cyclone-prone region of Australia (Crowder 1995). Nevertheless, whilst temporal variability of macroinvertebrate communities may be high in only one or two regions represented in this study, they represent a large portion of the continent. In particular, Humphrey *et al.* (1997) extrapolated the findings to suggest that the sensitivity of AUSRIVAS models developed for much of the drought-prone portion of eastern Australia, particularly NSW and QLD, could be compromised during (and possibly after) drought periods.

Possible implications of temporal variability for model construction and sensitivity

The UPGMA classification, combining long-term riffle data from two adjacent streams (South Alligator River and Magela Creek), together with other NT macroinvertebrate samples from riffle habitat, gathered from the late dry seasons of 1994 and 1995, are shown in Figure 10.2. Four classification groups are defined, separated at a dissimilarity cut-off value (horizontal scale) of *ca* 0.38. On superficial inspection, there are two features of the classification that are of concern. Firstly, the South Alligator River (SAR) data generally separate out into the two flow-states referred to above (1988 versus 1994 and 1995), although the three years of data for one site (SA-03) span three separate classification groups. Secondly, the long-term responses of macroinvertebrate communities of two adjacent streams are very different; SAR sites (SA-01 to SA-03) have changed markedly whilst the Magela Creek site (MC-01) has barely changed at all. On closer inspection of the data, however, it is evident that there is relatively high intra- and inter-site similarity across all the sites – see the overall small-scale of dissimilarity values in Figure 10.2 – suggesting that for family presence/absence data at least, the absolute changes occurring through time are not large. Nevertheless, further exercises such as this could be informative when extended to other regions of Australia. This would be particularly useful when extended to datasets gathered in drought and non-drought cycles, in order to examine the integrity of the classification groups over time.

In summary, drought in eastern Australia and major cyclonic disturbance in northern Australia seem to be the main factors that would restrict development of predictive models across the continent.

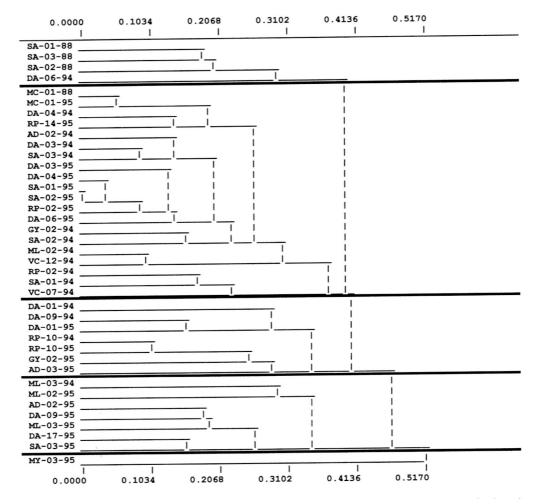

Figure 10.2. UPGMA classification of Northern Territory riffle macroinvertebrate samples, for late dry seasons 1988 (two streams only), 1994 and 1995, based on presence/absence data. Codes along left-hand margin refer to river (two-letter code)–site number–year of sampling. Bold horizontal lines define four classification groups in the dendrogram.

Results: sample processing errors

Humphrey & Thurtell (1997) showed that recovery of relative abundance data was met in most laboratory subsampled data (4 agencies), but recovery was much less successful in live-sorted data (5 agencies) where the major objective was to maximise taxa recovery (Davies 1994). The results of live-sort agency performance in recovery of community compositional data are discussed in the following sections.

Nature of live-sort errors using presence/absence data

It would be expected that if the objective of live-sorting is to maximise taxa recovery, then the LS/WSE ratio would exceed unity, i.e. live-sorting should be more efficient in achieving this aim than laboratory subsampling and sorting, the latter being the basis of WSE estimation. Humphrey & Thurtell (1997) reported a LS/WSE taxa number ratio less than 1 for 51% of live-sort samples processed in an external QA/QC audit. Thus, live-sorting is not particularly efficient at meeting the goal of maximising the recovery of taxa.

In terms of the quality of data achieved in live-sorting, two features of the data gathered by MRHI agencies appear to have the potential to create difficulties for MRHI model development, or to reduce the sensitivity of the model for diagnosing the quality of a site. These factors are under-representation of taxa and different rates of taxa recovery, dependent upon the efficiency of the operator. These factors and their possible contribution to errors in model development and output are discussed below.

Under-representation of taxa in live-sort samples

Factors contributing to poor taxa recovery in live-sorted samples include: (1) low live-sort sample size, (2) operator inexperience and (3) common taxa are missed.

(1). Low sample size. For live-sort sample size <300 animals, significant positive regression relationships were found between taxa recovery and live-sort sample size for combined agency live-sort data. These relationships are shown in Figure 10.3. Two regression equations were derived, each using different values of WSE for live-sort sample size <100; (i) WSE_N scaled to the same sample size as the live-sort sample, and (ii) WSE_{100} scaled to 100 animals. The derived regression equations for (i) and (ii) respectively are:

$$LS/WSE_N \quad = 0.856 + 0.000687 \ LS; \ (R^2 = 0.03, p = 0.05)$$

$$LS/WSE_{100} = 0.749 + 0.00124 \ LS; \ (R^2 = 0.14, p < 0.001)$$

where LS/WSE = ratio of number of taxa recovered by the live-sort and the whole-sample estimate procedures, and LS = live-sort sample size. (The two LS/WSE_N values >1.5 shown in Figure 10.3 were considered as outliers and were not included in the regression analysis).

Thus, low taxa number ratios (<1) typically accompany a small live-sort sample size (Fig. 10.3), a feature that is accentuated in WSE data normalised to 100 animals for live-sort sample size <100 animals. This result indicates that there is currently insufficient sorting effort for recovery of taxa under these conditions. Both regression lines meet the taxa number ratio value of 1 at a live-sort sample size of *ca* 200 animals (Fig. 10.3), although variation about the regression lines is very large. Partly on the basis of these results, Humphrey & Thurtell (1997) recommended that this value should be set as a minimum sample size target for future live-sorting under the MRHI. They observed that a factor contributing to low live-sort sample size is "low" overall abundance of animals in the sample.

(2). Operator inexperience. A second factor contributing to poor taxa recovery in live-sorted samples was operator inexperience. The least experienced operators tended to achieve poorer taxa recovery rates than more experienced operators (Fig. 10.4). This result was also corroborated by Growns, Chessman *et al.* (1997) who showed that experienced personnel sorted more than twice as many animals (and therefore more taxa) as inexperienced personnel in 30-min time trials.

(3). Common taxa that are missed. A feature of live-sorted data was the frequent absence of taxa that occur commonly in samples and across sites. This was a major factor contributing to poor taxa recovery in live-sorted samples, and is considered in more detail below.

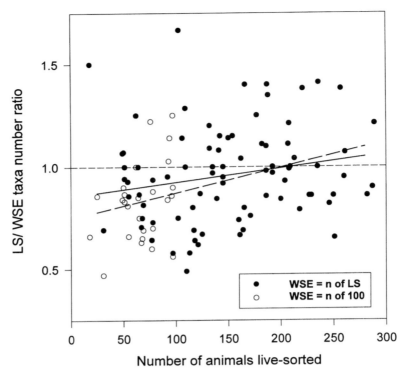

Figure 10.3. Relationships between live-sort taxa recovery (as measured by the LS/WSE ratios of taxa number) and total number of animals live-sorted. The unbroken line is a regression relationship using WSE scaled to the same sample size (WSE_N) as the live-sort sample for live-sort sample size <100. The broken line is a regression relationship using WSE scaled to 100 animals (WSE_{100}) for live-sort sample size <100.

Figure 10.4. Boxplots showing comparison of LS/WSE (presence/absence data) for operators of different levels of live-sorting experience using the LS/WSE ratios of taxa number. Each boxplot defines lower and upper quartiles divided at the median, with vertical lines showing the range of values that fall within 1.5 times the interquartile range; the asterisk indicates an outlier beyond these limits. Levels of operator experience are ranked as 1 = <2 years, 2 = 2–3 years, 3 = 3–4 years, 4 = 5 or more years.

Quantifying the recovery of key taxa

For MRHI, recovery of taxa that have a frequency of occurrence in a group of >50% is particularly important as these taxa are used in modelling and represent taxa expected at a site. To quantify the extent to which these key taxa were being missed from live-sort samples, taxa occurring in more than 50% of samples from any of the agencies, for either the live-sort or corresponding WSE component, were listed. (This is not the same as taxa occurring in 50% or more of samples from an agency classification group, a factor which would lead to some underestimation of actual taxa affected in the present analysis). For each of these taxa and for each agency, the percentage occurrence amongst all samples for which the taxon was found in both LS and corresponding WSE components, was recorded (Fig. 10.5).

In Figure 10.5, taxa have been ranked, from left to right, from greatest deficit to greatest surplus in occurrence in live-sort component compared to occurrence in corresponding WSE, when data were averaged across all live-sort agencies. Comparisons between occurrences of taxa present in the live-sort and corresponding WSE components show that similar taxa were either missed or better represented (in comparison to WSE occurrence) across all agencies and operators. Thus, there is consistency amongst all agencies in the biases in taxa recovery.

The results show that small and/or cryptic taxa are often overlooked during the live-sort process, regardless of agency. Thus, chironomid pupae and other small cryptic Diptera, such as ceratopogonids and empidids, were frequently missed during live-sorting (Fig. 10.5). This is also the case with the cryptic elmid larvae, hydroptilids (micro-caddis) and oligochaetes. Surprisingly, the fast-moving water mites (Acarina) are also frequently missed during live-sorting (Fig. 10.5). However, these data fail to reveal an additional problem of live-sorting, which is the potential for low recovery of chironomid subfamilies (Humphrey & Thurtell 1997). (Chironomidae are resolved to subfamily level for the MRHI but to family level for the present exercise).

Figure 10.5 also demonstrates that some taxa are better represented in live-sort data than WSE (= laboratory subsampled and sorted) data. Thus the large but less abundant taxa, such as the odonates, shrimps and adult beetles, are often missed during the more objective subsampling process. These results show the extent to which laboratory subsampling and sorting are biased in taxa recovery. In practice, this is minimised for most MRHI agencies which process samples in the laboratory, because an additional search of the entire sample for large taxa missed during the subsampling process is usually carried out.

Biases in taxa recovery are not necessarily a problem for classification and model development. The key requirement is that biases are consistent amongst agency staff. Whereas live-sorting is more efficient than laboratory procedures for recovering large, conspicuous and rare taxa, live-sorting is less efficient at retrieving most taxa and specifically small and cryptic taxa. The potential problem in live-sorting is that missed taxa are reasonably common both in samples and across sites (often occurring in >50% of samples for a given agency). Such common taxa, which are likely to have a high probability of occurrence at a site, are inherently important for MRHI classification and modelling. Moreover, many of the taxa that are commonly missed have been shown to be informative in Australian impact-assessment studies and are known to be sensitive to some types of water quality stress (Chessman 1995).

Conversely, the taxa that live-sorting is particularly effective at recovering are those that are uncommon in samples but also not particularly common across samples and sites (Fig. 10.5). These taxa would not be expected to be as influential in models. Thus, even if an additional screening of the sample was not undertaken by laboratory subsampling agencies, the loss of these taxa is likely to be of little consequence for model development and sensitivity.

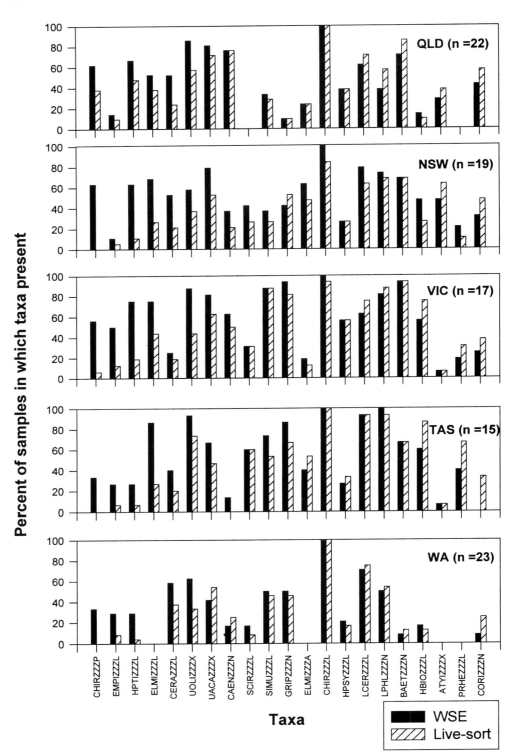

Figure 10.5 (*on facing page*). Taxa occurring commonly across samples for different MRHI agencies and their percentage occurrence (presence/absence data) in both LS (hatched) and corresponding WSE (solid) components of agency samples. n = number of samples examined per state. Taxa are coded as follows: ATYIZZZX, Atyidae; BAETZZZN, Baetidae; CAENZZZN, Caenidae; CERAZZZL, Ceratopogonidae; CHIRZZZL, Chironomidae; CHIRZZZP, Chironomidae; CORIZZZN, Corixidae; ELMIZZZL, Elmidae; ELMIZZZA, Elmidae; EMPIZZZL, Empididae; GRIPZZZN, Gripopterygidae; HBIOZZZL, Hydrobiosidae; HPSYZZZL, Hydropsychidae; HPTIZZZL, Hydroptilidae; LCERZZZL, Leptoceridae; LPHLZZZN, Leptophlebiidae; PRHEZZZL, Philorheithridae; SCIRZZZL, Scirtidae; SIMUZZZL, Simuliidae; UACAZZZX, Unidentified Acarina; UOLIZZZX, Unidentified Oligochaeta. The suffixes L, N, X, A, P on codes respectively refer to life stages – Larvae, Nymph, Life stage not identified, Adult and Pupae.

A broad range in taxa recovery observed amongst operators

Implicit in the findings of this study, and concurring with the results of others, is the fact that time-constrained sorting, unlike proportional or fixed sample-size sorting, is prone to varying rates of taxon recovery, depending upon the efficiency of the operator. Some superficial evidence for this is contained in Table 10.2, which shows the range in LS/WSE ratios amongst the samples examined within each agency. These values are quite broad, even for laboratory subsampled data where low ratios (<0.8) are the result of small numbers of animals in agency subsamples (Humphrey & Thurtell 1997). Operator experience is another contributing factor for live-sort agencies. Thus, the highest LS/WSE ratio of 2.3 from QLD (Table 10.2) was obtained for a sample sorted by the agency team leader, a very experienced stream biologist. In contrast, least experienced operators generally have the poorest rates of taxon recovery (see Fig. 10.4), a result consistent with the findings of others (Metzeling & Chessman 1996; Growns, Chessman *et al.* 1997).

Table 10.2. *Ranges of LS/WSE ratios for number of taxa (N) amongst the samples of each Australian agency. Sample processing was by live-sorting in the field (F) or by subsample and sort in the laboratory (L).*

Agency	N	Sample	Ranges of LW/WSE
QLD	22	F	0.75 – 2.30
NSW	19	F	0.42 – 1.42
VIC	17	F	0.56 – 1.38
TAS	15	F	0.58 – 1.09
WA	23	F	0.63 – 1.66
SA	13	L	0.58 – 1.22
ACT	10	L	0.82 – 1.01
NT	10	L	0.82 – 1.53
WA	10	L	1.11 – 1.77

Implications of "high" live-sort errors for model construction and sensitivity

The rate of bias against common taxa due to live-sorting (single agency and average of four agencies) was superimposed upon an AUSRIVAS dataset in which common taxa were well represented (ACT laboratory subsample agency). The consequences of missed common taxa for UPGMA classification were examined.

In the original ACT classification, six clearly defined groups were identified and a predictive model was successfully constructed. However, in the classifications derived after error rates

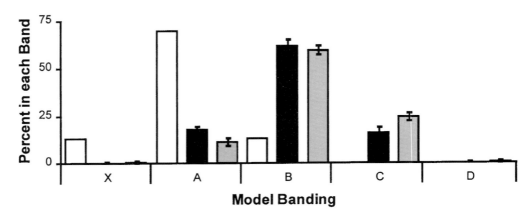

Figure 10.6. Mean (± 95% confidence limits) percent of samples recorded in each model banding when original ACT data (open columns) and the data derived from the ten simulations of the average agency (solid columns) and single agency (shaded columns) errors were run through the ACT edge-habitat model. (Band X = more taxa than predicted, A = equivalent number of taxa to reference condition, B = slightly impacted, C = moderately impacted and D = severely impacted.)

were applied to the ACT data, there was little evidence of preservation of group structure. All classifications exhibited dilation and breakdown or "chaining" in classification structure. There was no evidence that classifications based on average agency (with lower error rates) were an improvement on single agency classifications (higher error rates). Even for one or two (single agency) classifications for which chaining in classification was least evident, there was a loss of two or three groups, whilst dissimilarity cut-offs for the groups were found to be higher in the altered data, indicating introduction of errors (i.e. higher mean within-group dissimilarities).

Placement of the simulated data, site by site through the original ACT model, resulted in a high incidence of predictive failure (Fig. 10.6). When original data were run through the model, the majority of sites, by definition (Chapter 9), were recorded as "reference" (Band A), with *ca* 10% of sites in Bands X and B; none of the original sites was recorded in Bands C or D. However, average agency and single agency data were strongly skewed towards impacted, with the majority of sites in Band B, between 10 and 20% of sites in Bands A and C, and a small representation in Bands X and D. Approximately 80% of sites from simulated data were recorded as impacted, compared to 10% from the original data. There were slightly more sites recorded as Band C and fewer recorded as Band A for single versus average agency error, reflecting the poorer performance of the former agency (Fig. 10.6).

Part of the general failure to derive well defined classifications in both sets of simulations may be related to the level of taxonomic resolution used for MRHI. Family-level presence/absence data may be so coarse that any structure present in the classifications may be easily lost. The effect of errors due to differences in sorting efficacy will depend to a large extent on the magnitude of the real differences in the dataset being analysed; error will have a greater effect in a dataset with small differences (short gradients). This is likely the case for the ACT, where group definition based upon family-level presence/absence data could be expected to be quite subtle because of minimal biogeographical signal. All other agency classifications are derived for the entire state or territory, minimising this problem.

Discussion: dealing with temporal variability of macroinvertebrate communities

The ultimate test of whether or not temporal variability presents problems for predictive modelling lies in running long-term community compositional data for particular sites through agency classifications and models. In this context the severity or otherwise of any lack of community persistence – *within the bounds of sensitivity of the models* – can be fully measured. Misclassifications and poor predictions would indicate potential problems for model development. Possible approaches to dealing with temporal variability of macroinvertebrate communities include risk-based assessment using AUSRIVAS models, and accounting for temporal variability.

Risk-based assessment using AUSRIVAS models

As either an interim or definitive step, predictive regression relationships between temporal variability and environmental variables (see above), may be used to quantify degrees of "risk" of model failure for a particular location. This would give managers some indication of the accuracy of models developed for a particular location (i.e. the error associated with predictions if temporal variability was the sole factor of concern).

Accounting for temporal variability

As an improvement upon the above form of risk-based assessment, can temporal variability be accounted for?

(1). Modelling temporal variability. Seeking environmental correlates that may account for temporal variability is unlikely to be successful for a number of situations. These are: (i) seasonally-flowing streams where shifts in community composition over time may be associated with stochastic recolonisation processes (see also Wright 1995); (ii) longer-term (several years) recovery and recolonisation of streams following massive disturbance (e.g. Robe R, north-west WA, Table 10.1); and (iii) switches between different community "steady states" where triggers for the switch may be clearly identified, but the trajectory of community composition thereafter is either lagged, or unknown and unpredictable (e.g. South Alligator River (SAR) and Yuccabine Creek, north-east QLD, Table 10.1; see also Boulton & Lake 1992). Associated with these difficulties is the possibility of inter-catchment differences in community responses, as described above for the South Alligator River and Magela Creek (NT).

Modelling of drought-related changes to macroinvertebrate communities would be particularly useful for AUSRIVAS model development in eastern Australia. However, currently there is little understanding of the responses of macroinvertebrate communities to drought, including how responsive the fauna is to environmental change. Moreover, Humphrey *et al.* (1997) reported very different responses to drought across Australia at regional and inter- and intra-catchment scales. Examination of existing agency datasets, some of which span periods of major drought (e.g. QLD, 1994–1995), would assist in redressing these information deficiencies.

(2). Adjusting and updating model output. This would entail the re-sampling of suitable reference sites simultaneously in time with monitoring sites, in order to adjust model output by some factor. A problem with this approach is that it assumes the scaling or correction factor is similar across classification groups and between reference and disturbed sites. This assumption is unlikely to hold because, as described in (1) above, macroinvertebrate community response to a similar disturbance is likely to differ at different spatial scales. (In support of this, Weatherley & Ormerod (1990) also reported intra-catchment differences in persistence,

observing correlations between invertebrate persistence and altitude in Welsh streams). In addition, the degree of change to natural disturbance is likely to be greater for reference sites than for anthropogenically-disturbed sites. Hence there would be a need to include sufficient reference sites that were representative of each of the classification groups, as well as a need to incorporate re-sampling of selected disturbed sites, in order to derive appropriate scaling factors.

(3). Models for different climatic conditions (especially drought versus non-drought). Models empirically derived for different climatic conditions, such as drought versus non-drought, would have the advantage that fewer assumptions are made about the responses of macroinvertebrate communities in different habitats, between different parts of a catchment, amongst catchments, or across a disturbance gradient. The disadvantage in this approach is one of expense, whilst the (untested) assumption is made that responses to one drought will be the same as the next, even though droughts differ in their intensity. At best, interpolation and extrapolation between different models may enable some allowance to be made for different climatic conditions. Nevertheless, some of the current agency datasets span a period of drought and non-drought; processing of all these data, and derivation of different models for different climatic conditions, may be exceedingly valuable.

(4). Combined seasons models. There is little doubt that temporal variability would be reduced substantially by an approach in which data for different seasons of the year were combined. One disadvantage with this approach is the need to accumulate two or more seasons of data before an assessment of river health based upon macroinvertebrate communities can be made. Although this may provide some indication of longer term severity of a river health problem, it is contrary to the ethos of rapid biological assessment and rapid turn-round of results. Another disadvantage may lie in construction of a model so robust to natural environmental change that only impacts of a particularly severe nature are detected, whilst impacts restricted to one season may pass undetected.

Related to approaches (3) and (4) above, some agencies have constructed models by adding new reference sites (three seasons combined, UK RIVPACS) or existing reference sites for consecutive years of sampling (MRHI ACT agency) to an existing model. For regions where climatic variability is high, this last approach runs the risk of deriving models that are temporally confounded unless sampling of some common reference sites is undertaken simultaneously, to account for possible temporal variation. Where such variability is not evident, it has been argued that it is an advantage if the sites for the different classification groups come from a range of years, because this will better portray the "average" expected or "target" community for a site, by including both spatial and temporal coverage (R. T. Clarke, personal communication).

Inevitably, trade-offs will need to be made in the manner in which temporal variability is dealt with in predictive modelling, depending upon whether the management goal is aimed at detecting short-term impacts or tracking the health of a river over the long-term. Some combination of approaches (2) and (3) may provide adequate solutions to developing AUSRIVAS models for detecting short-term changes. Whether or not approach (4) and/or the accrual of reference site data over time are implemented specifically to inure models to environmental variability, the approaches can only serve longer term management needs. Regardless, for some geographical regions, temporal variability may be too large for useful predictive models to be developed. For these situations, it may be necessary to use more traditional hypothesis-testing approaches, involving BACI designs and derivatives (Underwood 1991; Faith *et al.* 1995; Keough & Mapstone 1995).

Discussion: sample processing errors

When viewed collectively, and as assessed by external QA/QC, data derived from live-sorting do not appear to meet the objective, as specified at the outset of the MRHI, of maximising taxa recovery (Davies 1994). Rather, live-sort data generally produce a poor recovery of small/cryptic taxa occurring commonly in samples and across sites, and variable recovery rates of taxa, depending upon the efficiency and/or experience of different operators sorting to a time limit (see also Metzeling & Chessman 1996; Growns, Chessman *et al.* 1997). These features of live-sort data suggest that taxa recovery rates for a large proportion of MRHI samples are poor.

The live-sort protocol specified for the MRHI in the period 1994–1996 was a prototype of the methods described by Chessman (1995), Metzeling & Chessman (1996) and Growns, Chessman *et al.* (1997). In relation to the first feature of live-sort data described above, implicit and explicit assumptions are made by these authors about the ready detection, and recovery from samples, of small and encased animals, because of their movement whilst alive. Our results show that even when advice is provided in protocols, at an agency level at least, a generally poor success rate has been achieved by MRHI staff in recovering small and cryptic taxa. None of the researchers cited above, whilst developing rapid biological assessment methods for Australian conditions, appears to have examined their sample residues to determine the nature and extent of possible biases in their proposed live-sort method!

Whilst it is possible that small teams of very experienced biologists can achieve results of the quality purported by these workers, we believe that there are a number of important revisions and training steps required of the existing and recommended protocols (Davies 1994; Chessman 1995; Growns, Chessman *et al.* 1997) before they can be applied further in national biological monitoring programs. Without detailed prescriptive protocols and extensive training, and given the reality of mixed experience staff amongst MRHI agencies and continued turnover in staff, approaches canvassed by Chessman (1995) and Growns, Chessman *et al.* (1997) ask too much of human capability.

Our findings strongly imply that time-based sorting is prone to the variable efficiencies of different operators in recovery of animals, and lend support to the need to prescribe a fixed sample size for retrieval of invertebrates in the live-sorting process, a view also supported by Chessman (1995) and Growns, Chessman *et al.* (1997). This need extends also to laboratory subsampling and sorting. Walsh (1997) advocated "fixed-count" subsampling and sorting procedures in macroinvertebrate studies, noting that this method more faithfully represented the similarity in community structure between samples/treatments than did proportional subsampling and sorting methods.

Chessman (1995) and Growns, Chessman *et al.* (1997) recommended a live-sort sample size of 100 animals for streams in south-eastern Australia. We note that whilst this target might be suitable for small, highly skilled teams of the type tested under controlled field conditions by Growns, Chessman *et al.* (1997), it does not appear to be applicable to MRHI agencies whose staff vary widely in levels of skill and experience, and who operate under a variety of field situations and conditions. Rather, our results from above and elsewhere (Humphrey & Thurtell 1997) suggest that a live-sort sample size of 200 animals should be targeted for relatively "fail-safe" recovery of a broad range of taxa.

As a consequence of the findings reported above, aspects of the live-sort protocol were revised for implementation during the First National Assessment of River Health in Australia (1996–97). The 30-minute time limit for sorting was replaced by a target sample size of 200 animals or sorting for one hour, whichever was reached first. In addition, agency staff were made aware of the taxa commonly missed in samples, so that training programs could be implemented to redress deficiencies. Additional changes to the protocol will follow as the results of further R&D appear.

It is not possible to reprocess live-sorted samples, as these are mostly discarded after sampling. However, it has been recommended to agency staff that poorly sampled sites (identified by low sample size) should be re-sampled to replace reference site data of dubious quality. Indeed, improvement in the procedures for taxa recovery would only stand to benefit ongoing monitoring programs if the quality of data for existing reference sites are also improved through a re-sampling, data replacement and re-modelling program. Until this is done, our simulation studies indicate that models based upon live-sort data gathered up to the end of 1996 will not be as sensitive to impacts as they should be.

Summary of future needs for refinement of AUSRIVAS

Recommendations for further investigations on sample processing procedures and temporal variability may be summarised as follows.

Further needs including R&D for sample processing

An extensive R&D project is required to fully revise live-sort protocols, ensuring more discipline, prescription and training elements to future sampling and sample processing. The outcomes from this research would complement changes already adopted to sample processing procedures, that are referred to above.

Internal and external QA/QC must accompany all future sampling and sample processing by MRHI agencies, so that unacceptable quality can be detected promptly to allow remedial action. Formal approaches to QA/QC, as applied in the UK (van Dijk 1994 and Chapter 5), should be implemented quickly.

Further needs including R&D for temporal variability

It would be useful to refine the predictive relationships of temporal variability and calibrate these to real rates of model predictive failures. Then, statements of risk of model failure associated with the use of AUSRIVAS for different regions can be stipulated in absolute rather than relative terms.

To quantify and possibly account for temporal variability present over most regions of Australia, a selection of reference (and possibly disturbed) sites should be re-sampled through time, to check on the extent of shifts in community composition.

The degree to which temporal variability of macroinvertebrate communities differs in different habitats, and the causes for this, need to be determined. Weatherley & Ormerod (1990) also observed that persistence of invertebrates was greater in riffles than in other habitats and drew attention to the possible management consequences of this observation (e.g. conservation of invertebrates in less stable habitats versus monitoring for pollutant effects in stable habitats).

There is a need to develop a further understanding of macroinvertebrate response to drought and non-drought cycles at all spatial scales (particularly within and amongst classification groups).

Collective needs in accounting for variability and error

Whilst some preliminary data simulations have been undertaken to determine the consequences – to model development and sensitivity – of temporal variability, as well as errors arising in live-sorting, a more complete sensitivity analysis is required to determine the full implications of collective error and variability (at various spatial scales) for model sensitivity. This analysis would include determining the sizes of various sources of error and variation, and their effects on the rates of misclassification to quality bands (*sensu* Clarke, Furse *et al.* 1996; Chapter 3).

Exemplifying the need to examine collective error and variability, the present study of temporal variability would have been improved had replicate data been available for particular sites sampled on particular sampling occasions. Variability over time could then be compared with that associated with replicate samples, the latter being represented by a dissimilarity measure calculated amongst samples and reflecting the combined effects of natural heterogeneity within a site, and error and variability associated with sampling and sample processing. This collective error and variability would then be "subtracted" from observed temporal variability to derive "true" temporal variability (R. T. Clarke, personal communication).

Until the sensitivity of the AUSRIVAS methodology has been fully assessed, and data quantity increased and quality improved, it would be prudent to be cautious in the promotion of AUSRIVAS for site-specific assessments.

Acknowledgements

We are most grateful to Tony Mount of the Environmental Research Institute of the Supervising Scientist (*eriss*) Information Technology section for writing the computer macros used in assessing quality of agency results and in data simulations. Justen Simpson, Richard Norris and Chris Williams at the Cooperative Research Centre for Freshwater Ecology, Canberra, are thanked for providing data, constructing the AUSRIVAS model used for data simulations and providing access to the model on the web. We also thank the staff of the various state and territory agencies, and independent researchers, for providing samples and data upon which to make the assessments. Ben Bayliss of *eriss* expertly prepared Figure 10.1. The paper was improved through the comments and suggestions made to an earlier draft by Ralph Clarke, John Wright and Mike Furse. This project was jointly funded by the Commonwealth Environment, and Primary Industry and Energy Departments through the Land and Water Resources Research and Development Corporation.

CHAPTER 11

The development of the BEAST:
a predictive approach for assessing sediment quality
in the North American Great Lakes

TREFOR B. REYNOLDSON, KRISTIN E. DAY AND TIM PASCOE

National Water Research Institute, Environment Canada, CCIW,
867 Lakeshore Road, Burlington, Ontario, L7R 4A6, CANADA

Summary

Ultimately, the purpose of environmental assessment and management is the maintenance of biological integrity; thus, we suggest that the setting of water and sediment quality objectives should involve the use of biological criteria rather than chemical surrogates. The objective of this study was to develop biological guidelines for sediment assessment in the Great Lakes of North America, based on invertebrate community structure and laboratory responses in terms of survival, growth and reproduction of benthic invertebrates. These guidelines can be used for assessment of sediment in harbours and embayments, for possible remediation, and for assessing sediment removed in navigational or other dredging projects.

345 site visits were made at 245 different sites over the study period (1991–1993) and 162 taxa (genus or species level) were identified. Using cluster analysis and ordination, six groups of sites supporting different communities were identified. Twelve habitat variables were then used in a discriminant model that predicted 88% of a set of test sites to the correct community group. This predictive model for BEnthic Assessment of SedimenT (BEAST) allowed the six community types to be used as the community structure guidelines for comparing test sites against reference sites in multivariate ordination space.

From the reference site data, three toxicological categories were established for each of 10 test end-points, in four species. The categories were: non-toxic, warning of potential toxicity, and toxicity. The delineations for these three categories were developed from the standard statistical parameters of population mean and standard deviation of each end-point, measured in all reference sediments.

Introduction

Environmental managers and regulatory decision-makers have traditionally established water and sediment quality guidelines using chemical concentrations. The primary advantage of a chemical approach is the apparent ease of numerical comparison. Concentrations of chemicals found in sediment are compared with levels of these same compounds that are believed to cause a toxic response in biota. However, the chemical approach has been criticized in recent years because it frequently fails to achieve its objectives (Cairns & van der Schalie 1980; Long & Chapman 1985; Chapman 1986, 1990) or because it is so excessively rigorous that it has limited value (Painter 1992; Zarull & Reynoldson 1992).

Because the purpose of environmental assessment and management is the maintenance of biological integrity, we suggest that the setting of water and sediment quality objectives should involve the use of biological criteria as well as chemical surrogates. Until recently, the development of numeric biological objectives was considered to be too difficult, due to the temporal and spatial variability inherent in biological systems. However, over the past 10 years, multivariate methods developed in the UK (Wright, Moss *et al.* 1984; Armitage, Gunn *et al.* 1987; Moss, Furse *et al.* 1987; Ormerod & Edwards 1987) and elsewhere (Corkum & Currie 1987; Johnson & Wiederholm 1989; Reynoldson, Bailey *et al.* 1995; Parsons & Norris 1996) have been used to predict the community structure of benthic invertebrates in clean (or "uncontaminated") sites, using simple habitat and water quality descriptors. This has been described as the *reference condition approach* (Reynoldson, Norris *et al.* 1997), which allows appropriate site-specific biological objectives to be set for ecosystems, from measured habitat characteristics, and also provides an appropriate reference for determining when degradation is occurring at a site from anthropogenic contamination. The acceptance of biological water and sediment quality objectives by regulatory authorities has been slow, but is now being given serious consideration, as shown by current work in Canada (Reynoldson & Zarull 1993; Reynoldson, Bailey *et al.* 1995); the USA (Hunsaker & Carpenter 1990; Besser, Giesy *et al.* 1996; Canfield, Dwyer *et al.* 1996), the UK (Wright 1995), and recent initiatives in Australia (Parsons & Norris 1996).

Criticisms of the complexity of the multivariate methods used in the reference condition approach have been made (Gerritsen 1995). There is validity to these criticisms in that application of the methods for routine site assessment can be difficult. Consequently, in three of the areas where large reference databases have been developed (Australia, Canada and the UK), complementary software has been produced to make the complex analyses routinely available to environmental managers. In the UK, the RIVPACS software is in a third iteration (Wright 1995). In Australia, the AUSRIVAS software has recently become available (http://enterprise.canberra.edu.au/AusRivAS.nsf). This chapter describes the development of the BEAST software (http://www.cciw.ca//nwri-e/aerb/sediment-remediation/BEAST/) based on a large database that has been assembled from reference sites in the Laurentian Great Lakes.

Methods

The fundamental concept behind the reference condition approach is to establish a database of sites that represent unimpaired conditions (reference sites) at which biological and environmental attributes are measured. The database is then used to: (1) examine and classify the normal variability observed at a series of reference sites – in the case of the Great Lakes this means the development of a classification based on the invertebrate community structure and also the use of information on the functional responses of selected invertebrates to sediment type; (2) develop methods to relate the variability in biological response to environmental attributes at reference sites; (3) develop methods to compare the observed biological conditions at a test site with the expected conditions based on the reference site database.

Selecting reference sites

The objective of this study was to develop biological guidelines to be used for the assessment of sediment in harbours and embayments for possible remediation, or for assessing sediment removed in navigational or other dredging projects. Therefore, the selection criteria for the Great Lakes reference sites were that they should (1) capture the range of biological variability expressed by the benthic invertebrate communities, (2) represent fine-grained sediment environments, (3) be located in shallow nearshore areas and (4) be unimpacted or clean. Seventeen ecodistricts were used to stratify sample sites. Within each ecodistrict, hydrographic charts were used to identify areas having fine-grained sediment material, and boundaries were drawn around those areas indicated on the hydrographic charts as having either a silt or mud substratum. These were identified as regions where sites could be located. Initially, sites were restricted to a maximum of 30 m water depth and within 2 km of shore. However, the absence of fine-grained material up to this depth in some areas required the inclusion of some deeper sites. Areas within 10 km of a point-source effluent discharge (Ontario Ministry of Environment 1990) were excluded as potential reference site locations. Avoidance of areas likely to be affected by nonpoint-source pollution was done using topographic maps to locate areas that had minimal agricultural or urban shoreline development.

Environmental variables

Three categories of environmental variables were measured: (1) geographic descriptors, which were large spatial-scale descriptors of where the site was located; (2) sediment descriptors, which were physical or chemical measurements that would relate to small-scale interactions between the organisms and their surrounding environment; (3) limnological descriptors, which relate the sediment to overlying lake-scale processes. A total of 43 variables was measured (Table 11.1). Details on sample handling, processing and analysis are available in Reynoldson, Bailey *et al.* (1995).

The location of each site was established in the field, using either Loran C or a hand-held Global Positioning System (GPS). Samples of water for chemical analyses were taken using a Van Dorn sampler from 0.5 m above the sediment–water interface. Sediments were characterized from samples taken from either a large box corer (50x50 cm) or mini box corer (40x40 cm). Samples for geochemical analysis were taken from the surface 2 cm of the box core.

Invertebrate community structure

Samples for the identification and enumeration of benthic invertebrates were taken using either a large box corer (1991) or a mini box corer (1992–93). Comparison of matched samples using the two box cores showed no differences in estimates of invertebrate community structure. The intact box core was treated as a section of sediment that has been taken to the surface. This was sampled by inserting five plexiglass tubes 10 cm in length (i.d. 6.5 cm, enclosed area 34.2 cm^2) into the sediment in the box core. Each core tube was considered to be a replicate sample unit. The contents of each core tube were removed and placed in a plastic bag and kept cool until sieved. The contents of each bag were sieved through a 250 μm mesh in the field immediately after sampling, or preserved in 4% formalin. Samples were sorted with a low-power stereo microscope and identified to species or genus level where possible. Slide-mounts of Chironomidae and Oligochaeta were made as required for high-power microscopic identification. Appropriate identification guides were used and voucher specimens of all identified specimens were submitted to experts for confirmation.

Whole sediment toxicity tests with reference sediments

A mini-ponar sampler was used at each site to obtain five separate samples of sediment for use in laboratory bioassays on benthic invertebrates. Care was taken at each site during the sampling process to obtain sediment that was not disrupted by a previous sample collection method. The contents of each mini-ponar were placed in a food-grade plastic bag which was

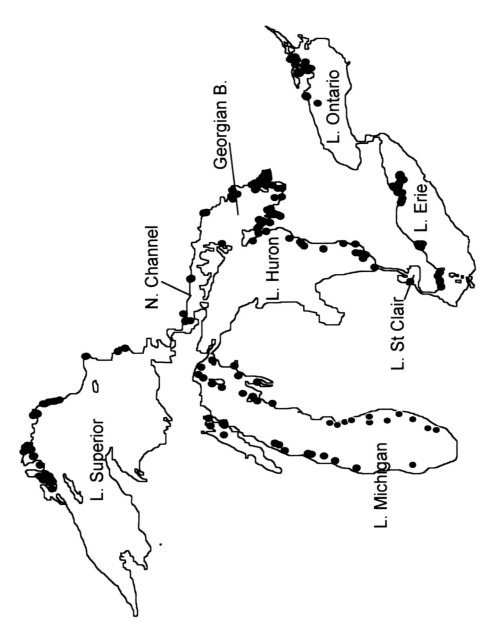

Figure 11.1. Location of reference sites in the Laurentian Great Lakes.

Table 11.1. *Measured environmental variables at reference sites in the Laurentian Great Lakes.*

Measured variable	Rationale	Use as potential predictor
Geographic (5 variables)		
Latitude	Geographic descriptors provide a	Yes
Longitude	synthesis of the effects of spatial	Yes
Lake basin	processes on animal distribution.	No – non-continous.
Ecodistrict		No – non-continuous.
Date		No – temporal effects examined separately.
Limnological (8 variables)		
Water depth	Integrates effects of temperature and oxygen on organisms.	Yes
Dissolved oxygen	Critical for most aerobic organisms.	No – modifed by seasonal processes.
pH	Modifies chemical interactions.	Yes
Temperature	Affects growth and reproductive processes.	No – requires temporal integration.
Alkalinity	Summarizes dissolved materials.	Yes
Total phosphorus	Affects nutrient status and primary producers.	No – modified by anthropogenic inputs.
Kjeldahl nitrogen	Affects primary producers.	No – modified by anthropogenic inputs.
Nitrate/nitrite-nitrogen	Affects primary producers.	No – modified by anthropogenic inputs.
Sediment (30 variables)		
Particle size (7 variables)		
(% gravel, sand, silt, clay, mean size, 75th and 25th percentiles)	Affect burrowing organisms; modify bioavailability of materials.	Yes
Major elements (10 variables) (oxides of Si, Ti, Al, Fe, Mn, Mg, Ca, Na, K, P)	Provide a good descriptor of overall sediment conditions; provide a regional signal.	Yes
Nutrients (4 variables) (TP, TN, loss on ignition, TOC)	Provide an indicator of food availability.	Yes
Metals (9 variables) (Totals for V, Cr, Co, Ni, Cu, Zn, As, Cd, Pb)	Provide a descriptor of anthropogenic inputs and general contaminant levels; allow verification of reference status.	No – modified by anthropogenic inputs.

tightly tied with a plastic tie. All samples of sediment were placed in a cooler on ice until they reached the laboratory. In the laboratory, the bags of sediment were placed in plastic pails with lids and refrigerated at 4°C in the dark until bioassays could be conducted with the sediment.

Sediment toxicity tests were conducted using functional responses as end-points. Four benthic invertebrates were used as test organisms. In three taxa, the non-biting midge *Chironomus riparius,* the amphipod *Hyalella azteca* and the burrowing mayfly *Hexagenia* spp., survival and growth were the end-points. In a fourth taxon, the oligochaete worm *Tubifex tubifex,* survival and reproduction (cocoons/adult, hatch rate, young/adult) were the test end-points. Thus, a total of four lethal and six sublethal end-points were measured.

The culture and testing of *Chironomus riparius, Hexagenia* spp., and *Tubifex tubifex,* are described in Hanes *et al.* (1990), Reynoldson *et al.* (1991), Bedard *et al.* (1992), Day *et al.* (1994) and Reynoldson, Bailey *et al.* (1995). The culture of *Hyalella azteca* was conducted according to the procedure described in Borgmann *et al.* (1989).

Data analysis

Frequency distributions of the toxicity test data on survival, growth and reproduction, for the four test taxa, were plotted as histograms to present a graphical picture of the responses of each organism to a variety of reference sediments collected in the Great Lakes. In addition, the descriptive statistics of mean, median, standard error, standard deviation, maximum and minimum values, and range, were determined for each end-point. The data were tested for normality and homogeneity of variance using SigmaplotRV.1.02 (Jandel Scientific). For purposes of analysis, the data pertaining to percent survival were transformed using the arcsine square root transformation.

The community data were examined using pattern analysis to investigate the structure of the data at the reference sites, and correlation and discriminant function analysis was used to relate the observed biological structure to the environmental characteristics. Structure in the data was examined using two pattern recognition techniques: cluster analysis and ordination. The mean values from the five replicates for the species counts were used as descriptors of biological condition for the classification analysis. The Bray–Curtis association measure was used because it has performed consistently well in a variety of tests and simulations on different types of data (Faith *et al.* 1987). Clustering of the reference sites was done using an agglomerative hierarchical fusion method with unweighted pair-group mean arithmetic averaging (UPGMA). The appropriate number of groups was selected by examining the group structure and, particularly, the spatial location of the groups in ordination space. Ordination was used to reduce the variables required to identify the structure of the data. A non-metric hybrid multi-dimensional scaling (MDS) method of ordination was used, i.e., semi-strong hybrid MDS (Belbin 1991). Hybrid MDS methods use metric and non-metric rank order rather than metric information, and thus provide a robust relationship with ecological distance. They do not assume a linear relationship, an inherent assumption in some dissimilarity measures used by other ordination techniques (Faith *et al.* 1987). This is of particular value when relating ordination scores to environmental characteristics. All clustering and ordination was done using PATN, a pattern analysis software package developed by CSIRO in Australia (Belbin 1992).

Of the 43 environmental variables measured in this study, 26 were examined for their relationship with the biological structure of the data (Table 11.1). We excluded those variables most likely to be influenced by anthropogenic activity, particularly those associated with sediment contamination. Thus, all of the metals were excluded from consideration as potential predictor variables. The variables used were general descriptors of sediment type, such as the major elements and particle size, as well as organic material – a potential indicator of nutritive quality. These, together with physical attributes such as water depth and also water chemistry, were considered as the most appropriate habitat descriptors that would be less prone to modification from human activity.

The relationship with the biological data was examined in two ways, summarized below.

Principal axis correlation (PAC). The procedure was PCC in PATN. This is a multiple-linear regression method that was used to describe how well the environmental data could be fitted to the ordination axes from the species matrix. The method took each environmental attribute and determined the location of the best-fitted vector in ordination space. These are represented as axes on an ordination plot, and a correlation of the axis with the ordination is provided. A Monte Carlo simulation was then performed to establish the statistical significance of the correlations.

Stepwise discriminant analysis (SDA). The procedure was STEPDIS in SAS, used to establish which of the environmental variables best described the biological groupings in the dataset.

Based on the results from these analyses, environmental variables were selected for use in multiple discriminant analysis (MDA), to relate the biological site groupings to the environmental characteristics of the sites. The SAS version of MDA was used with raw environmental data to generate discriminant scores, and to predict the probability of group membership. The more rigorous cross-validation method was used to verify the accuracy of the predictions from the discriminant model. Using this method each of the sites is in turn removed from the dataset, a new model is generated without that site, and then the removed site is predicted to a group. The predicted groupings and actual groupings can then be compared to provide a group and total error rate.

Selection of the optimal predictor variable dataset was done by iteration. Various combinations of predictor variables were selected from the stepwise discriminant analyses and PAC. The optimal set was defined as that with the lowest error rate from cross-validation in discriminant analysis.

Results

During the entire study period (1991–1993) a total of 345 site visits were made to 245 different sites (Fig. 11.1). For the current analyses, sampling was confined to the autumn and 304 samples were collected. They included visits to some sites in more than one of the three years.

Initial screening of the dataset from 304 samples, based on both toxicity and community structure data, resulted in 304 − 52 = 252 samples being included in the reference dataset. The exclusion criteria for 52 samples were: two or more toxicity end-points were below the acceptability criteria (< lower 5th percentile of the distribution), the sample had less than 50% survival for any test species, or the sample did not contain invertebrates. This does not preclude a sample from being reinstated as reference if it is equivalent to reference in future testing.

Invertebrate communities

A total of 162 taxa (genus or species level) were identified from the 252 reference samples from the Great Lakes. Using cluster analysis and ordination, six groups of sites were identified that support different communities; these are summarized in Table 11.2 and in the text below.

Community 1. Characterized by larvae of the midge *Chironomus* spp., and the bivalve mollusc *Dreissena* spp. Another common chironomid midge larva, *Procladius* spp., is also abundant in this community, as is the sphaeriid fingernail clam *Pisidium casertanum*. Numbers of *Chironomus* spp. are significantly ($p < 0.05$) greater than in the other five communities, and the leech *Helobdella stagnalis* is also characteristic of this community. Community 1 contains 29 sites; the majority are located in western and central Lake Erie.

Community 2. Characterized by the fingernail clam *Pisidium casertanum* and the amphipod *Diporeia hoyi*, which is indicative of a more oligotrophic community (Cook & Johnson 1974). Abundance of *D. hoyi* has been identified as an oligotrophic ecosystem objective by the International Joint Commission (Ryder & Edwards 1985). The more oligotrophic nature of Community 2 was also suggested by the location of the sites in ordination space, in which the first dimension represents a trophic and geographic gradient. Community 2 has more taxa (Table 11.2) than the other community groups, but is the least spatially defined. While the majority of sites in this group are located in Georgian Bay, it includes sites from Lakes Erie, Ontario, Huron, Michigan and the North Channel.

Community 3. Characterized by the predatory midge *Procladius* spp. and the fingernail clam *Pisidium casertanum,* but total abundance is generally low. One-half of the sites in this

Table 11.2. Above: *The geographic distribution of samples in the Laurentian Great Lakes (see Fig. 11.1) and the numbers placed in each of six groups (1 to 6) by cluster analysis.* Below: *Taxonomic composition of six corresponding communities, listing the major taxa and mean numbers per 34.2 cm² ± standard deviations.*

Lake	1	2	3	4	5	6
Erie	17	3	11	9	1	0
Ontario	7	6	9	0	2	4
St Clair	1	0	0	0	0	0
Huron	2	4	1	0	6	4
Georgian Bay	0	11	32	0	0	18
North Channel	2	8	11	0	1	14
Michigan	0	7	0	0	22	8
Superior	0	0	0	0	2	29

Taxa	1	2	3	4	5	6
Chironomus spp.	5.7 ± 5.8	0.9 ± 3.1	0.8 ± 1.3	1.3 ± 1.8	0.0	0.1 ± 0.4
Tanytarsus spp.	0.4 ± 1.3	4.7 ± 7.8	0.8 ± 1.5	0.1 ± 0.1	0.1 ± 0.3	0.5 ± 1.5
Heterotrissocladius spp.	0.2 ± 1.1	0.8 ± 2.5	0.0	0.4 ± 0.7	1.2 ± 1.7	1.6 ± 1.8
Procladius spp.	1.5 ± 1.9	1.9 ± 2.3	3.2 ± 2.7	2.0 ± 1.4	0.1 ± 0.3	0.2 ± 0.6
Diporeia hoyi	0.0	2.8 ± 6.2	0.3 ± 0.9	0.0	65.1 ± 41.8	10.4 ± 5.1
Valvata tricarinata	0.2 ± 0.4	0.7 ± 1.9	0.1 ± 0.2	1.7 ± 2.0	0.0	0.0
Dreissena polymorpha	5.1 ± 7.7	0.2 ± 1.0	0.2 ± 0.6	101.4 ± 78.1	0.0 ± 0.1	0.1 ± 0.7
Dreissena bugensis	1.8 ± 7.2	0.0 ± 0.1	0.0	122.8 ± 181.2	0.0	0.0
Pisidium casertanum	2.5 ± 2.8	4.4 ± 8.7	1.0 ± 1.8	0.8 ± 0.8	5.0 ± 8.4	0.6 ± 1.1
Stylodrilus heringianus	0.0	0.8 ± 1.8	0.0	0.0	10.2 ± 8.9	2.0 ± 3.8
Vejdovskyella intermedia	0.2 ± 0.5	2.3 ± 6.5	0.1 ± 0.2	1.5 ± 3.9	1.1 ± 2.0	0.3 ± 1.0
Potamothrix vejdovskyi	0.3 ± 1.2	4.8 ± 14.4	0.0 ± 0.2	6.2 ± 18.2	1.1 ± 3.9	0.1 ± 0.4
Spirosperma ferox	1.5 ± 5.2	4.0 ± 9.6	0.2 ± 0.5	0.4 ± 0.5	0.2 ± 0.7	0.5 ± 0.7
Helobdella stagnalis	0.2 ± 0.3	0.0 ± 0.2	0.0 ± 0.2	0.3 ± 0.3	0.0	0.0

community are from Georgian Bay; other sites are from Lake Erie (eastern basin) and the North Channel.

Community 4. This community occurs at only nine sites and these are dominated by very high numbers of two invading bivalve molluscs, *Dreissena polymorpha* and *D. bugensis*. However, Community 4 is similar to Community 1 with regard to the other taxa present. Both the location of the sites in Lake Erie, and their position in ordination space, suggest that these two communities are typical of the more mesotrophic Lake Erie (Table 11.2).

Communities 5 and 6. Both represent a *Diporeia hoyi/Stylodrilus heringianus* assemblage, the major differences between these two communities and all others being the greater abundance of the two species of worms, and the presence of the oligotrophic chironomid *Heterotrissocladius* spp. Community 5 has a higher abundance of both *Diporeia* and *Stylodrilus* than Community 6, but *Heterotrissocladius* is slightly less important numerically. Community 5 is primarily found in Lake Michigan. Community 6 occurs at the largest number of sites (77) and includes more than 90% of the Lake Superior sites, together with a large number of Georgian Bay and the North Channel sites (Table 11.2).

Relationship with habitat structure

Table 11.3. *Relationship between environmental variables and species, based on principal axis correlation (PAC) and stepwise discriminant analysis (SDA).*

Variable	Stepwise discriminant analysis		Principal axis correlation
	Partial r^2	Probability	r
Depth	0.519	0.0001	0.7458 (sig. p <0.01)
Latitude	0.405	0.0001	0.6496 (sig. p <0.01)
Total nitrogen (sediment)	0.216	0.0001	0.4131 (sig. p <0.01)
Alkalinity (water)	0.196	0.0001	0.5183 (sig. p <0.01)
K_2O (sediment)	0.098	0.0001	0.3138 (sig. p <0.01)
Longitude	0.085	0.0007	0.5639 (sig. p < 0.01)
CaO (sediment)	0.064	0.0066	0.4650 (sig. p <0.01)
MgO (sediment)	0.089	0.0004	0.2436 (sig. p <0.01)
pH (water)	0.065	0.0063	0.1815 (ns. p >0.01)
MnO (sediment)	0.054	0.0216	0.1362 (ns. p >0.01)
SiO_2 (sediment)	0.056	0.0170	0.3449 (sig.p <0.01)

Table 11.4. *Estimated error rates for discriminant models at species level, constructed using three sets of 11, 18 and 12 variables measured in the Laurentian Great Lakes.*

Selection method for variables:	Stepwise discriminant analysis	Principal axis correlation	Optimal iteration
Variables used:	11 (depth, lat., long., alk(w), pH, TN, K_2O, CaO, MgO, MnO, SiO_2)	18 (depth, lat., long., alk(w), TN, TP, TOC, LOI, CaO, Al_2O_3, SiO_2, K_2O, MgO, Na_2O, silt, sand, clay, particle size 75 percentile)	12 (depth, lat., long., alk(w), pH, TN, TOC, K_2O, CaO, MgO, MnO, SiO_2)
Total error rate for 252 samples:	32.4%	35.8%	30.1%
Error rates for a 20-site subset:			
Group 1 (n = 2)	0.00	0.00	0.00
Group 2 (n = 3)	0.00	0.33	0.00
Group 3 (n = 5)	0.40	0.60	0.40
Group 4 (n = 1)	0.00	0.00	0.00
Group 5 (n = 3)	0.00	0.00	0.00
Group 6 (n = 6)	0.33	0.33	0.33
Total error rate:	0.12	0.20	0.12

From PAC, 18 of the 26 variables considered as suitable predictor variables were significantly correlated (p <0.01) with the species ordination matrix. Eleven variables were selected by SDA (Table 11.3) as descriptors of the group structure. Two of these variables, pH (water) and MnO (sediment) were not significantly correlated with the species ordination matrix from PAC. From the relationship between site habitat attributes and species composition, a model can be constructed that allows a prediction to be made of the type of community assemblage that should occur at fine-grained nearshore locations within the Great Lakes basin. The predictive model is based on discriminant function analysis. This statistical method enables one to distinguish between two or more "groups", using a set of discriminating variables. In this case the "groups" have been established on species composition, and are defined as *community types;* the *discriminating variables* are a set of habitat attributes that are minimally affected by human activity.

The results (Table 11.4) for three models show little difference in total error rates between the stepwise (32.4%) and optimal models (30.1%). The third model, based on variables selected from principle axis correlation, was less accurate, with a total error rate of 35.8%. The optimal model uses 12 variables that are easily measured and describe geographic location (latitude and longitude), simple sediment attributes (TOC, total nitrogen and oxides of potassium, calcium, magnesium, manganese and silica) and general limnological conditions (water depth, alkalinity and pH of the water 0.5 m above the sediment–water interface). In an independent test using 20 sites, this model, and the stepwise model, predicted 88% of the test sites to the correct community group (Table 11.4).

Assessing impact

While there are a number of possible approaches for comparing reference sites and one or more test sites, our approach is again a multivariate method in which the entire community assemblage can be used. In this method the reference sites for the community type to which the test sites have been allotted are reordinated with the test sites and plotted in ordination space. The distribution of the reference sites provides the range of variation in unimpaired communities. By constructing probability ellipses based on the reference sites only, the community at the test sites can be compared with the range of conditions found amongst those reference sites with which the test site has the greatest probability of belonging. The greater the departure from reference state, as measured in ordination space, then the greater the difference from the reference condition. However, determining the degree of impairment, and what departure from the reference state is unacceptable, is ultimately a subjective decision.

A large river quality survey, conducted in the UK in 1990, provided the impetus for the development of methods to circumscribe the continuum of responses into a series of bands that represented grades of biological quality, from good to poor (Wright, Furse *et al.* 1991). Despite the simplification, it was seen as an appropriate mechanism for obtaining a simple statement of biological quality, allowing broad comparisons in either space or time that would be useful for management purposes.

We have adopted a similar approach for defining degrees of difference from the reference condition, using a multivariate approach, and based upon three probability ellipses (Fig. 11.2) constructed around reference sites. Sites inside the smallest ellipse (90% probability) would be considered *equivalent to reference;* sites between the smallest and next ellipse (99% probability) would be considered *possibly different;* sites between the 99% probability and the largest ellipse (99.9% probability) would be considered *different,* and sites located outside the 99.9% ellipse would be designated as *very different.*

Toxicity end-points and target values

Several statistical analyses were conducted in an attempt to correlate the responses for each end-point, and each species, with sediment characteristics such as particle-size distribution, TOC, LOI (loss on ignition), MgO, SiO_2, TP, TN, etc., for the reference sites. Both univariate (regression analysis with single variables) and multivariate statistics were used to determine if the range in any given response for a particular species in clean sediments could be correlated with specific characteristics of sediments. Although some trends were noted, especially with

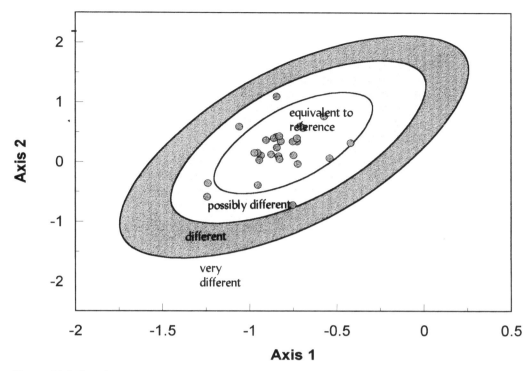

Figure 11.2. Impairment stress levels derived for reference sites in hybrid multi-dimensional scaling ordination space. Four bands, based on ellipses for 90%, 99% and 99.9% probability, are identified as: (1) equivalent to reference; (2) possibly different; (3) different; (4) very different.

regard to growth and percent silt or total organic content (TOC) in sediment, statistical significance with a single parameter could not be demonstrated. It was concluded that the range in each end-point, noted for the reference sediment dataset, represents the natural range in the responses of each organism in laboratory bioassays. Based on these results, a decision was made to treat each response for a species as a continuum of data points with a range, rather than to separate the responses into groups using multivariate analyses.

Chironomus riparius. Mean survival of *C. riparius* in 212 reference sediments was 85.9%, with a range of 53.5 to 100% and a coefficient of variation (CV) of 10.2%. Only 4.7% of the reference sediments, collected over the 3-year period from all five of the Great Lakes, caused mortality of *C. riparius* to be greater than 30%. American Society for Testing and Materials (1994) have set a minimum acceptable criterion of 70% for survival of *Chironomus* spp. in uncontaminated sediments used in toxicity tests. Our results show that this criterion is achievable in the majority of sediments collected from reference areas in the Great Lakes. The few reference sediments for which survival was below 70% were well within the 1 in 20 results that would fall outside the 95% confidence limits for any given test.

Growth of larval chironomids in a variety of reference sediments with a range of physico-chemical characteristics was variable, with dry weight of individual 4th-instar larvae at test termination (10 days) ranging from 0.19 to 0.60 mg, with a mean of 0.35 and a CV of 20.6%. All attempts to correlate this variability in growth with sediment characteristics were negative, although some parameters in the reference sediments, such as TOC, percent sand, percent clay, total nitrogen, total phophorus and concentrations of lead, zinc, and copper, were implicated in both single-parameter regressions and multivariate analyses.

Hyalella azteca. As with midge larvae, survival of juvenile *H. azteca* in 212 reference sediments was good, with a range of 52.0 to 100%, a mean of 87.5% and a CV of 10.6%. However, in 18.4% of the sediments tested, survival was below the minimum acceptable criterion of 80% which has been set for *H. azteca* in control sediments in a 10-day lethality test by ASTM (1994).

The growth of 3 to 9 day-old *H. azteca* in reference sediments with a variety of physico-chemical characteristics over a 28-day exposure to sediments, was more variable than growth in the midge bioassay, and ranged from 0.10 to 0.80 mg dry wt per juvenile amphipod, with a CV of 26.5%. A negative correlation with percent clay in the sediments was noted.

Hexagenia spp. Percent survival of larvae (nymphs) of the mayfly *Hexagenia* was excellent in all types of sediment (167 sites) and ranged from 66.0 to 100%, with a mean of 98.0% and a CV of 5.5%.

Growth of larvae during the 21-day test was more variable than survival, and ranged from 0.5 to 6.4 mg dry wt per individual with a CV of 34.0%. Strong positive correlations with LOI, TOC, TN, TP and SiO_2, as well as negative correlations with percent sand and percent silt, were noted in regressions.

Tubifex tubifex. Survival of adult *T. tubifex* was usually 100% in all bioassays with reference sediments (167 sites); only 3.6% of tested sediments recorded mortality between 10 and 20%. Based on these results, the acceptability criterion for percent survival of adult worms in nontoxic sediments can be set at >90%. Percent hatch of cocoons was also fairly high and constant, with a mean of 58±10% and a CV of 17.3%. The acceptability criterion for percent hatch of cocoons is thus set at >35%. The number of cocoons produced per adult worm was consistent, with a range of 4.8 to 14.5, a mean of 9.9 and a CV of 13.8%.

Categories of response to potential toxicity. As the purpose of a toxicity test with whole sediment is to determine if the biological response(s) of a cohort of organisms exposed to potentially contaminated sediment differ from the response(s) of a similar cohort of organisms to a negative control or reference sediment, the data from the reference sites were used to establish three categories of responses to test sediments. The three categories were: non-toxic, a warning of potential toxicity, and toxic. The delineations for the three categories were developed from the standard statistical parameters of population mean and standard deviation for an end-point measured in all reference sediments (Table 11.5). For each end-point, the non-toxic category was set at two standard deviations below the mean for the reference dataset; this represents the 95% confidence limit for that response (Table 11.5). At the 95% confidence level, 1 in 20 results (5%) would be expected to fall outside the limits by chance alone. The toxic category was set at three standard deviations below the mean of an end-point, which represents the 99.7% confidence limit (Table 11.5). At this confidence level, the probability of data falling outside the limits by chance alone is only 0.3% (one out of every 333 tests). The range of responses between two and three times the standard deviation represent the "warning of potential toxicity" category, and would indicate sediments that have some detrimental effects.

Table 11.5. *Criteria for determining three categories of toxicity for nearshore sediments of the Laurentian Great Lakes.*

Limits given for Category 1 (non-toxic) are 2×SD above and below the means (the upper limits indicate exceptionally high growth or reproduction). Limits given for Category 3 (toxic) are 3×SD above and below the means. Limits for Category 2 (warning of potential toxicity) are interposed between those of the non-toxic and toxic categories. Further explanation in the text.

Test species	Category 1 Non-toxic	Category 2 Warning	Category 3 Toxic
Chironomus riparius			
% survival	≥69.0	60.0 – 68.9	< 60.0
Growth	0.21 – 0.49	0.14 – 0.20	< 0.14
Hyalella azteca			
% survival	≥69.0	60.0 – 68.9	< 60.0
Growth	0.24 – 0.76	0.11 – 0.23	< 0.11
Hexagenia spp.			
% survival	≥85.0	80.0 – 84.9	< 80.0
Growth	1.00 – 5.00	0 – 0.99	—
Tubifex tubifex			
% survival	≥88.0	81.0 – 89.8	< 81.0
% hatch	37.8 – 78.2	27.7 – 37.7	< 27.7
No. of cocoons/worm	7.1 – 12.7	5.7 – 7.0	< 5.7
No. of young/worm	11 – 47	2.0 – 10.9	< 2.0

Applying the guidelines: the BEAST software

Employing the reference condition approach for the benthic assessment of sediment has the potential to provide an alternative to current environmental guidelines and criteria. It has been suggested that multivariate methods such as those developed in this chapter are too complex, require specialised practitioners, and are difficult to convey to managers and the public (Gerritsen 1995). However, limitations associated with multivariate methods can be attributed to the lack of a comprehensive tool for application. To date, those wishing to employ multivariate methods for sediment analysis have required several expensive and cumbersome software packages in order to achieve their goals.

The need for a simple, inexpensive software tool which encapsulates the requirements for multivariate analysis, has led to the development of the BEAST. Designed exclusively for the BEnthic Assessment of SedimenT, the software automates the methodology outlined in this account. Employing the RAISON Mapping and Analysis package from Environment Canada as a foundation, the BEAST combines new methods with a simple, software user-interface. The result is a powerful new tool for sediment analysis (Fig. 11.3).

Conceptual software design

The conceptual design for the BEAST calls for seven modules surrounding a central core of data (Fig. 11.3). The first module is a method for automating the entry of data to be compared with the reference database. Data in the BEAST are stored in an easily accessible, standard format, to limit the problems normally associated with complex datasets. Once data to be analyzed by the BEAST have been entered, data handling and statistical modules are required. One model predicts the reference group membership of each test site, using established predictor variables. The next is responsible for combining each test site with the appropriate

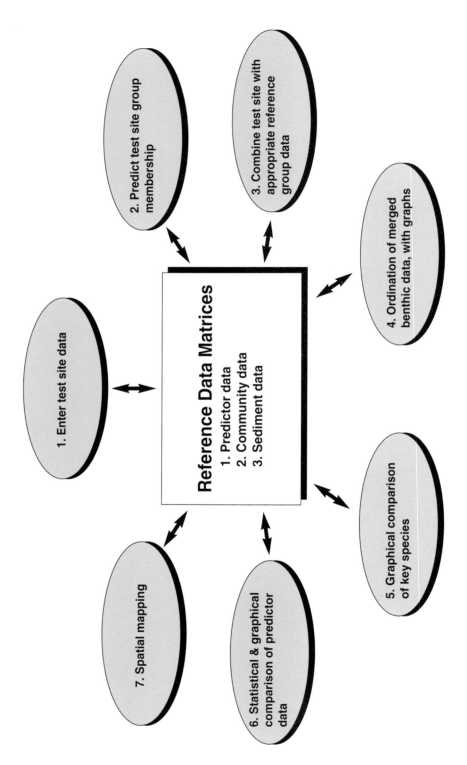

Figure 11.3. Components of the BEAST software package, developed for the Laurentian Great Lakes.

group of reference sites. The analysis of a test site's community structure is the fourth module. The final three modules are responsible for graphic analysis and comparison of results from the BEAST.

Data entry and storage

Microsoft™ Access file formats have been adopted for information storage and retrieval. A widely available relational database, Access is designed to accommodate the large, complex datasets common to benthic analysis. All of the data related to BEAST operation are stored in this format.

Entry of test data to the BEAST is achieved through the Benthic Information system for Reference Conditions (BIRC). Developed using Microsoft™ Access, BIRC is an automated data entry/management tool which provides a simple graphic user-interface and is available as stand-alone software. Data entry errors are reduced significantly by providing validation routines to ensure that data falls within acceptable ranges, and conforms to previously established formats and standards.

Unlike many other software packages, the manual generation of complex input files for analysis is also eliminated by BIRC. Test data can be selected by a user, and a database file containing all of the information – in the proper format for successful BEAST analysis – is automatically generated and placed in the appropriate location.

The BEAST is also designed to maintain any number of reference datasets, without the need for continual updating of the software itself. When a new reference database is developed (e.g. the Fraser River; see Chapter 12), the resulting Access file can be placed in the same directory as other reference database files within the BEAST file structure. Once there, it is automatically available for analysis in the BEAST.

The BEAST software

The BEAST maintains information for various analyses in a hierarchical format. The first step in analysis is the creation of a *project* with a unique name. Projects in the BEAST act as a container, establishing which reference and test databases are to be used each time the project is opened, and storing the results of analyses. Any number of projects can be maintained within the BEAST simultaneously, and can be deleted when they are no longer needed.

A project in the BEAST also has a subset of containers within it, called *scenarios.* Scenarios represent variations on the analysis of test data contained within a single project. Although the BEAST supplies an optimal set of predictor variables for MDA, some cases may occur where these variables are not available to the user. In these cases, the user must employ alternative variables, and the results for each of these discriminant models is stored as a scenario. This permits the user to compare the error rates of various discriminant analyses, and select the most accurate procedure for use in the BEAST.

Results from BEAST analysis can be viewed in several different ways. Error rates and probabilities of prediction to group are generated in a table format. Using the RAISON mapping engine, thematic maps of group membership and toxicology for each site can be produced. Bar graphs, comparing key species and environmental variables for a test site against the average for the most appropriate reference group, can be generated. Finally, bivariate probability ellipse plots can be displayed, showing the location of a test site in ordination space, in relation to the associated reference sites.

Concluding remarks

The process of determining whether an invertebrate community is impaired involves three stages: (1) sampling the community and measuring the predictor variables at the site of interest; (2) running the discriminant model with the reference database and one or more test sites to predict the expected community at each site; (3) comparing test sites with the reference sites, based on the group to which each test site was predicted to belong.

Once a site has been predicted to a community group, the species composition at the test site(s) is compared with the species composition at the equivalent reference sites. A data-file is constructed that includes the species counts for the appropriate reference sites and test sites. This is ordinated so that a matrix is calculated for reference and test sites. The sites can then be plotted in ordination space, showing the ordination dimensions that synthesise the biological attributes of the sites. Probability ellipses are calculated *only* for the reference sites. The location of each test site relative to the reference sites can then be determined. The assessment of the quality of a test site is based on all the ordination vectors, and the overall assessment of a site is based on its furthest distance from the swarm of reference sites in ordination space. The scale of the response, and the species that have been lost, determine the degree of difference between reference and test.

The assessment of the contribution of sediment toxicity to changes in community structure, using multiple end-points, is simplified by the use of criteria that rank sediment as non-toxic, potentially toxic, or toxic, based on data from multiple reference sites.

Acknowledgements

We wish to thank the following individuals without whom this study could not have been completed: Sue Humphrey of Ontario Region, Environment Canada, whose efforts provided the resources by which this study was conducted; Danielle Milani and Cheryl Clark who performed most of the sediment toxicity tests; Craig Logan and Scott Hughson who sorted and identified the invertebrate samples; Dave Lam and Isaac Wong who converted our concepts into software. We also thank John Wright, John Hilton and Mike Furse for making possible the preparation of this contribution.

CHAPTER 12

Establishing reference conditions in the Fraser River catchment, British Columbia, Canada, using the BEAST (BEnthic Assessment of SedimenT) predictive model

DAVID M. ROSENBERG[1], TREFOR B. REYNOLDSON[2] AND VINCENT H. RESH[3]

[1]*Department of Fisheries and Oceans, Freshwater Institute, 501 University Crescent, Winnipeg, MB R3T 2N6, CANADA*

[2]*National Water Research Institute, Environment Canada, CCIW, 867 Lakeshore Road, Burlington, ON L7R 4A6, CANADA*

[3]*Department of Environmental Science, Policy & Management, 201 Wellman Hall, University of California, Berkeley, CA 94720, USA*

Summary

A biomonitoring program based on the BEAST predictive model is described for the Fraser River, British Columbia, Canada. The BEAST model is a three-stage multivariate approach to establishing reference conditions. Reference sites (representative of the "best available condition") were chosen using ecoregions and stream orders within ecoregions. A small number of test sites (suspected of being impacted) were used for comparison with the reference sites when developing the model. Environmental variables representing map, site, channel and water-column scales were measured at each site. Single macroinvertebrate samples were collected from riffle habitats at each site using a kicknet sampler (400-µm mesh) for 3 minutes. Sites in the Fraser River catchment were sampled in the autumn of 1994, 1995 and 1996. Results from the 1994 and 1995 field seasons used 127 reference sites and produced five reference groups based on macroinvertebrate community structure. Ten optimum predictor variables were identified for matching new sites to the appropriate reference group, and included map, site, channel and water-column measurements. The error rate for predicting test sites to particular reference groups in cross-validation studies was 37%. The model was capable of discriminating the most impacted of the test sites used.

Introduction

Traditional methods of establishing control sites in field-oriented biomonitoring studies of water quality are largely limited to areas upstream of impacts in lotic waters, and areas near impacts in lentic waters. Such designs are often "confounded" (Eberhardt 1978; Hurlbert 1984). Moreover, reliance on only one or a few control sites is problematic because of limited capacity to extrapolate to other locations, limited ability to calculate variance estimates, and difficulties in addressing problems of a nonpoint-source nature (Hughes 1995).

The reference condition approach offers a powerful alternative to the above-described traditional methods because the sites themselves serve as replicates; this is in contrast to the multiple collections within sites that are the replicates in designs using inferential statistics (Reynoldson, Norris *et al.* 1997). We define the "reference condition" as being ". . . *representative of a group of minimally disturbed sites organized by selected physical, chemical and biological characteristics"* (Reynoldson, Norris *et al.* 1997).

In this study, we use the BEAST model (BEnthic Assessment of SedimenT) (Reynoldson, Bailey *et al.* 1995; Reynoldson, Norris *et al.* 1997; and see Chapter 11), in which an array of reference sites characterizes the biological condition of a region, and a test site is compared with an appropriate subset of reference sites. The probability of a test site belonging to each of the subsets or classification groups is determined, and the test site is assigned to the highest probability group. In other multivariate models based on the reference condition approach, the probabilities are computed for a test site being a member of each classification group, and the prediction for the test site is weighted in relation to the probabilities for each classification group (RIVPACS (Wright 1995 and Chapters 1 to 3) and AUSRIVAS (Parsons & Norris 1996, and Chapters 9 to 11)). Another reference condition approach, multimetrics (e.g. Barbour *et al.* 1995; Barbour, Gerritsen *et al.* 1996) is considered in Chapters 13 and 19.

The reference condition approach is well-suited for large-scale biomonitoring programs because reference sites can be scattered throughout the catchment. Furthermore, local knowledge and expertise, published information, or simple reconnaissance trips, can be used to identify sites that represent "best available condition" for use in building the reference site model. The model can represent either a one-time investment (Rosenberg *et al.* 2000) or it can be continually improved (e.g. Wright 1995). The reference condition approach already forms the basis of large-scale biomonitoring programs in the UK (e.g. Wright 1995), Australia (e.g. Parsons & Norris 1996) and Canada (Reynoldson, Bailey *et al.* 1995). The objective of this contribution is to describe a Canadian program on the Fraser River, British Columbia (BC), one of Canada's largest rivers, and to report results from the first two years of field research. We include a description of the biotic groups formed from the reference sites, and an assessment of sites suspected of being impacted.

The Fraser River catchment

The Fraser River catchment (Fig. 12.1) covers *ca* 230,000 km^2 or 25% of British Columbia (BC Ministry of Environment, Lands and Parks and Environment Canada 1993). The Fraser River mainstem (>1350 km long) has a mean annual discharge of 3620 m^3 s^{-1}, which makes it the fourth largest river in Canada after the St Lawrence (10,800 m^3 s^{-1}), the Mackenzie (9910 m^3 s^{-1}) and the Yukon (6370 m^3 s^{-1}) (Dynesius & Nilsson 1994). Two-thirds of British Columbia's population, or *ca* 1,700,000 people, live in the Fraser catchment, mostly in its southern regions.

The Fraser River mainstem is one of the last unregulated large rivers of North America. However, the catchment has a variety of land-use and management problems, which include forest harvest and pulp mills throughout the catchment, widespread agricultural activities (e.g. ranching, fruit growing and other crops), flow regulation for hydroelectric power generation on some of the tributaries, and urban development in the lower Fraser River, near Vancouver (Richardson & Healey 1996). Mining, fishing and wilderness recreation and tourism are additional pressures (Environment Canada 1995). All of these activities pose a threat to the health of the Fraser River ecosystem, a fact recognized by the establishment of the Fraser River Action Plan (FRAP) in 1991 by Environment Canada (Environment Canada 1995). The research described in this chapter was funded by the FRAP, to address the problem of pollution in the Fraser River by developing a biomonitoring program for water quality assessment. The

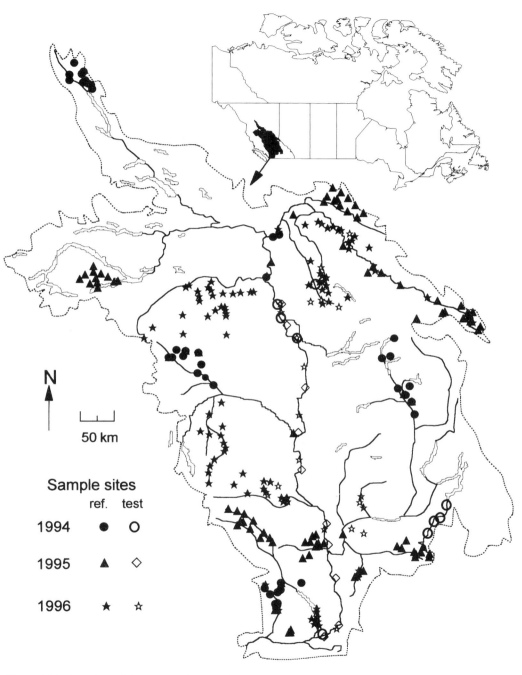

Figure 12.1. Location of the Fraser River catchment in British Columbia, Canada, showing the mainstem river, major tributaries and sampling sites (1994–1996). ref. = reference site.

Fraser River is the first Canadian river to which the reference condition approach, using benthic macroinvertebrates, has been applied.

Methods

Design of the program

The multivariate methods used to match test sites to a subset of reference sites require a substantial initial investment in sufficient sites to characterize both the different conditions in a catchment and the variability associated with these conditions. Generally, *ca* 250 sites are required to characterize variability adequately, and to build appropriate predictive models (e.g. see Reynoldson, Bailey *et al.* 1995; Wright 1995). A small set of additional (test) sites, which may or may not be impacted, is included to verify performance of the reference site model during its development. A minimum ratio of five reference sites to one test site is recommended because the BEAST combines test and reference sites in a new ordination matrix, so the test sites will affect the distribution of reference sites in ordination space (see below; Reynoldson, Norris *et al.* 1997).

Two spatial scales, ecoregion and stream order within an ecoregion, were used to maximize the diversity of sites chosen. The ecoregion scale ensured the inclusion of different climatic and landscape conditions, whereas the stream-order scale ensured that a range of hydraulic conditions was included (Rosenberg *et al.* 2000). A series of workshops with local experts served to identify subcatchments that were unimpacted and those that had different degrees of impact. Reference and test sites were randomly selected from the appropriate subcatchments (Rosenberg *et al.* 2000).

Two temporal scales, annual and seasonal, were also examined. Most of the reference sites were visited only once, in the autumn, because of the large geographic scale of the study. The autumn period was chosen because it is a low-water period in the long-term hydrograph of the Fraser River, which is important in terms of accessibility to streams in the catchment. Thus, our intent was to examine the effects of annual and seasonal variability on the accuracy of the predictive model. Annual variation was examined by re-sampling *ca* 10% of sites visited initially, in the second and third years of the study. Seasonal variation was examined by sampling six sites monthly over a 2-year period (Dymond 1998). Preliminary results of the seasonal study indicated unpredictable effects of season on the predictive models, so Dymond (1998) recommended that sampling should be restricted to the autumn or done over multiple seasons. However, the overall results of temporal investigations are not available at this time and will be reported elsewhere.

Site selection

Thirty-nine subcatchments (including the Fraser River mainstem) were sampled over the 3-year field study (Rosenberg *et al.* 2000). Fifteen of these were reference (unimpacted) subcatchments. The Fraser mainstem flows through seven ecoregions; tributaries individually flow through a maximum of three ecoregions. A maximum of seven stream orders was sampled in a subcatchment.

A total of 266 sites (233 reference, 33 test) was visited over three years (Fig. 12.1): 46 in 1994 (37 reference, 9 test), 99 in 1995 (90 reference, 9 test) and 121 in 1996 (106 reference, 15 test). In addition, nine sites were re-sampled in 1995 and 1996 to measure annual variability. Thus, the sampling program approximated the target level of 250 reference sites, and it achieved the guideline of a 5:1 ratio of reference to test sites (the actual ratio was *ca* 7:1).

Test sites came from the Fraser mainstem (pulp and paper mill impacts), the Salmon River (agricultural impacts), and the Willow River (logging impacts). For the Fraser mainstem sites, FRA13 is *ca* 50 km downstream of Prince George and its pulp mills; FRA14 is *ca* 100 km downstream of Prince George and *ca* 10 km upstream of Quesnel; FRA16 is *ca* 20 km downstream of the pulp mill at Quesnel; FRA28 is *ca* 400 km further downstream, at Hope, and away from pulp mill influences. For the Salmon River sites, SAL1 is upstream of most agricultural activity, which progressively increases downstream from SAL2 to SAL4. Three replicated samples taken at SAL3, as part of an earlier sampling design, were included. A single test site came from the logged-over Willow River (WIL1).

Environmental variables measured

Environmental variables are used to relate habitat conditions to subsets of sites selected, based on similarities in macroinvertebrate communities, and to build the predictive model for matching new sites to the appropriate subset of reference sites (see below). An optimum set of predictor variables cannot be determined *a priori,* so a maximum number of likely variables had to be chosen beforehand. Those variables came from previously published multivariable studies that examined the relationship between environmental characteristics and community structure of lotic benthic macroinvertebrates. The list of variables was discussed, amended and supplemented at the initial Fraser River workshop (Rosenberg *et al.* 2000). The final list (Table 12.1) was measured at all sites, using methods described in Rosenberg *et al.* (2000).

Variability of environmental measurements was assessed by sampling 26 (*ca* 10%) of the sites in triplicate. Coefficients of variation (CV) were calculated for each site, and overall mean CVs were calculated for each variable measured.

Table 12.1. *The environmental variables measured in the Fraser River biomonitoring program, listed under various scales (map, site, channel and water).*

(1) Diameter (cm) of the dominant substratum: one of seven categories at each site (>0.1–0.2; 0.2–0.5; 0.5–2.5; 2.5–5.0; 5.0–10.0; 10.0–25.0; >25 cm), averaged for all sites in a group.

(2) Diameter of the next dominant substratum (see note (1) above).

(3) Degree of exposure of the dominant substratum: one of five categories ranging from completely embedded (score = 1) to unembedded (score = 5) at each site, averaged for all sites in a group.

Map	Site	Channel	Water
Latitude	Date of sampling	Wetted width	pH
Longitude	Flow state	Mean channel depth	Dissolved oxygen
Altitude	Macrophyte cover	Maximum channel depth	Conductivity
Ecoregion	Riparian vegetation (%)	Bankfull width	Temperature
Stream order	[grasses, shrubs,	Slope	Total phosphorus
	deciduous, coniferous]	Water velocity [mean, max.]	Nitrate-nitrite and
	Canopy cover	Framework[1]	Kjeldahl nitrogen
	Extent of logging in	Matrix[2]	Alkalinity
	riparian zone	Interstitial material (%)	Total suspended
		[silt/clay, sand, gravel]	solids
		Embeddedness[3]	
		Periphyton biomass	
		Periphyton chlorophyll-*a*	

Community structure of benthic macroinvertebrates

Benthic macroinvertebrates were collected from the riffle areas of small streams and the cobble shoulders of large streams/rivers using a triangular kicknet (38.5 cm on each side), as described by Rosenberg, Davies *et al.* (1977). The kicknet was inexpensive to construct, durable and easy to transport and use. A series of calibration studies revealed that a single sample per site, collected for 3 minutes using a 400 μm mesh, provided an optimal combination of taxon recovery and cost effectiveness (Rosenberg *et al.* 2000).

Samples were subsampled using a Marchant box (Marchant 1989), and the first 200 specimens, located at random in the box, were counted (see Rosenberg *et al.* 2000 for details). Barbour & Gerritsen (1996) reported that fixed-count subsampling discriminated better than other subsampling methods, including fractions, in a study of Florida lakes. A subsample containing 200 organisms required about 4 hours to sort and identify, which represented *ca* 1/30 of the time required to process three full replicates from each site.

The eventual need for non-specialists to identify benthic macroinvertebrates is a special concern of the Fraser River study. Only results from the family level are reported here, but a final calibration step will involve a comparison of the efficacy of identification at family level and lower taxa (mostly genus and species) for establishment of site groups and in model development.

Reference condition statistics

A three-stage procedure (Reynoldson, Bailey *et al.* 1995) was used to analyze the Fraser River data.

Stage 1. Pattern recognition techniques (cluster analysis and ordination) were used to describe the biological structure of reference site data. The Bray–Curtis association measure was used to describe the species matrix because it performs well under a variety of conditions (Faith *et al.* 1987). Clustering was done using an agglomerative hierarchical fusion method with unweighted pair-group mean arithmetic averaging (UPGMA). Groups were selected by examining group structure and spatial location of the groups in ordination space. Ordination (semi-strong hybrid multidimensional scaling; Belbin 1991) was used to reduce the variables required to identify structure of the data. All clustering and ordination was done using PATN (Belbin 1992).

Stage 2. The observed biological structure was related to environmental variables. Variables that were most likely to be influenced by anthropogenic activity (e.g. total phosphorus and chlorophyll-*a*) were excluded from the analysis. The relationship was examined in three ways.

(a). Principal axis correlation (PAC) in PATN – a multiple-linear regression method that determines how well a set of attributes (environmental variables) can be fitted to an ordination matrix space (the species). The method determines the orientation of the best-fit vectors for each environmental variable in ordination space. These vectors can be represented as axes on an ordination plot, and correlation values of axes with the ordination are provided. Monte Carlo simulations can be used to establish the statistical significance of the correlations.

(b). ANOVA in SAS – to identify the environmental variables that differed significantly among biological groups.

(c). Stepwise discriminant analysis (STEPDIS in SAS) – to identify the variables that best described the biological groups (and to minimize effects of auto-correlation among those variables).

Key environmental variables, identified by the above three analyses, were used in multiple discriminant analysis (MDA in SAS) to relate the biological groups to environmental variables. Untransformed environmental data were used to generate discriminant scores and to predict the probability of group membership of individual sites. Cross-validation was used to verify the accuracy of predictions from the discriminant model. In this method, each of the sites is in turn removed from the dataset, a model is generated without that site and then the group to which the site belongs is allocated probabilistically. Allocated and actual groups are then compared to provide group and total error rates based on the percentage of sites allocated correctly.

The optimal set of predictor variables was chosen by iteration. Various combinations of predictor variables were selected from the stepwise discriminant analyses and principal axis correlations. The set of variables having the lowest error rate was regarded as optimal.

Stage 3. The final stage is devoted to assessing the biological condition (i.e. equivalent to reference or impacted) of new sites tested. The first step is to assign the new site to one of the reference groups by comparing community composition of the benthic macroinvertebrates. Values of the optimal predictor variables are used to assign the new site to one of the reference groups, using a multiple discriminant analysis (PROC DISCRIM in SAS). Reference sites are then combined with the new site to create a new data-matrix, which is ordinated using semi-strong hybrid multidimensional scaling (see Stage 1). Test sites having a similar probability of belonging to more than one group are compared to each of those groups; the current protocol involves sites having a probability of membership >30%. All sites are re-plotted in ordination space, and probability ellipses are constructed around the reference sites (SCATTER-PLOT in SYSTAT). A new site is considered to be equivalent to reference if it is located inside the 90% probability ellipse, and impacted if it falls outside the 90% probability ellipse. Other probability ellipses (i.e. 99% and 99.9%) can be used to measure the degree to which impacted sites differ from the reference condition (e.g. see Chapter 11).

Results and discussion

Variability of environmental measurements

Mean coefficients of variation for nine variables concerned with channel characteristics, and eight variables connected with the water column, revealed a range from <1% to 87%. Measures of substratum composition (CV = 10 to 87%) and biomass of benthic algae (CV *ca* 35%) were the most variable in the channel group, whereas water variables (e.g. pH, nutrients, total suspended solids) had CVs <25%. We were unable to separate the relative contributions of field and laboratory procedures on the variables measured. In the end, values of the available CVs for variables used as optimal predictors at the family level ranged from 5 to 87%.

Model building at the family level

The three-stage process of model building using the BEAST, as described above, was applied to the 127 reference sites sampled in the 1994 and 1995 field seasons. A further 106 reference sites from 1996 remain to be completed. The model derived from the complete dataset will be reported in subsequent publications.

A total of 131 families was identified but only 39 families, each one of which accounted for ≥0.5% of total abundance, were used in the analysis. These 39 families included 99.7% of the organisms collected. Taxa having abundances <0.5% were deleted, because the presence of large numbers of rare taxa adds unwanted noise to the classification analysis (Reynoldson, Bailey *et al.* 1995).

Thirteen families represented more than 90% of total numbers; predominantly these were the

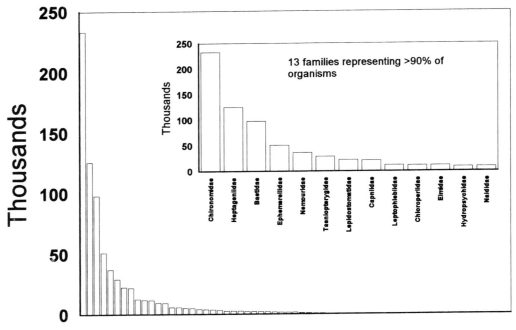

Abundance of 63 families

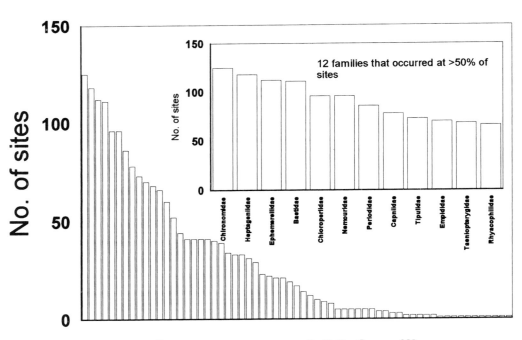

Occurrence of 63 families

Figure 12.2 (*on facing page*). The most abundant families and most frequently occurring families of macroinvertebrates in the Fraser River study during 1994 and 1995.

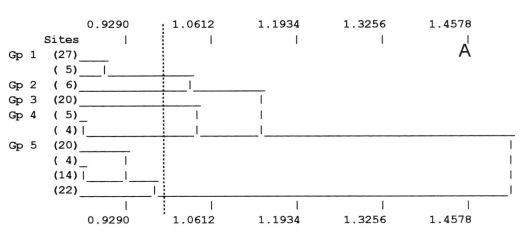

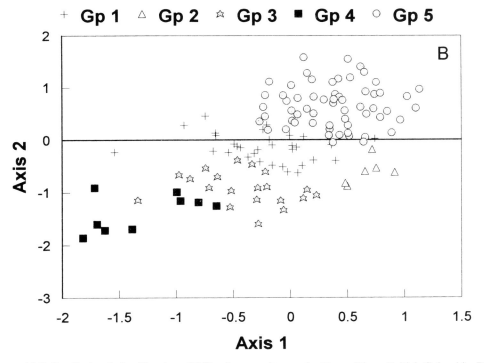

Figure 12.3. Family-level classification of 127 reference sites on the Fraser River, British Columbia. Data are from the 1994 and 1995 field seasons. Gp = Group. (A) Cluster diagram; vertical dotted line indicates the cut-off point for group formation. (B) Ordination of five macroinvertebrate groups; stress level = 0.1728.

Chironomidae and three families of Ephemeroptera (Fig. 12.2). Twelve families occurred at more than 50% of all the sites, once again led by the Chironomidae and the three families of Ephemeroptera.

Stage 1. We identified five groups of sites formed by the macroinvertebrate families from the cluster analysis and ordination (Fig. 12.3). Figure 12.3B presents the ordination of taxa data only; the contribution of individual taxa to the ordination will be reported elsewhere. The distribution of sites along axis 1 (Fig. 12.3B) suggests a strong gradient, although we have not examined the nature of that gradient. Twenty-eight of the 39 common families contributed significantly (p <0.01) to the ordination axes, according to the PAC. Each of the five site groups had a characteristic family composition, which is shown in Table 12.2 for the ten families contributing most to the structure observed in the ordination analyses. No geographic pattern was obvious (Fig. 12.4), which suggests that geographic distribution at the family level is not an important consideration in the Fraser River catchment.

Table 12.2. *Relative occurrence at sites (%) and relative abundance of families (%) best correlated with five groups of sites (Gp 1 to Gp 5) formed from 127 reference sites in the Fraser River catchment. The mean numbers of individuals (per family) collected in each group of sites are given, and the total number of sites in each group is also shown.*

PAC r = principal axis correlation coefficient.

Families	PAC r	Occurrence at sites	Total abundance	Mean numbers per kicknet sample in each group				
				Gp 1	Gp 2	Gp 3	Gp 4	Gp 5
Chironomidae	0.615	98.4	31.4	326	110	48	26	3692
Heptageniidae	0.543	92.9	16.9	342	444	63	8	1843
Baetidae	0.503	87.4	13.2	172	71	129	6	1492
Nemouridae	0.487	74.8	5.0	96	105	7	10	367
Leptophlebiidae	0.461	33.9	1.7	16	0	0	0	202
Taeniopterygidae	0.461	53.5	3.9	73	1848	146	15	213
Perlodidae	0.450	66.1	0.8	22	49	14	23	73
Empididae	0.426	55.1	0.5	11	6	2	2	57
Chloroperlidae	0.425	75.6	1.6	72	99	24	2	144
Tipulidae	0.403	55.9	0.7	14	11	3	2	73
Total no. of sites:	—	127	127	32	6	20	9	60

Stage 2. PAC revealed ten variables that were important to predicting macroinvertebrate community structure: (1) two map variables – altitude and longitude; (2) two site variables – maximum water velocity and percent grasses; (3) five channel variables – mean channel depth, percent gravel, percent sand, percent silt/clay and framework (dominant substratum diameter); (4) one water variable – alkalinity.

Table 12.3 shows the mean values of these optimal predictor variables for each reference site group, as well as the PAC value between the variables and the family ordination matrix. Overall similarity of variables in Table 12.3 may reflect the use of riffles as a standardized habitat for sampling. Cross-validation procedures to test the accuracy of predictions from the discriminant model, using the ten predictor variables, resulted in an overall error rate of 37% (Table 12.4).

Reference-site groups

1	+
2	▲
3	★
4	■
5	●

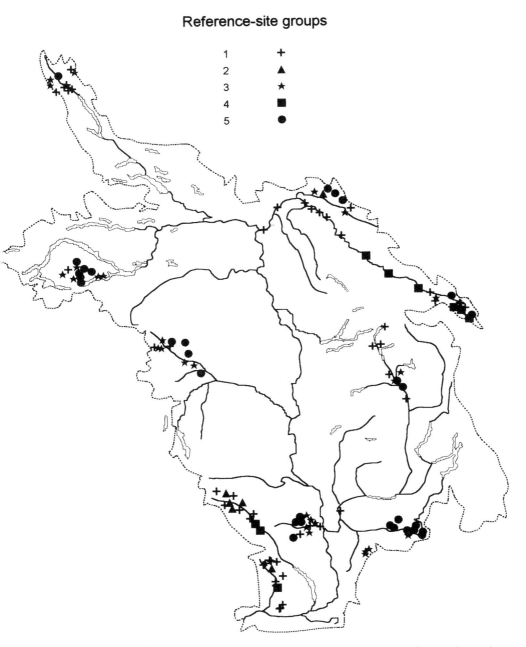

Figure 12.4. Geographic distribution of each of the five reference groups of macroinvertebrates throughout the Fraser River catchment.

Table 12.3. *Mean values of predictor variables selected by stepwise discriminant analysis in five reference groups (Gp), and principal axis correlation (PAC r), with the ordination matrix rank given in parentheses.*

(1) Presence or absence at each site, averaged for all sites in a group.

(2) Diameter (cm) of the dominant substratum (see note (1) in Table 12.1 for explanation).

Predictor variables	PAC r	Gp 1	Gp 2	Gp 3	Gp 4	Gp 5
Altitude (ft amsl)	0.343 (9)	3113	2688	2234	2766	3784
Longitude (°.decimal mins)	0.193 (21)	123.00	122.88	121.50	120.50	122.60
Grasses (% occurrence)[1]	0.476 (1)	22	17	5	0	52
Framework (cm)[2]	0.353 (7)	6.1	7.2	7.2	5.3	5.8
Interstitial material (%)						
Silt/clay	0.327 (12)	0.17	4.24	1.32	1.96	0.26
Sand	0.419 (3)	71.4	84.2	75.6	86.3	63.4
Gravel	0.432 (2)	27.3	11.5	19.2	13.1	35.3
Mean channel depth (cm)	0.409 (4)	31.0	22.3	35.3	25.0	20.4
Maximum velocity (cm s^{-1})	0.398 (5)	0.58	0.52	0.74	0.66	0.51
Alkalinity (mg l^{-1})	0.349 (8)	37.4	23.9	24.4	23.5	50.0

Table 12.4. *Prediction of family groups (Gp) by discriminant analysis. Overall error rate = 37%.*

Error rate	To Gp 1	To Gp 2	To Gp 3	To Gp 4	To Gp 5
From Gp 1	14 (44%)	0	6	2	10
From Gp 2	1	2 (33%)	1	1	1
From Gp 3	2	0	14 (70%)	3	1
From Gp 4	0	1	0	8 (89%)	0
From Gp 5	5	2	7	4	42 (70%)

Stage 3. The last stage assesses test sites, suspected of being impacted, against the reference site groups, and requires reordination of the appropriate reference site group with the test sites. All of the test sites were predicted to occur in either reference Group 1 or reference Group 5 (Fig. 12.5). The Fraser mainstem sites were predicted to Group 1; FRA16 had a similar probability of belonging to either group, so it was included in Group 1. FRA13, FRA14 and FRA16 fell well outside the 90% probability ellipse, indicating probable pulp and paper mill impacts at these sites; FRA13 and FRA16 were more affected than FRA14. The downstream FRA28 site seems to be unimpacted.

The remaining test sites were predicted to occur in Group 5 (Fig. 12.5). The WIL1 site appears to have been marginally affected by past logging activities in its catchment. For the Salmon River sites, SAL1 and SAL2 are equivalent to reference. The evidence for agricultural impacts at SAL3 and SAL4 is equivocal because of the proximity of SAL4 and two of the three SAL3 replicates (SAL3.l, SAL3.2) to the 90% probability ellipse. In addition, SAL3.3 is equivalent to reference.

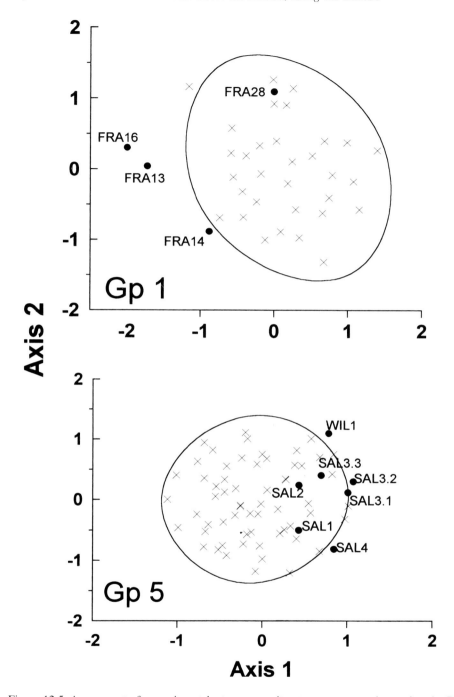

Figure 12.5. Assessment of macroinvertebrate community structure at test sites, using the BEAST model and the 1994 and 1995 data from the Fraser River, British Columbia. Groups (Gp) 1 and 5 are shown along with their 90% probability ellipses. Crosses = reference sites. Solid circles = test sites (FRA = Fraser River mainstem; SAL = Salmon River; WIL = Willow River; see Methods for description of test sites). Two dimensions were used for Gp 1, stress level = 0.2334. Three dimensions were used for Gp 5, stress level = 0.1850; only the first two axes are shown for Gp 5.

Conclusion

We have developed a family-level predictive model that uses five reference groups based on macroinvertebrate community structure, and requires ten predictor variables. Our error rate is 37% for predicting reference sites to a group.

Preliminary assessment of test sites using the BEAST model indicates that a variety of environmental perturbations can be evaluated. Eventual use of the full dataset should provide a valid method for setting numerical criteria for decision-making over large geographic scales. The resulting reference database can be used by itself or added to, over time, as funding becomes available. The database, models, and eventual software development, will enable routine assessment of sites suspected of being impacted in the Fraser River catchment.

Acknowledgements

We thank J. Hilton and J. Wright for making possible the preparation of this paper. D. Cobb and R. Stewart reviewed earlier drafts of the manuscript. Environment Canada's Fraser River Action Plan provided funding for this study. We also thank T. Tuominen and field and laboratory personnel for their support throughout the project.

CHAPTER 13

Selection of benthic macroinvertebrate metrics for monitoring water quality of the Fraser River, British Columbia: implications for both multimetric approaches and multivariate models

VINCENT H. RESH[1], DAVID M. ROSENBERG[2] AND TREFOR B. REYNOLDSON[3]

[1]*Department of Environmental Science, Policy & Management, 201 Wellman Hall, University of California, Berkeley, CA 94720, USA*

[2]*Department of Fisheries & Oceans, Freshwater Institute, 501 University Crescent, Winnipeg, MB R3T 2N6, CANADA*

[3]*National Water Research Institute, Environment Canada, CCIW, 867 Lakeshore Road, Burlington, ON L7R 4A6, CANADA*

Summary

Rapid bioassessment protocols are widely used in the USA and are based on the multimetric approach in which scores for several individual metrics (or measures) are evaluated against thresholds developed from reference sites, and a composite score is then calculated. The multimetric and multivariate approaches that use benthic macroinvertebrates in assessments of water quality (e.g. RIVPACS, AUSRIVAS, the BEAST), are similar in their data collection methods, but differ in the way reference sites are selected, test sites are classified and test site assessments are made.

Forty-four metrics were calculated from collections of benthic macroinvertebrates made at seventeen sites in the Fraser River catchment, British Columbia, Canada, in 1994. They included measures of richness (17 metrics), numbers of individuals (16), functional feeding groups (10), and a biotic index (1). Richness measures had the lowest variability in mean values across the five basins (or subcatchments) examined, and the lowest coefficients of variation based on replicate samples collected at a single site within each basin. Most (59.1%) metrics could be calculated at all sites examined in this study, and most (55.3%) correctly indicated impairment when impaired and unimpaired sites were compared. However, incorrect indications of impairment were noted in 40 to 60% of the metric comparisons made between unimpaired sites located in different ecoregions, between unimpaired sites in different streams of the same ecoregions, and between unimpaired sites in the same stream.

Richness metrics consistently had the lowest error rates of all the metrics examined. Incorporation of non-richness metrics into multivariate approaches may increase incorrect indications of impairment (i.e. Type I errors).

Multimetric approaches should consider incorporating multivariate analyses for defining reference conditions and assessing impairment of test sites. Collaboration among users of multimetric and multivariate approaches can enhance both types of water quality monitoring and assessment programs.

Introduction

Various approaches employed for water quality monitoring have become closely identified with their countries of origin and development, examples being the Saprobien index from Germany (Cairns & Pratt 1993) and RIVPACS from the UK (see Chapter 1). The rapid bioassessment protocols developed in the mid-1980s (Plafkin, Barbour *et al.* 1989) are most identified with monitoring in the USA. Rapid bioassessment attempts to provide an integrated assessment of an aquatic resource, comparing habitat (e.g. physical structure, flow regime) and biological measures with empirically defined reference conditions (Barbour, Gerritsen *et al.* 1999).

Resh *et al.* (1995) have noted that in almost all its permutations (see the appendix in Resh & Jackson 1993), rapid bioassessment approaches use techniques that attempt to evaluate assemblages of benthic macroinvertebrates at reduced costs relative to those associated with traditional, more quantitatively rigorous assessments. The effort (and cost) of benthic analysis is reduced with rapid bioassessment because of four specific features. First, a single relatively large sample, covering an area several-fold larger than that in traditional quantitative collections, is taken instead of several replicate samples. Second, a standardized subsampling procedure is used (e.g. the first 100 to 300 organisms randomly sorted), which both reduces the number of organisms processed and provides a relatively consistent unit of effort for the processing of all samples. Third, identification is often only to family level. Fourth, the results of surveys can be summarized in ways that can be understood by non-specialists, such as managers, other decision makers, and the concerned public.

Rapid bioassessment protocols in the USA are based on the use of multimetrics. This approach attempts to provide an integrated analysis of the biological community at a site, by calculating various metrics (or measures) representing functional or structural aspects of the community, and summing these into a single score. Their use has not been without controversy; for example, potentially important ecological information may be lost by aggregating individual measures into an index (e.g. Suter 1993; Polls 1994). In addition, some metrics are too variable to detect impairment consistently (or may indicate impairment when it does not occur) and are based on subjective criteria (Resh & Jackson 1993; Hannaford & Resh 1995). However, supporters have argued that the advantage of a multimetric approach is that it incorporates ecological information on how aquatic organisms feed, reproduce, and exploit their habitats (Fore *et al.* 1996) into assessments of water quality. They suggest that reliance on combinations of multiple measures minimizes the weaknesses of individual metrics (Barbour, Gerritsen *et al.* 1999, among others). These debates are often "apples and oranges" in content, and the resolution of these differences seems to be far from over.

The use of the multimetric approach in biological monitoring has expanded greatly in the USA over the past decade. Currently, 47 of the 50 states use benthic macroinvertebrates as the "target assemblages" (Utah, Nevada, and South Dakota do not, probably because their wadeable streams flow intermittently); 31 states also use fish and five use periphyton in bioassessments (Barbour *et al.* 1995; Barbour, Gerritsen *et al.* 1999). Benthic macroinvertebrates are the basis for most biomonitoring programs currently in use worldwide (Rosenberg & Resh 1993b), and the reasons for this choice are clear (Rosenberg & Resh 1996). State programs in the USA are usually based on modifications of a national program developed and promulgated by the United States Environmental Protection Agency (USEPA) (Plafkin, Barbour *et al.* 1989).

The purpose of this chapter is to determine which metrics are most appropriate for examining impairment in the Fraser River catchment, Canada, and to examine how these results could influence users of multimetric and multivariate approaches. To do this we examine a range of metrics in two ways: (1) do they detect impairment when impairment occurs and (2) do they give incorrect indications of impairment when no impairment occurs (Type I errors)?

How do multimetric and multivariate approaches differ?

Both approaches involve similar methods for collecting benthic macroinvertebrates, but the range of environmental variables used in the multivariate predictive models are not generally measured when multimetric collections are made. Instead, a habitat assessment supplements the biological information collected in the multimetric approach (Plafkin, Barbour *et al.* 1989; Hannaford *et al.* 1997). The two approaches diverge further once the samples have been collected, sorted, and specimens identified. In multimetric analysis, sites are grouped *a priori* based on their geophysical attributes, and final classification is based on taxonomic composition. In multivariate approaches, sites are classified into groups using clustering methods based on the similarity of their species composition.

In multimetric analysis, selection of reference sites for comparison with a test site is based on the geographical or physical attributes of the site, whereas in multivariate approaches, selection may be based on the sites in the reference group with which the test site has the highest probability of inclusion, using a discriminant model (e.g. the BEAST, Chapters 11 and 12). Alternatively, the selection may draw on information from several reference groups, according to the weighted probabilities with which the test site would be included in those reference groups (e.g. RIVPACS and AUSRIVAS, Chapters 1 to 10). Finally, test site assessment in the multimetric approach is based on quartile distributions of additive metrics. In the multivariate approach, it may be based on a comparison of the test and reference sites in taxa ordination space, using probability ellipses constructed around reference sites (the BEAST) or a comparison of the taxa observed at the test site and those expected to be present at the site, based on weighted probabilities of taxon occurrence (RIVPACS and AUSRIVAS). The above distinctions are discussed in detail by Reynoldson, Norris *et al.* (1997).

Reynoldson, Norris *et al.* (1997) compared two multivariate predictive models (the BEAST and AUSRIVAS) with a multimetric analysis. The latter was done using two groups of metrics. First, a fixed list of metrics modified from Plafkin, Barbour *et al.* (1989) was used, which included calculation of the following: (1) number of individuals; (2) number of families; (3) percent of Ephemeroptera, Plecoptera and Trichoptera (EPT) individuals; (4) percent of Chironomidae individuals; (5) ratio of the number of EPT individuals/number of EPT + Chironomidae individuals; (6) ratio of the number of Hydropsychidae individuals/number of Trichoptera individuals; (7) percent dominance of a single taxon; (8) the Family Biotic Index (Hilsenhoff 1998). Based on input from M. T. Barbour and J. Gerritsen (Tetra Tech Inc.), a second multimetric analysis was carried out in which the number of individuals was deleted, and the ratio of the number of EPT individuals/number of EPT + Chironomidae individuals was replaced with the ratio of the number of Baetidae individuals/number of Ephemeroptera individuals. A composite score was then calculated, based on the similarity of metrics to the appropriate reference site classification. Precision (i.e. whether all replicates at a single site were consistently designated as impaired or unimpaired) and accuracy (i.e. designations of unimpaired sites as unimpaired) of multimetric assessments were estimated. The precision and accuracy of the two groups of metrics were then compared within ecoregions, stream order, and biotic classifications.

The results of this comparison indicated that the two multivariate models performed consistently better than either of the fixed metric designs (Multimetric 1 and 2 in Table 13.1). In one comparison of precision, the BEAST performed less well than AUSRIVAS. However,

AUSRIVAS failed to designate a known impaired site as impaired, which the BEAST did designate as impaired.

Table 13.1. *Comparison of precision (A) and accuracy (B) of four methods employed for assessing water quality by macroinvertebrate composition at sites in the catchment of the Fraser River, Canada. Results are expressed as percentages of correct assessments for impaired and unimpaired sites.*

(See Reynoldson, Norris *et al.* 1997 for additional details).

Method of assessment	Ecoregion	Stream order	Biotic grouping
(A). Designation of replicates at each site as either ALL impaired or ALL unimpaired			
Multimetric 1	40	80	60
Multimetric 2	60	80	80
BEAST	80	100	80
AUSRIVAS	100	100	100
(B). Designation of unimpaired sites as unimpaired			
Multimetric 1	50	38	75
Multimetric 2	69	38	88
BEAST	100	100	100
AUSRIVAS	100	100	100

Table 13.2. *Description of sampling sites in the catchment of the Fraser River, Canada, used for the analysis shown in Tables 13.3 and 13.4.*

* Sites where replicate samples were taken.

Subcatchment	(Site)	River	Order	Ecoregion	Impacts
Salmon	(01)	Salmon River	3	Thompson-Okanagan Plateau	None
	(02)	Salmon River	4		None
	(03)*	Salmon River	4		Agriculture, logging
	(04)	Salmon River	3		Agriculture, logging
Chilcotin	(04)	Cluska River	4	Fraser Plateau	None
	(05)*	Palmer Creek	4		None
	(08)	Cluska River	4		None
Clearwater	(03)	Hobson Creek	2	Southern Rocky Mt. Trench	None
	(06)*	Hemp Creek	2		None
Pitt	(01)	Pitt River	2	Pacific Ranges	None
	(02)	Pitt River	2		None
	(03)	Pitt River	3		None
	(06)*	Pitt River	3		None
	(07)*	Pitt River	4		None
	(08)	Pitt River	4		None
Stuart	(02)*	Condit Creek	2	Omeineca Mts, Fraser Basin	None
	(04)	Lion Creek Trib.	2		None
	(06)	Lion Creek	3		None

Methods

Study area

The analysis is based on benthic macroinvertebrate collections made in the Fraser River, a catchment that covers *ca* 230,000 km^2 or 25% of British Columbia, Canada's westernmost province (see Chapter 12 for further description). Although the Fraser is one of the last unregulated large rivers of North America, urban and industrial pressures pose a severe threat to the health of this ecosystem. The research described here attempts to address the problem of pollution in the Fraser River catchment, through the development of a biomonitoring program for assessing water quality using benthic macroinvertebrates.

Sampling methods and analysis

Eventually, the Fraser River study will involve analysis of benthic macroinvertebrate data from more than 250 sites. In the analysis presented here, we use results from second to fourth order sites in five subcatchments from five different ecoregions of the Fraser River catchment (Table 13.2).

Rosenberg *et al.* (2000) provide details of the sampling and laboratory sorting program. The data used for this present study were obtained from 18 sites located throughout the Fraser River catchment (Table 13.2). Samples were collected from riffles using a triangular kicknet sampler (38.5 cm on each side). Either one sample unit or 3–5 replicate sample units, each of 3 minutes duration, were collected on each site; subsamples of the first 200 organisms encountered were subsequently sorted and identified from each sample unit.

Benthic macroinvertebrates were identified to the lowest taxonomic level (genus and in some cases species) in the Fraser River study. In this analysis, metrics were calculated in two ways: (1) at family level, because this is the approach used in many rapid bioassessment programs; (2) at genus or species level when possible (e.g. not with the Family Biotic Index or percent Chironomidae), as used in other programs. A total of 44 metrics was examined, including the same nine metrics used by Reynoldson, Norris *et al.* (1997) in the analysis described in Table 13.1, and an additional 35 metrics chosen from Barbour, Gerritsen *et al.* (1999).

The 44 metrics can be divided into four groups: measures of richness; numbers of individuals (or enumerations); functional feeding group ratios; and a biotic index. Analysis of each metric involved calculating the coefficients of variation (CV) for sites in six streams (marked with an asterisk in Table 13.2) in the Fraser River catchment. Test sites included a known impaired site (Salmon River 04) and known unimpaired sites. These designations were determined by personnel who are knowledgeable with this area (see the description of the workshop conducted for this purpose, in Rosenberg *et al.* 2000), examination of the area around a site (by helicopter) before sampling, and examination of a site while sampling.

To determine if impairment could be detected at the known impaired sites and, conversely, to determine if impairment would be incorrectly indicated (Type I error) at known unimpaired sites, we compared: (a) known impaired sites with known unimpaired sites (Salmon 03 cf. 01, and 03 cf. 02); (b) unimpaired sites of the same stream order in different ecoregions (selected because of their geomorphic similarity, e.g. Clearwater 06 cf. Stuart 02); (c) unimpaired sites in different streams of the same order in the same ecoregion (without regard to geomorphic similarity, Clearwater 03 cf. 06, Chilcotin 04 cf. 05, 05 cf. 08, Stuart 02 cf. 04, 02 cf. 06); (d) sites of the same or ±1 order in the same stream (Pitt 01 cf. 06, 02 cf. 06, 03 cf. 06, 07 cf. 08). Statistical analysis of these comparisons involved one-tailed t-tests at $p = 0.05$, as recommended by Barbour, Gerritsen *et al.* (1999); a one-tailed test was used because the metrics change in one direction (e.g. a decrease in number of taxa present with impairment).

Because we were using known impaired or unimpaired sites, and examining metric response individually, a Bonferroni correction was not necessary.

Results

Variability of 44 metrics

The first analysis examined the variability of 44 metrics, which included both the fixed list of metrics advocated by Plafkin, Barbour *et al.* (1989), marked with an asterisk in Table 13.3, and other metrics proposed for use in Barbour, Gerritsen *et al.* (1999). Mean values and CVs (expressed as percent) for all metrics varied greatly, sometimes by over an order of magnitude at the six sites in different basins (Table 13.3).

Table 13.3. *Mean metric values/coefficients of variation (CV %) for selected metrics at six stream sites in the catchment of the Fraser River (see Table 13.2 for descriptions of sites) for which replicate samples were collected.*

* Metrics that were typically used in the fixed-metric approach of Plafkin, Barbour *et al.* (1989); for a complete description of metric calculation see Barbour, Gerritsen *et al.* (1999).

— indicates that the metric could not be calculated at that site.

N = number of Families or Taxa; values for families may be higher than values for taxa because some smaller specimens could be identified only to family. EPT = Ephemeroptera, Plecoptera and Trichoptera combined.

(1) Ratio of EPT Individuals/Chironomidae + EPT Individuals.

CHI = Chilcotin subcatchment; CLR = Clearwater subcatchment; PIT = Pitt River subcatchment; SAL = Salmon River subcatchment; STU = Stuart subcatchment (see Table 13.2).

Metrics	CHI 05	CLR 06	PIT 06	PIT 07	SAL 03	STU 02
Richness:	(n = 5)	(n = 5)	(n = 3)	(n = 5)	(n = 3)	(n = 5)
Total N Taxa	27.6/11.0	28.4/ 6.9	12.0/25.0	19.8/ 8.3	26.0/ 6.7	21.0/21.6
*Total N Families	20.0/ 8.7	16.4/14.0	10.3/14.8	14.2/12.7	14.7/10.4	13.2/12.4
N EPT Taxa	9.6/16.3	15.4/14.2	9.0/15.1	7.5/11.1	8.7/ 8.7	14.4/19.4
N EPT Families	9.6/11.9	11.2/9.8	7.7/15.1	8.6/13.3	7.7/19.9	10.2/16.1
N Ephemeroptera Taxa	3.0/62.4	5.2/21.1	3.0/0	6.2/13.5	1.3/43.3	5.6/24.0
N Ephemeroptera Families	4.0/ 0	4.4/12.5	4.0/0	3.0/0	3.7/15.8	4.0/17.7
N Trichoptera Taxa	3.6/15.2	2.8/46.6	2.0/0	1.3/43.3	3.3/17.3	1.6/55.9
N Trichoptera Families	3.2/14.0	2.6/43.9	2.0/0	1.3/43.3	3.0/33.3	1.4/39.1
N Plecoptera Taxa	6.0/ 0	7.4/12.1	4.0/0	4.0/0	4.0/0	7.2/15.2
N Plecoptera Families	2.4/47.5	4.2/20.0	3.0/0	4.6/ 9.3	1.0/0	4.8/17.4
N DipteraTaxa	8.8/23.3	13.6/13.9	5.3/39.0	9.2/11.9	14.3/10.7	7.2/26.7
N Diptera Families	3.6/34.3	3.2/26.2	2.0/ 0	3.2/13.1	3.3/34.7	2.4/22.8
N Chironomidae Taxa	5.6/32.4	11.6/13.1	3.3/62.5	6.2/17.9	11.3/18.4	5.8/37.4
N Odonata Taxa	— —	— —	— —	— —	— —	— —
N Odonata Families	— —	— —	— —	— —	— —	— —
N Coleoptera Taxa	2.4/22.8	— —	— —	— —	1.0/ 0	— —
N Coleoptera Families	1.0/0	— —	— —	— —	1.0/ 0	— —

(Table 13.3 is continued on facing page)

Metrics	CHI 05	CLR 06	PIT 06	PIT 07	SAL 03	STU 02
Number of Individuals:						
*N EPT Ind/Ch+EPT Ind[1]	0.6/22.0	0.5/13.1	1.0/2.1	0.6/2.0	0.6/23.3	0.7/12.6
*% EPT Individuals	45.4/22.2	46.5/12.8	94.1/2.9	81.4/3.0	49.6/32.8	66.7/12.8
% Ephemeroptera	36.3/19.5	26.1/23.0	56.6/12.4	28.7/8.5	27.6/20.8	55.4/10.4
% Plecoptera	4.0/50.0	17.7/6.5	35.9/24.5	52.2/24.5	6.1/102.3	10.2/23.4
% Trichoptera	5.1/34.2	2.7/28.1	1.6/0	0.6/34.6	16.1/72.9	1.1/49.8
*% Chironomidae	25.9/38.2	49.4/12.9	2.1/91.7	11.7/13.0	31.7/25.5	32.1/26.1
% Coleoptera	2.4/31.6	— —	— —	— —	1.0/108.7	— —
% Odonata	— —	— —	— —	— —	— —	— —
% Tribe Tanytarsini	19.3/37.9	17.0/48.2	— —	0.8/47.1	18.1/31.6	26.7/30.8
% Diptera+non-insects	46.3/18.8	56.2/10.8	7.5/47.6	19.1/13.1	57.0/15.7	34.4/23.3
*% Dominant Taxon	17.9/22.6	17.5/29.2	39.3/ 6.2	36.7/ 2.6	21.6/17.6	32.7/8.7
% 2 Dominant Taxa	30.5/12.0	30.6/19.9	64.7/ 6.4	54.7/ 7.2	37.6/14.4	55.1/7.0
% Contribution of 5 Dominant Taxa	57.3/ 5.3	56.4/8.0	92.5/ 6.1	73.2/ 2.1	65.2/ 5.1	79.0/4.2
*% of Trichoptera that are Hydropsychidae	53.3/40.1	20.0/0	— —	75.0/47.1	52.2/25.3	88.9/21.7
% of Ephemeroptera that are Baetidae	38.0/42.7	31.3/9.6	59.0/14.6	61.5/14.0	16.2/57.4	48.2/15.4
*Total Abundance	11,191.6/23.3	12,904.2/20.5	324.3/41.0	414.6/44.0	4,325.0/19.1	4,216.4/23.3
Functional feeding measures:						
% Gatherers	53.6/8.6	76.4/3.3	89.1/0.6	79.0/2.3	45.6/10.8	86.1/3.4
% Gatherer Families	37.9/9.9	51.8/13.7	51.9/6.2	42.1/5.2	48.1/10.8	48.0/15.7
% Filterers	21.7/34.2	8.3/74.1	— —	1.9/60.0	10.0/63.8	— —
% Filterer Families	19.2/17.2	10.9/18.2	— —	8.4/28.9	11.2/27.2	— —
% Predators	3.3/43.7	3.8/42.2	8.7/8.7	11.7/ 9.8	10.9/50.7	5.8/24.8
% Predator Families	17.7/37.0	16.4/53.4	39.3/14.2	24.7/38.9	21.0/42.6	30.9/28.9
% Scrapers	18.3/18.4	16.1/38.1	54.4/16.9	55.3/6.0	7.8/120.8	23.6/113.5
% Scraper Families	18.0/12.5	24.9/37.4	42.0/5.3	21.4/12.8	18.0/13.2	26.8/23.6
% Shredders	3.9/38.9	21.7/30.1	— —	4.2/31.0	30.1/49.8	5.9/41.7
% Shredder Families	11.1/37.4	30.2/30.4	— —	17.1/24.1	20.6/10.8	21.2/11.8
Biotic Indices:						
*Family Biotic Index	3.3/11.1	2.9/8.9	2.2/7.9	1.6/11.8	3.0/16.3	3.0/16.9

Richness measures showed low variability in terms of either mean values or CVs (Table 13.3). Among sites, mean values ranged over less than a 2-fold difference for the following: number of families; number of Ephemeroptera, Plecoptera and Trichoptera (EPT) taxa and families; number of Ephemeroptera families; number of Plecoptera taxa; number of Diptera families; the ratio of EPT individuals to EPT+Chironomidae individuals; the contribution of the five dominant taxa; the percentage of gatherer taxa and families (Table 13.3). Coefficients of variation showed the lowest range for number of families (8.7 to 14.8%) and the highest range for percent Chironomidae individuals (12.9 to 91.0%). The lowest CV values were obtained for the following: number of taxa ($\leq 25.0\%$ at all six sites) and families ($\leq 14.8\%$); number of EPT taxa ($\leq 19.4\%$) and EPT families ($\leq 19.9\%$); number of Ephemeroptera families ($\leq 17.7\%$); number of Plecoptera taxa ($\leq 15.2\%$); percentage of Ephemeroptera ($\leq 23.0\%$), two dominant taxa (19.9%) and five dominant taxa ($\leq 8.0\%$); percentage of gatherer taxa ($\leq 10.8\%$) and families ($\leq 15.7\%$); Family Biotic Index ($\leq 16.9\%$).

Detection of impairment in twelve sites

In the second analysis, twelve among-site comparisons were made for the detection of impairment. For each site, metrics were calculated when the information required to do this was available from collections at the site; e.g. calculation of the number of Trichoptera taxa would require that Trichoptera occurred at the site. With this restriction, 6 of 17 richness metrics, 12 of 16 enumerations, 7 of 10 functional feeding group metrics, and the Family Biotic Index, were calculated in the twelve comparisons (Table 13.4).

Table 13.4. *Summary of one-tailed t-test evaluations (p = 0.05) comparing metrics in terms of:*
(a) how often data were available for a statistical comparison, from 12 sites;
(b) correct indications of impact (n = 2);
(c to e) incorrect indications of impact in terms of site comparisons in different rivers from
(c) different ecoregions (n = 1), (d) the same ecoregion (n = 5), (e) different sites in the same river (n = 4).

(1) Ratio of EPT Individuals/Chironomidae+EPT Individuals.
EPT = Ephemeroptera, Plecoptera and Trichoptera combined.

N = number of Families or Taxa. See text on sampling methods for sites involved in the comparisons.

| | | | Did the metric incorrectly indicate impairment when sites were compared in: | | |
Metrics	(a) No. of sites for calculation	(b) Metric indicated impairment	(c) Different ecoregions?	(d) Different rivers?	(e) The same rivers?
Richness:					
Total N Taxa	12	Yes	Yes	Yes (2/5)	Yes (1/4)
Total N Families	12	Yes	No	Yes (4/5)	No (0/4)
N EPT Taxa	12	Yes	No	Yes (1/5)	No (0/4)
N EPT Families	12	Yes	No	Yes (2/5)	No (0/4)
N Ephemeroptera Taxa	9	Yes	No	Yes (1/5)	No (0/1)
N Ephemeroptera Families	6	No	No	Yes (1/3)	—
N Trichoptera Taxa	9	Yes	No	Yes (4/5)	Yes (1/1)
N Trichoptera Families	12	No	No	Yes (4/5)	Yes (1/4)
N Plecoptera Taxa	6	No	No	No (0/3)	—
N Plecoptera Families	7	—	No	Yes (1/5)	No (0/1)
N DipteraTaxa	12	No	Yes	Yes (4/5)	Yes (1/4)
N Diptera Families	9	No	No	Yes (3/5)	No (0/1)
N Chironomidae Taxa	12	No	Yes	Yes (4/5)	Yes (1/4)
N Odonata Taxa	0	—	—	—	—
N Odonata Families	0	—	—	—	—
N Coleoptera Taxa	3	—	No	Yes (2/2)	—
N Coleoptera Families	3	—	No	Yes (2/2)	—
Number of Individuals:					
N EPT Ind/Ch+EPT Ind[1]	12	No	Yes	Yes (3/5)	Yes (1/4)
% EPT Individuals	12	No	Yes	Yes (3/5)	Yes (1/4)
% Ephemeroptera	12	Yes	Yes	Yes (4/5)	Yes (1/4)
% Plecoptera	12	No	No	Yes (3/5)	Yes (3/4)
% Trichoptera	9	No	No	Yes (3/5)	Yes (1/1)
% Chironomidae	12	Yes	Yes	Yes (3/5)	Yes (1/4)
% Coleoptera	4	No	—	Yes (2/2)	—
% Odonata	0	—	—	—	—

(Table 13.4 is continued on facing page)

Metrics	(a) No. of sites for calculation	(b) Metric indicated impairment	Did the metric incorrectly indicate impairment when sites were compared in:		
			(c) Different ecoregions?	(d) Different rivers?	(e) The same rivers?
% Tribe Tanytarsini	9	Yes	No	Yes (3/5)	Yes (1/1)
% Diptera+non-insects	12	Yes	Yes	Yes (4/5)	Yes (1/4)
% Dominant Taxon	12	Yes	Yes	Yes (4/5)	Yes (3/4)
% 2 Dominant Taxa	12	Yes	Yes	Yes (4/5)	Yes (2/4)
% Contribution of 5 Dominant Taxa	12	Yes	Yes	Yes (3/5)	Yes (1/4)
% of Trichoptera that are Hydropsychidae	7	Yes	—	Yes (4/4)	Yes (1/1)
% of Ephemeroptera that are Baetidae	12	Yes	Yes	Yes (2/5)	Yes (2/4)
Total Abundance	12	Yes	Yes	Yes (4/5)	Yes (2/4)
Functional feeding measures:					
% Gatherers	12	Yes	Yes	Yes (4/5)	Yes (2/4)
% Gatherer Families	12	Yes	Yes	Yes (3/5)	Yes (3/4)
% Filterers	7	No	No	Yes (2/3)	No (0/1)
% Filterer Families	7	Yes	Yes	Yes (2/3)	No (0/1)
% Predators	12	No	No	Yes (3/5)	Yes (2/4)
% Predator Families	12	No	No	No (0/5)	Yes (2/4)
% Scrapers	12	Yes	No	Yes (5/5)	Yes (4/4)
% Scraper Families	12	No	Yes	Yes (3/3)	Yes (4/4)
% Shredders	12	No	Yes	Yes (1/5)	No (0/1)
% Shredder Families	9	Yes	Yes	Yes (3/5)	No (0/1)
Biotic Indices:					
Family Biotic Index	12	No	No	Yes (3/5)	Yes (2/4)

With regard to correct indications of impairment (i.e. impairment was noted when it occurred; e.g. Salmon River 01 and 02 cf. 03 comparisons), 6 of 12 richness metrics, 10 of 15 enumeration metrics, 5 of 10 functional feeding group metrics, but not the Family Biotic Index, had t values higher than expected at $p = 0.05$ (Table 13.4).

Incorrect designations of impairment when a site was not impaired (Type I error) were as follows. For unimpaired streams in different ecoregions, errors were found for 3 of 15 richness metrics that were calculable, for 10 of 13 enumerations, and for 6 of 10 functional feeding groups metrics. In different rivers of the same ecoregion, errors were found for 35 of 65 richness comparisons, for 49 of 71 enumerations, for 26 of 44 functional feeding groups metrics, and for 3 of 5 Biotic Index comparisons. Unimpaired sites in the same river had the lowest errors, with errors in richness being 5 of 32, enumerations 21 of 47, functional feeding groups 17 of 28, and Family Biotic Index 2 of 4 (Table 13.4).

Combining error rates across different scales (different ecoregions, different rivers, sites in the same river), by summing the last three columns in Table 13.4, indicated that the best performing metrics were all richness metrics: number of taxa (only 4 errors in 10 comparisons); families (4 of 10); EPT taxa (1 of 10) and families (2 of 10); Ephemeroptera taxa (1 of 7) and families (1 of 4); Plecoptera taxa (0 of 4) and families (1 of 7).

The lowest error rates occurred when unimpaired sites in the same rivers were compared, and this was especially evident for richness metrics. Fewer incorrect designations occurred (although only one site comparison was used) when sites in different ecoregions (located several hundred km apart) were picked because of physical habitat similarities, than when streams in the same ecoregion were compared (Table 13.4).

Discussion

This analysis of metrics, calculated from macroinvertebrate collections from the Fraser River, clearly shows three main points. (1) Richness metrics are the most useful of all the types of metrics tested, in terms of ability to indicate impairment when it occurs and not indicating impairment when it does not occur. (2) The fixed metric approach of Plafkin, Barbour *et al.* (1989), which attempts to include a variety of structural and functional measures of benthic communities (i.e. those marked by an asterisk in Table 13.3), would not be significantly improved by substitution of other metrics (i.e. those without an asterisk in Table 13.3), because it is mainly the richness metrics that perform well. (3) There are more classification errors (i.e. incorrect indications of impairment) with the multimetric approach when sites in different rivers are compared than when sites in the same river are compared, and two sites in different ecoregions selected because of geomorphic similarity may have fewer classification errors than sites in the same river or region.

The high variation in mean values for the six sites in Table 13.3 indicates that rather than having geographically broad-based thresholds reflecting unimpaired conditions, local thresholds must be established. Given that these streams have different underlying geology, nutrient bases, geomorphology, etc., the variability observed in mean values of benthic macroinvertebrate metrics between subcatchments is not unexpected. Consequently, even for metrics that have high CVs, finding statistically significant differences in the absence of impairment is not surprising. Other studies have examined the appropriateness of benthic macroinvertebrate metrics for different regions, and their results indicated that some metrics could be used successfully in different regions (Table 13.5) but most could not. Although these studies examined a range of metrics, it is important to note that only the richness measures seem to be reported as consistently useful across studies.

What can the multimetric approach tell us about RIVPACS-type models? Water quality monitoring agencies worldwide are considering the use of multivariate models as the basis for monitoring programs. Although reliance on the use of a few fixed metrics (e.g. percent EPT) may be appropriate for developing countries (Resh 1995; Sivaramakrishnan *et al.* 1996), this certainly goes against international trends. Because the regulatory agencies in the USA have based most of their benthic macroinvertebrate biomonitoring programs on the multimetric approach (Resh & Jackson 1993; Resh *et al.* 1995), Reynoldson, Norris *et al.* (1997) recommended that a safe, cost-effective strategy for these agencies may be to (1) supplement the multimetric biological collections, which are fundamentally the same as those used for multivariate approaches, with similar environmental measurements required for multivariate analyses, and (2) do multimetric and multivariate analysis side-by-side and base the ultimate decision of site impairment on analysis and interpretation of both approaches.

RIVPACS and other multivariate approaches (e.g. AUSRIVAS) develop predictive models using the presence or absence of species as the basis for predictions of faunal occurrence in test sites, although data on density (e.g. the BEAST) and abundance (e.g. RIVPACS) are also used in these models. From the other chapters in this volume, it is apparent that a trend in the future development and expansion of multivariate models is to include non-richness metrics that reflect other structural and functional aspects of benthic macroinvertebrate communities (e.g.

Table 13.5. *Benthic macroinvertebrate metrics found to be useful in previous analyses.*

Kerans *et al.* (1992) determined success of a metric if no differences or consistent differences were found between the sampling devices that were used, between riffles and pools, and year-to-year differences.
Barbour *et al.* (1992) used ability to distinguish classes (montane versus valley/plains).
Resh & Jackson (1993) used low variability between sites and years, and consistent patterns of difference between impacted and unimpacted sites.
Kerans & Karr (1994) used concordance with water quality and fish assemblage analyses, and variability across habitats and ecoregions.
Fore *et al.* (1996) distinguished disturbed sites from minimally disturbed sites.

Kerans *et al.* (18 metrics)	Barbour *et al.* (17 metrics)	Resh & Jackson (20 metrics)	Kerans & Karr (18 metrics)	Fore *et al.* (30 metrics)
Plecoptera richness	No. of taxa	No. of taxa	Taxa richness	Taxa richness
Intolerant snail and mussel richness	EPT richness	No. of EPT taxa	Intolerant snail & mussel richness	Ephemeroptera richness
% Individuals in two numerically dominant taxa	Pinkham-Pearson index	No. of families	Ephemeroptera richness	Plecoptera richness
% Omnivores	Quantitative similarity index	Margalef's index	Trichoptera richness	*Pteronarcys* richness
% Gatherers	Biotic index	Family biotic index	Plecoptera richness	Trichoptera richness
% Grazers	% Dominant taxa	% Scrapers	% *Corbicula*	Intolerant taxa richness
% Predators	Dominants in common for five most abundant taxa		% Oligochaeta	Sediment-intolerant taxa richness
			% Omnivores	
% Filterers	Ratio of individuals of Hydropsychidae to total Trichoptera		% Filterers	Sediment-tolerant taxa richness
% Shredders			% Grazers	
% Chironomidae	% Scrapers		% Predators	% Tolerant species
	% Shredders		% Individuals in two numerically dominant taxa	% Sediment-tolerant species
	Quantitative similarity index for functional feeding groups		Total abundance	% Dominance of the three most abundant taxa

see Chapter 9). However, the analysis performed in this study showed that richness metrics were most accurate in detecting impairment and avoiding classification errors; it should be expected that predictive, multivariate models incorporating non-richness measures will also produce higher misclassification rates. A comparison of the BEAST and AUSRIVAS (Reynoldson, Norris *et al.* 1997) indicated that although data on presence and absence alone (in AUSRIVAS) has lower rates of classification errors, the inclusion of density (as in the BEAST) may make the model more sensitive in detecting impairment. This suggestion needs further testing; however, it does underscore the potential problems of increased misclassification but also the benefits of increased sensitivity from including non-richness metrics.

Taxon richness is the most widely used evaluation measure in benthic macroinvertebrate studies of pollution effects (Resh & McElravy 1993). Why did richness measures work better than enumerations, functional feeding group and biotic index metrics in this study? The success of using presence or absence information would suggest that with impairment, taxon abundance is not just reduced, but rather that taxa are eliminated. Furthermore, changes in density can result from either impairment-related or non-impairment-related sources. Problems with functional feeding group designations and biotic indices may involve issues of methods: the need for correct designation of feeding groups (or the concept itself), and correct designations for tolerances of individual taxa, respectively. The above questions require far more experimental study.

The present analysis also has implications for the multimetric approach. Each of the metrics in a test site that is compared to a reference site value, using percent similarity or interquartile ranges, could also be compared using a multivariate analysis. This inclusion could bring federal and local regulatory agencies in the USA more in line with worldwide trends in approaches to monitoring water quality, and lead to greater international cooperation and collaboration that can advance the performance of all water quality monitoring programs (Resh & Yamamoto 1994).

Acknowledgments

We thank M. Barbour and C. Faulkner for making a draft version of the 1999 USEPA rapid bioassessment protocols available to us, T. Pascoe for assistance with database management, and D. W. Sutcliffe, J. F. Wright and an anonymous reviewer for their comments on the manuscript of this chapter.

CHAPTER 14

Running-water biomonitoring in Spain: opportunities for a predictive approach

JAVIER ALBA-TERCEDOR[1] AND ANA MARÍA PUJANTE[2]

[1]*Departamento de Biología Animal y Ecología, Facultad de Ciencias, Universidad de Granada, 18071-Granada, SPAIN*

[2]*Departamento de Biología Animal, Universitat de València, Dr Moliner 50, 46100 Burjassot (València), SPAIN*

Summary

In Spain, the practical application of biotic indices in biological monitoring underwent considerable development during the 1980s. In general, the indices used were modifications of procedures developed in the UK and France, although they also included new approaches developed in Spain. Towards the end of the 1980s the development of a Spanish version of the British BMWP system led to the new index being widely used throughout Spain. However, despite these recent trends, the use of biomonitoring to assess river quality has lagged behind other European countries. Recent attempts to develop a RIVPACS-type system for the Mediterranean rivers of the Castellón, València and Alicante provinces have demonstrated the viability of this approach in Spain, but have also highlighted some of the problems that must be faced. These include the difficulty of finding suitable reference sites at low altitudes, the need to integrate information from very different biogeographic zones and hydrological regimes, and the poor taxonomic knowledge of the Spanish macroinvertebrate fauna at species level.

Introduction

The recent developments and experience gained in biomonitoring in Spain have not been followed by legal obligations on public authorities. In fact, except for the use of bacteria to evaluate the suitability of water for drinking purposes, the use of biomonitoring to assess river quality in Spain has lagged behind some other European countries, and it has not been incorporated into legislation for routine surveys.

For routine surveillance throughout the country a "General Quality Index" (ICG, Indice de Calidad General) is used, based on chemical variables (Mingo 1980). This index is defined as the weighted sum of nine basic variables (BOD, COD, dissolved oxygen, suspended solids, pH, conductivity, total coliforms, total phosphates, and nitrates) and 14 complementary parameters (which include heavy metals and salts such as sulphates and chlorides). Thus:

$$ICG = \sum (Qi \times Pi) \tag{1}$$

In eqn (1), Qi is a characteristic function of each parameter and Pi weights the importance of each parameter as follows:

$$Pi = (1/ai) \div \sum (1/ai) \tag{2}$$

In eqn (2), *ai* takes values from 1 to 4, according to the degree of importance attributed to each parameter.

The ICG varies from 0 to 100, and particular ranges of the values correspond to five water quality classes.

Four hundred and fifty-three automated surveillance sites have been established on stretches of the principal river basins (named the COCA web). Data are sent to a control centre by satellite, thereby giving early warning of potential problems. There are provisions to increase the number of automated surveillance sites to 1053.

In Catalonia, a simplified index of quality has been developed which also has a range of values from 0 to 100. This uses only five parameters (temperature, COD, suspended solids, dissolved oxygen and conductivity). The analysis of data is easily automated, thus providing instantaneous information on water quality (Queralt, Godé *et al.* 1995).

Official reports of water quality in Spain are therefore based on physical, chemical and bacteriological analysis. However, in many cases where environmental impacts may occur, studies of macroinvertebrate communities and the use of biotic indices to assess the river quality are also required by water authorities, when operating conditions for engineering schemes are being negotiated.

In Spain, the practical application of biotic indices in biological monitoring started at the end of the 1970s and underwent considerable development during the1980s. Little attention was paid to saprobic methodologies and most studies used methods based on the "Biotic Score" of Chandler (1970) and the biotic indices developed by Woodiwiss (1964) and by Tuffery & Verneaux (1967). Examples included Alba-Tercedor & Prat (1992) and Alba-Tercedor *et al.* (1992). In addition, some adaptations or new approaches to biological indices have been developed in Spain (Table 14.1).

Table 14.1. *Spanish adaptations or new approaches to biological indices.*

(1) Adapted from the biotic score of Chandler (1970).
(2) Adapted from the biotic indices of Woodiwiss (1964) and Tuffery & Verneaux (1967).

Indices	References
Mancha[1]	González del Tánago *et al.* (1979a, 1979b)
Jarama[1]	Garcia de Jalón & González del Tánago (1980)
Llobregat and Besòs (BILL)[2]	Prat *et al.* (1983)
Duero	González del Tánago & Garcia de Jalón (1984) and Garcia de Jalón & González del Tánago (1986)
Segre (IBS)[2]	Palau & Palomes (1985, 1986)
Spanish adaptation of the "Biological Monitoring Working Party" score system (BMWP')	Alba-Tercedor & Sánchez-Ortega (1988)

One example is the "Biotic Index of the Duero Basin" (BIDB) (González del Tánago & Garcia de Jalón 1984; Garcia de Jalón & González del Tánago 1986). This index takes the river zoning concept into account and is calculated from the expression:

$$BIDB = f1(E) \times f2(C) \tag{3}$$

In eqn (3), $f1(E)$ is a function of the community structure as a synecological factor (in practice, $f1(E)$ is Shannon's H diversity value) and $f2(C)$ is a function of the community composition as an autoecological factor, and thus is different in each zone of the river:

Rhithron zone: $\qquad f2(C) = 2(S_{int}) + (S_{ind}) - 2(S_{eut}) - 5(S_{poll})$ (4)

Epipotamon zone: $\qquad f2(C) = 3(S_{int}) + (S_{ind}) - 0.5(S_{eut}) - 5(S_{poll})$ (5)

Mesopotamon zone: $\qquad f2(C) = 3[4(S_{int}) + (S_{ind}) - 10(S_{poll})]$ (6)

In eqns (4) to (6), S corresponds to the number of species present, which are classed as intolerant (int), indifferent (ind), indicators of eutrophy (eut) or indicators of pollution (poll).

In the 1980s the development and use of biological indicators in Spain followed the same trend as in other countries. Thus, the comment by Bartsch & Ingram (1966) that *"there are about as many procedures [in North America] as number of biologists working in this field"*, also applied to Spain. However, towards the end of the decade, the development of BMWP' (Alba-Tercedor & Sánchez-Ortega 1988) led to this new index being widely used throughout Spain (see Table 14.1).

The BMWP', a Spanish adaptation of the British Biological Monitoring Working Party (BMWP) score system

The BMWP' (Alba-Tercedor & Sánchez-Ortega 1988) is an adaptation of the British BMWP score system (Armitage, Moss *et al.* 1983). The modifications have included the addition of new families, changes in some scores (Table 14.2) and division of scores into five classes, representing varying degrees of pollution (Table 14.3). The BMWP' families and their scores, included in Table 14.2, correspond to a recent updating (Alba-Tercedor 1996), and the five levels of river quality in Table 14.3 were established according to the "Extended Biotic Index" (after Ghetti, Bernini *et al.* 1983). In cartographic presentations of survey data, river stretches are presented as one of five different colours according to their assigned quality class.

Apart from the addition of families and changes in score values between the BMWP and BMWP' systems, the sampling procedure was also modified. When the BMWP system is used in conjunction with RIVPACS, macroinvertebrate sampling is for a fixed period of three minutes kick-sweep sampling, which includes proportional collection from each of the different microhabitats present. However, when applying the Spanish BMWP' no specific sampling time is laid down and sampling stops when further searching by eye adds no more new families. This permits samples to be sorted in the field.

The river quality classes are artificial divisions of a continuum, and hence there are difficulties in establishing strict limits to them. By adding or subtracting five to the final score, a site may move from one quality class to another. In these circumstances, the final assessment must be considered intermediate between two classes. In that case the cartographic colour representation must be made by alternating the colours of both quality classes. For example, a final score of 62 would fit into Class II, but should be considered intermediate between Classes II and III because, by subtracting five units, the resulting score of 57 would cause the site to move into Class III. The cartography of the stretch is then represented by alternating green and yellow colours (Alba-Tercedor & Sánchez-Ortega 1988; Alba-Tercedor 1996). This intermediate definition of river quality classes is similar to that used in Italy for the routine application of the Extended Biotic Index (Ghetti 1997).

The high correlation between the BMWP' index and other biotic indices (Rico, Rallo *et al.* 1992) and its acceptance as a meaningful and interpretative system (Palau 1990; Zamora-Muñoz & Alba-Tercedor 1996) justify the adoption of this index by the Spanish Society of Limnology, and its general acceptance all over Spain.

Table 14.2. *Families of macroinvertebrates and corresponding scores according to the BMWP'*
(a Spanish adaptation of the British BMWP score system).

Changes and innovations with respect to the original table by Armitage, Moss *et al.* (1983) are indicated as follows:
families in italics have new scores and new families are shown in **bold**.

Families	Score
Siphlonuridae, Heptageniidae, Leptophlebiidae, Potamanthidae, Ephemeridae Taeniopterygidae, Leuctridae, Capniidae, Perlodidae, Perlidae, Chloroperlidae Aphelocheiridae Phryganeidae, Molannidae, Beraeidae, Odontoceridae, Leptoceridae, Goeridae, Lepidostomatidae, Brachycentridae, Sericostomatidae **Athericidae, Blephariceridae**	10
Astacidae Lestidae, Calopterygidae, Gomphidae, Cordulegastridae, Aeshnidae Corduliidae, Libellulidae Psychomyiidae, Philopotamidae, **Glossosomatidae**	8
Ephemerellidae, **Prosopistomatidae** Nemouridae Rhyacophilidae, Polycentropodidae, Limnephilidae, **Ecnomidae**	7
Neritidae, Viviparidae, Ancylidae, **Thiaridae** Hydroptilidae Unionidae Corophiidae, Gammaridae, **Atyidae** Platycnemididae, Coenagrionidae	6
Oligoneuriidae, Polymitarcidae Dryopidae, Elmidae, **Helophoridae, Hydrochidae, Hydraenidae**, Clambidae Hydropsychidae Tipulidae, Simuliidae Planariidae, Dendrocoelidae, **Dugesiidae**	5
Baetidae, *Caenidae* *Haliplidae, Curculionidae, Chrysomelidae* **Tabanidae, Stratiomyidae, Empididae, Dolichopodidae, Dixidae, Ceratopogonidae, Anthomyiidae, Limoniidae, Psychodidae, Sciomyzidae, Rhagionidae** Sialidae Piscicolidae **Hydracarina**	4
Mesoveliidae, Hydrometridae, Gerridae, Nepidae, Naucoridae, **Pleidae, Veliidae,** *Notonectidae, Corixidae* Scirtidae, *Hydrophilidae, Hygrobiidae, Dytiscidae, Gyrinidae* Valvatidae, Hydrobiidae, Lymnaeidae, Physidae, Planorbidae, **Bithyniidae, Bythinellidae**, Sphaeriidae Glossiphoniidae, Hirudinidae, Erpobdellidae Asellidae, **Ostracoda**	3
Chironomidae, **Culicidae, Ephydridae, Thaumaleidae**	2
Oligochaeta (whole class), **Syrphidae**	1

Table 14.3. *Five classes of river quality in Spain, with their meanings and cartographic colours for values of the BMWP'.*

Class	Quality	Score	Meaning	Colour
I	Good	>150	Very clean waters (pristine)	Blue
		101–150	Not polluted, or not noticeably altered system	Blue
II	Passable	61–100	Evidence of effects of mild pollution	Green
III	Dubious	36–60	Polluted waters (altered system)	Yellow
IV	Critical	16–35	Very polluted waters (very altered system)	Orange
V	Very critical	≤15	Strongly polluted waters (strongly altered system)	Red

In Spain, biotic indices were often criticised because it was not always possible to demonstrate a significant correlation between the prevailing physical and chemical conditions, and the biological condition of sites, as indicated by the index values. However, it is now generally accepted that this apparent contradiction can result from the physical and chemical data measuring the conditions at the time of sampling only, whereas the structure of the biological communities represents a summation of a temporal sequence of past conditions.

Particular criticism has also been levelled at some biotic indices because of their pronounced variability (Murphy 1978), or because they were designed for use within a limited region and may be inappropriate for use in other geographical regions (Hellawell 1978; Washington 1984). In addition, the most consistent criticism of the biotic indices based on macroinvertebrate communities has been that seasonal changes in index values may not be due to changes in river quality. Instead, it has been argued, changes in index values may result from the natural changes in assemblage structure associated with the life cycles of the species present and the natural dynamics of their populations. However, wide applicability of the BMWP' system within the Iberian Peninsula has demonstrated, beyond any doubt, that the index values obtained using the BMWP' system, and the river quality derived from them, are not seasonally dependent (Alba-Tercedor & Prat 1992; Zamora-Muñoz, Sáinz-Cantero *et al.* 1995).

Experience with classification and prediction techniques in Spanish rivers

TWINSPAN (Hill 1979a), a polythetic, divisive classification technique, has been widely used to characterise stretches of Spanish river basins (Pardo 1992; Zamora-Muñoz 1992). Using a site classification based on faunal composition as the starting point, multiple discriminant analysis (MDA) (Klecka 1975) can then be used to link the biological information to the known physical and chemical characteristics of each site. The next step is to use this physical and chemical data to predict the classification group and hence the macroinvertebrates expected at a new site, based on their physical and chemical conditions, as in RIVPACS (Wright *et al.* 1993). An early version of this package (RIVPACS I) was used successfully to predict macroinvertebrate communities at family level in two rivers from north-western Spain (Armitage, Pardo *et al.* 1990). However, as was pointed out by Wright (1994): *"Britain has a restricted range of families of macroinvertebrates compared to Spain and there are very substantial differences in the fauna at species level. Hence the faunal and also the environmental database which has been developed for rivers in the UK can never have a direct application to the full range of environmental conditions and macroinvertebrate assemblages within Spain".*

More recently, in south-eastern Spain, Pujante, Furse *et al.* (2000) also demonstrated the applicability of this technique for assessing the biological condition of rivers.

The development of a preliminary version of RIVPACS
for the Mediterranean rivers of the Valencian region

This study was the first attempt to develop a RIVPACS-type system in the Iberian peninsula, and followed the original procedures adopted in Great Britain (Wright *et al.* 1993). The objective was to develop a system for predicting the macroinvertebrates to be expected at sites on eastward-flowing "Mediterranean" rivers in Spain and, on the basis of the predictions, to evaluate the ecological quality of the sites.

For this trial, the provinces of Castellón, València and Alicante, in the central eastern region of Spain, were selected. In this region the landscape ranges from mountains to coastal plains, and from areas of low to high rainfall. Also, it can be subdivided into separate biogeographic areas.

The predictions generated by RIVPACS represent the fauna that is to be expected at sites of known environmental character in the absence of significant environmental stress. This implies that, ideally, the initial database from which predictions are derived should comprise high quality information on pristine river sites. This ideal is difficult to attain and, in the absence of pristine conditions, the reference sites must be as little affected as possible by any kind of environmental stress, particulary those of human origin. It is also imperative to cover all the variability of natural types of rivers in the area. The selection of the representative sites or reference sites is an arduous task but one that is vital to the effectiveness of the system.

Preliminary selection of reference sites for rivers in the Valencian region

In an earlier study in this region, Pujante (1993) sampled 96 sites from 41 rivers. There were large and very evident differences in the quality of these rivers, which were commonly related to their geographical location. In the north (Castellón province) there were many good quality sites, whereas in the south (mainly Alicante province) widespread and severe pollution of the river systems was common. This separation is a consequence of the demographic and socio-economic conditions in the study region.

The three provinces of the study region are much more densely populated in the coastal plain than in the mountains. Throughout the plain, as a result of climatic conditions, agricultural activities are very well developed and heavily dependent on irrigation. Thus, most of the lowland watercourses have suffered all kinds of alterations (e.g. channelisation, realignment, impoundment and abstraction) and the water is intensively used. As a result, some of the main rivers run completely dry at their mouths. Industrial activities are also very well developed in the coastal strip, and the legislation on effluent discharge is not always complied with. This leads to the lowland rivers being highly polluted chemically as well as organically, and these impacts are each exacerbated by the low flows.

Low flows also result from climatic conditions, as well as from high agricultural, industrial and domestic demand. The Mediterranean climate shows an extreme cycle of flooding and drought in this part of the country. Consequently, a characteristic river type in the study area is the "rambla", an ephemeral watercourse that flows only during periods of heavy rain. In general, few studies have been made of the ecology, chemistry and biology of these streams (Vidal-Abarca *et al.* 1992). Whilst the ramblas are common in the region, it is difficult to select suitable reference sites because aquatic assemblages can be supported only for the short periods of flow. Furthermore, these periods of flow are more closely related to the incidence of heavy and prolonged rain than to the season of the year.

Other problems affecting the development of a RIVPACS-type model were related to the biogeography of the region and difficulties of identifying some of the Spanish aquatic macroinvertebrate fauna. For example, distinct differences exist between the species representatives of certain genera or families in the different biogeographic units, as Sanz & Pinkster (2000) demonstrate for the three study provinces, and these may be important in distinguishing river types. A disadvantage of using administrative boundaries for setting up study regions is that they do not necessarily coincide with the territorial limits of the biogeographic regions. Inclusion of different biogeographic units within the same classification may also result in taxa being predicted to occur at sites which lie outside their particular distribution range. This factor was recognised in the UK, where RIVPACS III included separate systems for the contiguous mainland of Britain (England, Wales and Scotland) and for Northern Ireland. It has also resulted in the development of a multiplicity of different classification and prediction systems for different administrative regions of Australia (see Chapter 8).

Taxonomic difficulties arise because the Iberian fauna contains a large proportion of endemic species, and lack of knowledge on the larval stages of many insects makes specific identification of numerous groups difficult at present. In their study, Pujante, Furse *et al.* (2000) worked at species level for groups of taxa where this was consistently possible, but frequently at a coarser, though more reliable level, where species identification was not achievable.

Refining the selection of reference sites for rivers in the Valencian region

As a consequence of some of the problems outlined above, selection of reference sites from the north of the study region was straightforward, but all of the southern sites had to be rejected. Similarly, it was easy to select reference sites in the mountains but increasingly difficult to find good quality sites with decreasing altitude. The primary criterion used to select the first set of reference sites was that they should be in the BMWP' quality Class 1 (Alba-Tercedor & Sánchez-Ortega 1988). For the rejected sites, secondary criteria of acceptance were set up, based on minimum acceptable levels of ASPT' and the number of taxa (Pujante, Furse *et al.* 2000). A total of 48 sites met the selection criteria but an equal number failed to do so and were rejected.

A second, detailed survey of the region was therefore undertaken to find possible reference sites for the poorly represented river types. In practice, several gaps could be filled but this proved to be impossible for sites close to the sea in the lowland area. Absence of the latter types of sites meant that any RIVPACS-type system resulting from the study could not be used to make reliable predictions for the coastal strip.

From the set of sites sampled during the second survey, 21 were considered to be of sufficiently good quality to be suitable as potential reference sites for the development of a RIVPACS system for the study area. Developmental procedures, as described above, involved site classification by TWINSPAN (Hill 1979a), followed by the use of MDA (Klecka 1975) to mathematically link the biological classification to the values of a set of environmental variables.

The environmental variables selected for use in MDA were the ones already available from the earlier work of Pujante (1993), together with latitude and longitude. This set of variables was broadly similar to those used for RIVPACS development (Wright *et al.* 1993). However, future development of this system in Iberia, particularly over a wider geographic area, should involve more detailed assessments of the variables that most influence species distribution, and hence the predictive accuracy of a RIVPACS-type system. It may transpire that different suites of variables are most effective in different biogeographic units.

The first classification of sites was made using the original 48 sites that were selected as meeting defined quality criteria from the work of Pujante (1993). MDA was used to compare the observed and expected BMWP' index values of each of these 48 sites, together with the values for the 48 rejected sites, plus those for the 21 additional sites selected from the second survey. A new set of criteria was devised to select the best quality sites from the 117 that were evaluated, to provide a secondary classification. Criteria were based on observed to expected ratios for these sites (Pujante, Furse *et al.* 2000) and followed standards previously operated in Great Britain for the 1990 River Quality Survey (Sweeting, Lowson *et al.* 1992).

A total of 60 sites met the new criteria and these were used to develop the second classification. This classification comprised eight end-groups with a minimum group size of three sites. A re-substitution test of the system assumed that a site was placed in its biological end-group, on the basis of its environmental data, if it had the highest probability of membership of that group when MDA was applied. By this criterion, 85% of the 60 sites were assigned to their "correct" biological group. Comparison between success rates achieved for different classifications is complicated by, amongst other factors, the different numbers of end-groups, numbers and intrinsic variability of sites, and number and suitability of predictor variables. However, as a guide, in the forerunner to RIVPACS, using species-level data for 268 sites, the range of success varied between 69.4% and 79.1% of correct site allocations (Furse, Moss *et al.* 1984). On this basis, the results for Iberia must be seen as encouraging.

The same classification of 60 sites was also used to assign each of the 117 available sites to one of four quality classes, in the same manner that was used for RIVPACS when assessing the results of the 1990 River Quality Survey (Sweeting, Lowson *et al.* 1992). Full details of this process and the most important predictor variables are given in Pujante, Furse *et al.* (2000).

Opportunities for a predictive approach in Spain under objectives of the European Directive on Ecological Quality of Surface Waters

In 1994 the European Community (EC) published a draft proposal for a Council Directive (94/C 222/06) on the Ecological Quality of Water (Council of the European Communities 1994). Subsequently, in June 1998, the EC published an updated draft proposal (9265/98 ADDI, DGI) to monitor the "ecological status" of surface waters (Council of the European Union 1998). In this document, ecological status was defined as *"an expression of the quality of the structure and functioning of aquatic ecosystems associated with surface waters"*. For this purpose, at least one of four biological communities is to be studied (phytoplankton, macrophytes and phytobenthos, benthic invertebrate fauna, and fish fauna) and data shall be expressed as a numerical ratio with values between zero and one, *"representing the relationship between the values of the biological parameters observed for a given body of surface waters and the value for these parameters in the reference conditions applicable to that body"*.

It is well known that aquatic communities integrate many factors representative of the health of river basins (Rosenberg & Resh 1993b). From a practical viewpoint, it is considered unrealistic to take account of all groups of parameters. Therefore, it has been suggested that to assess river quality at least one of four parameters should be required, with an understanding that to characterise the ecological quality of the river, the biological parameters are the most important (Prat *et al.* 1997).

Docampo (1995) has proposed an ecological quality index for rivers of the Basque country and, following the recommendations of the EC (Council of the European Communities 1994), Prat *et al.* (1996) have developed an ecological index for the two Catalan rivers, the Llobregat and Besòs. In the Catalan system, ecological quality is assessed from each of the following: (1) 12 physical and chemical parameters, (2) the eutrophy (measured as biomass of the alga *Cladophora*), (3) biomonitoring with macroinvertebrates, (4) an evaluation of the riparian vegetation according to the EC Habitats Directive (Council of the European Communities 1992) and (5) the vertebrate communities. Here, biomonitoring with macroinvertebrates uses the Llobregat and Besòs Index – BILL (Prat *et al.* 1983), which involves BMWP' and the ratio E/S (where E = the number of taxa of Ephemeroptera+Plecoptera captured at a site, and S = the total number of taxa captured at that site).

Prat *et al.* (1996) conclude that the most important factors required to define river quality are the biological parameters of the river itself, and to a lesser degree the structure of the riparian vegetation. It is important to recognise that a well developed river-bank vegetation may occur, which can support a diverse bird community, under a wide range of river quality conditions. Thus, these varied results need to be integrated and it may be necessary to consider other parameters such as land-use within the river basin, as suggested by Roth *et al.* (1996).

The need to develop standard techniques throughout Spain

Given the number of different approaches that have been adopted in Spain for assessing the ecological quality of watercourses, and the number of parameters that may need to be taken into account in applying European directives, it is becoming increasingly important to develop a series of standard techniques. The adoption of standard techniques would benefit from the creation of a national organisation, like the Environment Agency in England and Wales. Such an organisation could be responsible for unifying and coordinating the relevant scientific teams working on river ecology, so that they employ a standard sampling method that would make the results among different areas comparable. In this standard method, factors such as the macroinvertebrate sampling device, the timing for each sample, the sampling procedure, the sampling seasons, the level of identification, the environmental variables to record, etc., would be stipulated. At present the use of different methodologies has been the norm (González del Tánago *et al.* 1979a; Prat *et al.* 1983; Garcia de Jalón & González del Tánago 1986; Palau & Palomes 1986; Docampo 1995), and the collection of data is so non-homogeneous that often they cannot be used for other purposes, such as the development of a RIVPACS-type system in the Iberian peninsula.

In Pujante's pilot study in the Valencian Community, the standardisation of sampling method was not a problem because it was all undertaken by the same small team from the University of València, adopting the same approach as that used to develop RIVPACS. However, when larger geographic areas are being considered, such as the whole of Spain, many more people and organisations would need to be involved and all should adopt compatible procedures.

Using a RIVPACS-type predictive system in Spain

The preliminary development of "RIVPACS" for the Valencian Community has shown that there is no conceptual reason why such a system should not work in Spain. RIVPACS, and its preliminary Spanish derivative, predict expected values of the BMWP/BMWP' indices in the absence of environmental stress. This system fits well with the underlying philosophy of the European directives, that ecological quality should be expressed in terms of the extent to which prevailing biological and environmental conditions meet expectations.

The Valencian trial version of RIVPACS used the BMWP' system (Alba-Tercedor & Sánchez-Ortega 1988) which is becoming widely accepted in Spain. A good correlation has been demonstrated between the BMWP (and BMWP') and the different biotic indices used within Europe (Alba-Tercedor & Sánchez-Ortega 1988; and an unpublished exercise (CEN/TC230/WG2/TG1) carried out by the European Committee for Standardisation in 1993). The delay in incorporating biomonitoring protocols into Spanish legislation may now prove advantageous, because it may be simpler to adopt a methodology under the directive relating to the field of water policy (Council of the European Union 1998).

Whilst there may be no conceptual difficulties in applying predictive systems such as RIVPACS, in Spain, numerous practical difficulties remain to be solved (Wright 1994), many of which applied to the Valencian system. Firstly, it may be difficult to find reference sites at low altitudes (Alba-Tercedor *et al.* 1992; Pujante, Furse *et al.* 2000) or for particular types of rivers, such as ramblas. Secondly, very different biogeographic zones (with a poorly known fauna at species level and many endemic species), and different hydrological regimes (from alpine, snow-dependent rivers, to Mediterranean streams with no water for long periods) have to be accommodated, and each one represents a big challenge. Thirdly, because of poor taxonomic knowledge, it may not even be realistic to defend the idea of a predictive system at species level. However, the high diversity of macroinvertebrate families inhabiting Iberian rivers makes it possible to produce a predictive system, first to family level and later to generic or even species level. The initial requirement is the collection of reference site data, first identified to family level but then retained for future appraisal at more precise taxonomic levels as this becomes possible.

Spain already has the scientific and human resources to undertake the task of developing a RIVPACS-type system, based on standard field and laboratory procedures. It also has good relationships with the RIVPACS team in England. The task is a realistic one but critically the financial resources are now required to launch this project.

Acknowledgements

We are indebted to Mike Furse and John Wright for valuable suggestions and corrections to an earlier version of the manuscript.

CHAPTER 15

Effects of taxonomic resolution and use of subsets of the fauna on the performance of RIVPACS-type models

CHARLES P. HAWKINS[1] AND RICHARD H. NORRIS[2]

[1]*Department of Fisheries and Wildlife,
Watershed Science Unit and Ecology Center,
Utah State University, Logan, Utah 84322-5210, USA*

[2]*Cooperative Research Centre for Freshwater Ecology,
University of Canberra, Canberra 2601, AUSTRALIA*

Summary

Models designed to predict assemblage composition and measure biological impairment of stream ecosystems can be built with biological data described at different levels of taxonomic resolution, and can include all or part of the invertebrate assemblage present at sites. Models based on identifications at family level appeared to be adequate for assessing biotic conditions in Australia, whereas we found that models at species level were required for montane streams of California, USA. Chironomid midges (Diptera) are a conspicuous component of the invertebrate fauna of many streams, but in the USA and elsewhere they are frequently excluded from analyses, or identified only to subfamily, because of the time and cost involved in identifying them to species.

We tested three hypotheses about the relationships between taxonomic resolution, completeness of taxonomic coverage, and the ability of models to discriminate between streams with different biological composition. The first hypothesis was that the adequacy of family-level models would be inversely related to the amount of adaptive radiation occurring within families. The second hypothesis was that the exclusion of chironomid midges from samples would reduce the ability of species-level models to discriminate between streams. The third hypothesis was that models based solely on chironomid taxa would perform as well as models based on all taxa. We tested the first hypothesis by comparing the error rates of discriminant functions models built from data at family and species level, with the number of mayfly, stonefly and caddisfly genera per family in Great Britain, Australia, and California. We tested the second and third hypotheses by comparing values for observed/expected ratios obtained from three species-level models built from the Californian data: one with complete taxonomic coverage, one that excluded chironomid midges, and one with chironomid taxa only. Our results were consistent with the first hypothesis, but did not support the second and third hypotheses. These results imply that the taxonomic resolution and completeness of taxonomic coverage needed to develop models of acceptable sensitivity may vary greatly among the biotic regions of the world.

Introduction

Aquatic invertebrates are used extensively to monitor and assess the biological condition of freshwater ecosystems in many countries. The value of using aquatic invertebrates in monitoring and assessment rests with the fact that they can provide a direct and time-integrated measure of the effects of pollutants on aquatic biota (Karr 1991) and be cost-effective relative to traditional physical-chemical measures (Norris & Georges 1986; Ohio EPA 1987; Brinkhurst 1993). The specific costs associated with using aquatic invertebrates depend on both the costs of field sampling and sample processing. The latter typically consists of sorting, identifying and enumerating animals from preserved samples; thus the time and cost to process a sample depends on both the breadth of taxonomic groups examined and the level of resolution used in the identification of individual organisms. Water quality managers would like to maximize the information gained for the effort or cost expended; thus it is important to know how taxonomic resolution and completeness of taxonomic coverage affect our ability to detect the effects of pollution.

Recently, we evaluated how well predictive RIVPACS-type models (Moss, Furse *et al.* 1987; Wright 1995; Norris 1996) could detect biological impairment of mountain streams in California that are associated with silviculture activity (Hawkins, Norris *et al.* 2000). Predictive models were built from collections of stream invertebrates identified to the near-species level (hereafter called "species"). All groups of aquatic insects were identified to species level, including chironomid midge larvae. Non-insect macroinvertebrates (generally ≥ 1 mm) were also included in the models, but the taxonomic level of resolution varied from species to class, depending on the group.

We found that models based on identifications at species level detected the effects of logging, whereas models based on identifications at family level did not. In making RIVPACS-type assessments, discriminant functions models (DFMs) are used to estimate the probabilities of a site belonging in previously defined classes of sites. For the model built for California streams, the classification errors associated with the DFM were high (*ca* 45%) for the family model and low (*ca* 20%) for the species model, implying that differences in classification errors may have been responsible for the difference in sensitivity between models at family and species level. The relative magnitude of DFM errors between the family-level and species-level models in the Californian study, contrasts with analyses performed in both Great Britain and Australia, where only minor to moderate differences in DFM errors occurred between family-level and species-level models (Furse, Moss *et al.* 1984; Norris 1996). One reason why models at family level might have high error rates in some areas, but not in others, is that the amount of adaptive radiation occurring within families might vary among continents and biogeographic regions. In areas with few species per family, identifications at family level would provide much of the ecological information contained in data at species level. In contrast, in areas with many species per family, identifications at family level would provide less ecological information about the fauna, especially if species differed in their ecological requirements and tolerances.

Of the 293 taxa collected from the sites examined by Hawkins, Norris *et al.* (2000), 31% were chironomid midges. Identifying chironomid larvae to species level more than doubled the time of sample processing and hence both the cost of the study and the time-span between field sampling and reporting the results. However, several midge species appeared to be adversely affected by silviculture activity within the study basins, and excluding midges from predictive models might reduce their reliability in detecting overall biological impairment at test sites. Furthermore, because of their ecological diversity and wide distribution, assessments made from chironomids alone could conceivably provide accurate descriptions of overall biotic conditions. If this were true, rapid assessments based on easily collected and identified exuviae of chironomid pupae (Coffman & Ferrington 1996) might be useful in assessing the condition of a wide variety of aquatic habitats.

Here, we describe analyses designed to test three hypotheses: (1) that the difference in error rates between species-level and family-level DFMs would be related to regional differences in the number of species per family, (2) that exclusion of midges from models would result in a significant reduction in our ability to discriminate between unimpaired and impaired sites, and (3) that use of midge taxa alone would produce assessments comparable to those based on all taxa.

Materials and methods

Test of hypothesis (1)

To test our first hypothesis, we used estimates of DFM misclassification rates taken from Furse, Moss *et al.* (1984) for Great Britain, Norris (1996) for the Australian Capital Territory, Marchant, Hirst *et al.* (1997) for Victoria, Australia (unpublished error rates provided by R. Marchant), and Hawkins, Norris *et al.* (2000) for California, together with estimates of genus to family ratios (GFRs) compiled from Wright, Blackburn *et al.* (1996) for Great Britain, Marchant, Hirst *et al.* (1997) for Victoria, Australia, and Hawkins, Norris *et al.* (2000) for California. For comparison with the individual Australian studies, we have included mean family DFM errors, mean number of sites sampled, and mean number of groups in the classification derived from the 40 family models described by Simpson and Norris in Chapter 9. We assumed that the GFRs for all Australian sites were similar. We then examined how the magnitude of misclassification errors associated with the family-level and species-level DFMs varied with GFRs.

We recognize that estimates of DFM errors can vary with the method used to assess error, the completeness of the faunal survey, the number of sites and classification groups, and the choice of predictor variables. Furse, Moss *et al.* (1984) used re-substitution to measure error, which gives lower error rates than the cross-validation used by Norris (1996), Marchant, Hirst *et al.* (1997) and Hawkins, Norris *et al.* (2000). To minimize confounding associated with number of groups, we used the 8-group datasets provided by Furse, Moss *et al.* (1984, their Table 8). Although we could not control or adjust for the number of sites or predictor variables, we considered the potentially confounding effects of both these factors when interpreting analyses. Similarly, we could not control for differences among studies in the number of habitats sampled. Of the studies considered here, only Furse, Moss *et al.* (1984) sampled biota from multiple types of habitats. They also based analyses on combined data collected from three different seasons. All other studies restricted sampling to one main type of habitat. Norris (1996) and Hawkins, Norris *et al.* (2000) sampled riffles during the summer period. Marchant, Hirst *et al.* (1997) used combined data from samples collected on four to six occasions, and they restricted their analysis to samples collected from bankside habitats. No statistical tests were performed because we had only four sets of data on which to base analyses. We therefore visually determined if trends in the data were consistent with the hypothesis.

We based estimates of GFRs on data from three orders: mayflies (Ephemeroptera), stoneflies (Plecoptera), and caddisflies (Trichoptera). These orders were used because the taxonomy of these three taxa is most consistently known on a worldwide basis and they are broadly distributed across the world. We used the number of genera to families rather than species to families, as a measure of adaptive radiation, for two reasons. First, the consistency of identifications at species level appeared to vary substantially among the three geographical regions, whereas genera seemed to be consistently identified. Second, Wiggins & Mackay

(1978) suggest that differences in ecological specialization among aquatic insects occur primarily among genera, with mainly subtle differences occurring among species within genera.

Test of hypotheses (2) and (3)

We tested the second and third hypotheses by two methods. First, we compared how observed/expected ratios (O/E) calculated from the three different species-level models (with midges, without midges, and midges only) varied between reference and test sites. Second, we calculated regression statistics describing how well the partial taxa models (without midges and midges only) predicted O/E values calculated from the full model with midges. For these analyses, we calculated two different measures of O/E based on probability of occurrence thresholds (Moss, Furse *et al.* (1987) of ≥0.01 and ≥0.5, hereafter referred to as O/E_{01} and O/E_{50}, respectively. Procedures used in building the models are described in detail by Norris (1996) and Hawkins, Norris *et al.* (2000).

   Models were built with biological and physical-chemical data from 254 reference sites, and the condition of each of 234 test sites was then evaluated by examining O/E values. We previously showed that test site O/E values were inversely related to the amount of logging activity upstream of a site (Hawkins, Norris *et al.* 2000). If the without-midges model predicted substantially fewer impaired sites than the model with midges, the data would be consistent with hypothesis (2). In addition, weak or no correlation between test site O/E values for the without-midges and with-midges models would be consistent with hypothesis (2). Hypothesis (3) would be supported if the midge-only model assessed the same number of impaired sites as the with-midge model, and if O/E values for the two models were strongly correlated with a slope of 1.0 (i.e., the midge-only model was an unbiased predictor of the with-midges model O/E values).

Results

Hypothesis (1)

Discriminant functions model (DFM) error rates. In general, mean family-level DFM error rates were about 50% higher than mean species-level error rates (Table 15.1). Only Norris (1996) reported a greater error rate for the species model than for the family model. The difference between family and species models was highest for the models that we constructed for Californian streams (Hawkins, Norris *et al.* 2000). Differences between family and species DFM error rates were associated with relatively large variation, among the three regions, in DFM error rates of the species-level models.

Genus to family ratios (GFRs). The number of genera per family calculated over all three orders varied from a low of 1.5 for the data from Victoria, Australia, to a high of 2.9 for the data from California (Table 15.2). There was little difference in the GFRs for mayflies between regions. Californian streams had the highest GFRs for stoneflies, and Great Britain had the highest GFRs for caddis.

Relationship between DFM error rates, GFRs, number of sites and number of groups. The magnitude of family-level DFM error rates was positively related to GFRs as hypothesized (Fig. 15.1). However, family-level DFM error rates were also highly correlated with the number of sites and the number of groups included in each of the classifications. In contrast to classification errors for family models, classification errors for species models were unrelated to GFRs ($r^2 = 0.05$), number of sites ($r^2 = 0.03$), or number of groups ($r^2 = 0.09$).

Table 15.1. *Classification error rates associated with the discriminant functions models (DFM) for species-level and family-level data from sites in Great Britain, Australia and California.*

Numbers that are separated by slash marks (/) under the columns for Groups and Variables refer to the numbers of groups and predictor variables used in species and family models, respectively.

(1) Classification errors estimated by re-substitution and are probably underestimates relative to other studies.

(2) Mean values for 40 models.

Source	Sites	Groups	Variables	DFM errors (%) Species	Family
Furse, Moss *et al.* (1984)[1]	268	8 / 8	28 / 28	27	43
Norris (1996)	51	4 / 3	4 / 4	42	34
Marchant, Hirst *et al.* (1997)	49	3 / 4	5 / 4	12	26
Simpson & Norris (1999)[2]	103	− / 4.7	− −	−	31
This study	254	10 / 7	11 / 9	18	45

Table 15.2. *Genus to family ratios for mayflies, stoneflies, caddisflies and combined data for the three orders in (1) Great Britain, (2) Australia and (3) California.*

Source	Mayflies	Stoneflies	Caddisflies	Combined
(1) Wright, Blackburn *et al.* (1996)	2.1	2.0	3.2	2.7
(2) Marchant, Hirst *et al.* (1997)	2.2	1.3	1.4	1.5
(3) This study	2.3	3.3	2.4	2.9

Table 15.3. *Means ± standard deviations for O/E values from reference and test sites in Californian mountain streams, calculated with and without midge taxa and for two different probability of capture thesholds* ($p \geq 0.01 = O/E_{01}$, and $p \geq 0.50 = O/E_{50}$).

Model	No. of taxa	Reference Sites Mean O/E_{01}	Mean O/E_{50}	Test Sites Mean O/E_{01}	Mean O/E_{50}
With midges	226	1.03±0.28	1.02±0.17	0.92±0.26	0.87±0.18
Without midges	147	1.03±0.30	1.02±0.17	0.90±0.30	0.86±0.20
Midges only	79	1.04±0.38	1.01±0.25	0.97±0.33	0.87±0.29

Hypothesis (2)

Number of test sites predicted as impaired. Excluding midges from the predictive models did not affect the overall statistical distributions of O/E values for either reference or test sites (Table 15.3). The only apparent effect of excluding midges was a slight (<15%) increase in the standard deviations of the O/E values. This increase was more noticeable for test sites than for reference sites, and was slightly greater for O/E_{01} values than O/E_{50} values.

Correlations between model outputs. Without-midge O/E values were highly, but not perfectly, correlated with O/E values calculated for with-midges (Fig. 15.2). Between 15 and 27% of the

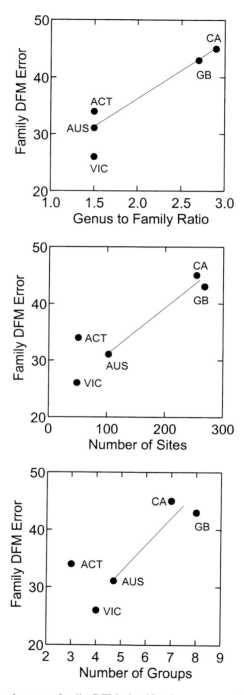

Figure 15.1. Relationships between family DFM classification errors and the genus to family ratio (top panel), number of sites classified (middle panel), and number of groups used in the classification (bottom panel). Lines are fitted by eye and forced through the point (AUS) describing the mean values calculated from 40 models (see Chapter 9). ACT = Australian Capital Territory, CA = California, GB = Great Britain, VIC = Victoria, Australia. (Further explanation in the text)

variation in with-midge O/E values was not predicted by without-midge O/E values. Furthermore, the slopes of all four relationships shown in Figure 15.2 were significantly less than 1.0, implying that the non-midge O/E values gave biased estimates of O/E values based on models containing midges. Without-midge O/E values slightly underestimated high O/E values based on all taxa, and slightly overestimated low O/E values based on all taxa.

Hypothesis (3)

Number of test sites predicted as impaired. For reference site data, mean O/E values for the midge-only models were nearly identical with those calculated from models based on all taxa for both O/E_{01} and O/E_{50} models (Table 15.3). Mean midge-only O/E values were also identical to values observed for test sites based on O/E_{50} models, but not for the O/E_{01} model. This latter midge-only model implied that test sites were more similar on average to reference sites than either the with-midge or without-midge models. In addition, the standard deviations of all midge-only O/E values were higher than those observed for the with-midge and without-midge models.

Correlations between model outputs. The midge-only models were poorer predictors of with-midge O/E values than were the without-midge models (Fig. 15.3). Between 29 and 46% of the variation in with-midge O/E values was not predicted by midge-only O/E values. In addition, the magnitude of bias (deviation from slope = 1.0) in predicting with-midge O/E values was higher than for the without-midge models.

Discussion

Hypothesis (1)

The observed variation in family DFM error rates is consistent with at least two explanations. The positive relationship between error rates and GFRs (Fig. 15.1) shows that the adaptive radiation hypothesis is plausible. However, similar positive relationships between error rates and number of sites and groups (Fig. 15.1) suggests that differences in family-model errors were caused by differences in the number of sites and groups included in the classifications. The data alone can not discriminate between these two alternative hypotheses, although the latter explanation appears to be more parsimonious because it does not require a biological explanation. Consideration of other evidence, however, lends support to the adaptive radiation hypothesis. First, if the observed error rates were simply a statistical consequence of varying the number of sites or groups, then similar relationships – as observed between family DFM error and number of sites and groups – should have occurred with species-model error rates. However, error rates from species models were unrelated to either the number of sites or groups. Second, little of the variation in error rates among the 40 family models that are listed by Simpson and Norris (Fig. 9.3, Chapter 9) was related to either the number of sites or number of groups (r^2 with number of sites = 0.11, p = 0.039; r^2 with number of groups = 0.05, p = 0.15), implying that the differences in error rates among the British, Australian and Californian models may be primarily related to something other than number of sites or groups. It is therefore worth exploring how differences among faunas, in the degree of adaptive radiation within families, could influence DFM prediction errors.

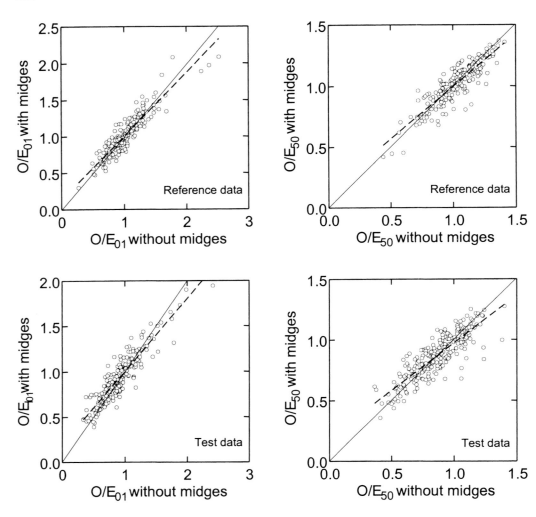

Figure 15.2. Relationships between with-midge (O/E_{wm}) and without-midge (O/E_{wom}) values calculated for probabilities of capture (p_c) of both ≥ 0.01 and ≥ 0.5. Relationships are given for both reference and test sites from mountain streams in California, USA. Dashed lines are the fitted regression lines and solid lines show the theoretical line of perfect fit. Regression models describing each of the relationships are as follows.

(1) Reference sites where $p_c \geq 0.01$: $O/E_{wm} = 0.131 + (0.872 \times O/E_{wom})$; $r^2 = 0.85$, n = 203.

(2) Reference sites where $p_c \geq 0.5$: $O/E_{wm} = 0.138 + (0.858 \times O/E_{wom})$; $r^2 = 0.77$, n = 203.

(3) Test sites where $p_c \geq 0.01$: $O/E_{wm} = 0.204 + (0.799 \times O/E_{wom})$; $r^2 = 0.83$, n = 234.

(4) Test sites where $p_c \geq 0.5$: $O/E_{wm} = 0.193 + (0.781 \times O/E_{wom})$; $r^2 = 0.73$, n = 234.

If ecological diversity exists within any particular taxonomic level, treating all individuals within that taxon as identical will produce a less robust classification, and the potential magnitude of classification errors should be a direct function of the amount of ecological diversity occurring within groups of taxa. It is easy to understand how adaptive radiation of species within families would affect the ability of family-level DFMs to predict sites into the

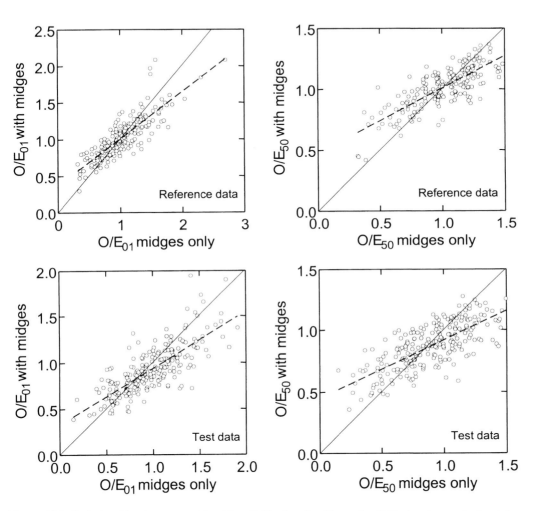

Figure 15.3. Relationships between with-midge (O/E_{wm}) and midge-only (O/E_{mo}) values calculated for probabilities of capture (p_c) of both ≥ 0.01 and ≥ 0.5. Data as in Figure 15.2. Regression models describing each of the relationships are as follows.

(1) Reference sites where $p_c \geq 0.01$: $O/E_{wm} = 0.367 + (0.642 \times O/E_{mo})$; $r^2 = 0.71$, n = 203.

(2) Reference sites where $p_c \geq 0.5$: $O/E_{wm} = 0.474 + (0.535 \times O/E_{mo})$; $r^2 = 0.62$, n = 203.

(3) Test sites where $p_c \geq 0.01$: $O/E_{wm} = 0.328 + (0.611 \times O/E_{mo})$; $r^2 = 0.60$, n = 234.

(4) Test sites where $p_c \geq 0.5$: $O/E_{wm} = 0.451 + (0.471 \times O/E_{mo})$; $r^2 = 0.54$, n = 234.

correct biological groups. If all families in a region each contained one species, then species and family DFMs would contain identical biological information and thus would have identical error rates. In a region with many species per family and high ecological divergence within families, species within the same family would tend to inhabit very different ecological conditions. In this situation, knowing the family to which an individual belonged would provide us with little information to predict what type of stream it came from. Hence, DFMs would tend to have high misclassification rates and our ability to predict impairment would be compromised. Although the amount of ecological divergence within a family is unlikely to be perfectly correlated with the number of genera or species within the family, the fact that no two species have identical ecological requirements suggests that within-group taxon richness should be a good first approximation of ecological diversity.

Although the adaptive radiation hypothesis clearly needs to be more rigorously tested, it has great practical significance if it is true. In some parts of the world, predictive models based on family-level data may not perform well enough to allow reasonably sensitive detection of biological impairment. In addition to the mountainous streams of California, streams in the Appalachian and Rocky Mountains, USA (Lenat 1983, 1987; Ward 1986), Malaysia (Bishop 1973), north-eastern Australia (Pearson et al. 1986; Dean & Cartwright 1987; Rosser & Pearson 1995), Japan (Kubo, Inoue et al. 1975) and Venezuela (A. Flecker, Cornell University, unpublished data), appear to contain high numbers of mayfly, stonefly and caddisfly species, relative to other regions (Vinson 1998). Family-level models, if constructed for these areas, may not perform well.

If the adaptive radiation hypothesis is true and the relationship observed here between family DFM errors and GFRs is a general one, stream researchers and managers should be able to anticipate the level of taxonomic resolution that will be needed before the collection and processing of biological samples. Such knowledge could at least prevent researchers from making the potentially costly assumption that family-level data are sufficient, an assumption that might require re-processing of samples, if not complete re-sampling, before an acceptable model could be built.

Hypothesis (2)

Although the level of taxonomic resolution distinctly affected the ability of the Californian predictive models to detect impairment (Hawkins, Norris et al. 2000), the exclusion of chironomid midges from species models had only a subtle effect on the assessments. Considering the number of species of chironomids that occurred in the study streams, their ecological diversity, and the fact that more species of chironomids appeared to be sensitive to logging effects than any other taxonomic group (Hawkins, Norris et al. 2000), we were surprised to find that the results from without-midge models were so similar to the results from with-midge models. Evidently, the biological information contained in the midge fauna is largely redundant compared with that contained in the rest of the invertebrate assemblage that we sampled.

However, although the with-midge and without-midge models gave essentially identical results on average (i.e. Table 15.3), the without-midge models did not give especially precise predictions of individual with-midge O/E values, and they produced slightly biased estimates relative to with-midge model O/E values. The latter varied by as much as 0.30 O/E units for a given non-midge O/E value (Fig. 15.2). Assuming that O/E values from the with-midge model represent the truest measure of biological condition, this latter fact implies that excluding a substantial component of the fauna may significantly contribute to the various forms of error associated with measuring the biological condition of a site. The bias present in without-midge

O/E models also implies that models in which portions of the taxa are excluded will be less sensitive in detecting real degradation of highly diverse faunas than models based on a more complete set of taxa. Although the reasons for this bias are not completely clear to us, biases of high magnitude could significantly compromise the utility of predictive models in assessing the condition of stream faunas.

The lack of perfect agreement between without-midge and with-midge model O/E values notwithstanding, our results have important practical implications for the development and application of predictive models in streams having diverse without-midge faunas. Considering how time-consuming and costly it is to process and identify midges, it may be possible to ignore this taxon when building models for some regions. Streams in mountainous terrain tend to have diverse non-midge faunas, and without-midge models may perform adequately in these regions. In contrast, chironomids contribute an even higher percentage of the biological diversity in many lowland and low-gradient streams, and we suspect that excluding midges may severely compromise the ability of models to detect impairment in these types of streams.

Hypothesis (3)

Although chironomid midges are among the most ecologically diverse groups of freshwater invertebrates, models based on these taxa alone performed relatively poorly in terms of discriminating between test and reference sites. If banding schemes based on deviation from reference site O/E values were used to score biological condition, the relatively high reference site standard deviations would require test sites to have lower O/E values than in the with-midge or without-midge models, in order to be judged impaired. The fact that the relationships between with-midge O/E values and both without-midge and midge-only O/E values had slopes <1.0 (cf. Figs 15.2 and 15.3) implies that the tendency of partial-taxa models to underestimate high quality sites and overestimate low quality sites is related to the number of taxa used in the model. This issue needs to be carefully studied for at least two reasons. First, if we can only build partial-taxa models because of logistical constraints or lack of taxonomic knowledge, we need to have some idea of how well these models perform relative to models based on more complete faunas. Second, it may be difficult to compare assessments based on models that differ in the proportion of fauna used in predictions. For example, one goal of the United States Environmental Protection Agency is to provide national estimates of the condition of freshwater resources. RIVPACS-type predictive models provide a potential basis for allowing a standard measure of biological condition that can be directly compared across states and regions. However, if regional models differ in the proportion of taxa used in making assessments, our ability to make direct comparisons may be compromised.

Conclusions

The predictive modelling approach first developed by J. F. Wright and colleagues is a powerful tool for biological monitoring and assessment of stream ecosystems. Although the basic approach is clearly sound, tests are needed to examine how well models that are based on species and families work outside Great Britain and Australia. Refinements in either model development or application will likely be needed for streams that differ either physically or biologically from those in the UK and Australia. In this contribution we have also provided tentative evidence of how exclusion of part of the fauna might affect model performance. However, our work was based on how well the models detected a relatively mild form of pollution stress – that associated with timber-harvest practices. Additional work that compares performance across more severe gradients of pollution, and under a wider variety of environmental conditions, is needed to more rigorously examine the consequences of excluding taxa from models. Such work will provide needed practical information to the world's water monitoring community.

Acknowledgements

We thank the organizers of the RIVPACS International Workshop for allowing us to participate in this stimulating workshop. CPH is grateful to the Cooperative Research Centre for Freshwater Ecology at the University of Canberra for providing travel funds to Canberra where the initial modelling of the California data was done. Mark Vinson provided helpful comments on two drafts of the manuscript and shared his as yet unpublished data on global trends in stream insect biodiversity. This chapter is dedicated to Jim Hogue, who spent more than two years sorting and identifying midges; our studies would not have been possible without his efforts. He is still sane and still loves streams.

CHAPTER 16

The 1995 national survey of Swedish lakes and streams: assessment of ecological status using macroinvertebrates

RICHARD K. JOHNSON AND WILLEM GOEDKOOP

*Department of Environmental Assessment, Biodiversity Section,
Swedish University of Agricultural Sciences, Box 7050, S-750 07, Uppsala, SWEDEN*

Summary

Some 700 streams (riffle habitats) and 500 lakes (littoral sites) were sampled for benthic macroinvertebrates in the autumn of 1995 as part of the Swedish national survey. Correlation showed that geographic position influenced the indicator metrics. Hence the data were analysed on national and regional (ecoregion) scales. Stream communities were more taxon-rich (23.2 ± 0.32 taxa) and had higher numbers of individuals per unit effort (1591±95 NPUE) than lake littoral communities (15.9 ± 0.3l taxa and 696 ± 44 NPUE). Three of the most frequently occurring taxa were found in both lakes and streams. However, no clear-cut functional differences were found between stream and lake littoral communities. Mean acidity index values for lakes were slightly lower than for streams. Very acid conditions were indicated in 25% of the lakes but only 7% of the streams. In contrast, streams showed a higher degree of organic enrichment than lakes (lower Saprobien and ASPT values). Relatively high contents of humic matter occur naturally in Swedish waters, and these confounded the use of indices for acidity and organic pollution. Altitude, substratum and vegetation best explained the community composition of lakes. A principal component of two variables, substratum and vegetation, was selected in three of the five ecoregions. For stream communities, chloride concentration accounted for the largest portion of explained variability.

Introduction

National monitoring of lakes and watercourses in Sweden has been performed on various spatial and temporal scales since the early 1960s. At the onset, monitoring programs were principally focussed on discharges of nutrients and metals to Sweden's four largest lakes and marine coastal areas, but during the late 1980s a number of sub-programs were implemented to monitor the effects of acidification and liming. In the early 1990s the Swedish Environmental Protection Agency (SEPA) proposed a revised program (Wiederholm, Johnson *et al.* 1992), addressing the overall objective for the nation's freshwater resources: *"Native species should occur in stable, well-balanced populations, and pollution should not limit the value of water as a fisheries, recreation, and raw water resource"* (SEPA 1990a). To meet the monitoring objectives mandated by SEPA (1990b), it was decided that there was a need for unbiased characterisation of the status of lakes and watercourses, and determination of whether populations are improving, degrading or have remained unchanged, as well as the rate at which these processes may be occurring (see, for example, Wiederholm & Johnson 1997).

A nested sampling design with three tiers was implemented, with (1) national lake and watercourse surveys every fifth year, using physico-chemical and biological indicators to determine spatial patterns of ecological quality, (2) annual monitoring of reference lakes and watercourses to determine among-year variability and trends of indicator metrics, and (3) more intensive monitoring of lakes and watercourses to better understand the importance of interactions between physico-chemical and biological processes within and between sites and their watersheds (e.g. the importance of complex, trophic-level interactions on selected indicator metrics) (Wiederholm, Johnson *et al.* 1992). Moreover, the monitoring of lakes used as reservoirs for water abstraction (e.g. drinking-water) and/or for recreation, limed lakes and watercourses, as well as areas of national interest, are all in various stages of implementation.

National surveys of surface water quality have been performed since the mid-1970s. Past surveys have used only physico-chemical indicator metrics and have been restricted to lakes. In 1995, the national survey also included the sampling of small streams (catchment areas from 15 to 250 km²) and macroinvertebrates as an indicator of ecological quality. Furthermore, lake sampling was coordinated for the first time as a Nordic project, with Sweden, Norway, Finland and Denmark participating, as well as parts of Russia (the Kola peninsula) and Scotland. However, Sweden was the only Nordic country to sample streams and use macroinvertebrates as an indicator metric, i.e. the other countries restricted their programs to the use of physico-chemical indicators. A first integrated evaluation of lakewater chemistry data and acidification status was published recently by Henriksen, Skjelvåle *et al.* (1998).

Methods

Site selection and sampling

The Swedish national survey of lakes and streams was done in the autumn of 1995. In the first national survey of stream biodiversity, it was decided that emphasis would be placed on relatively small streams (Wiederholm, Johnson *et al.* 1992). The national catchment and stream registers were combined, resulting in a total of 3191 streams with catchments between 15 and 250 km² (Johnson, *et al.* 1995). Six hundred streams were randomly selected from two catchment size-classes (n = 1200 streams), and checked for accessibility using topographic maps (scale 1:50000). Sites that could not be accessed within 600 m by car were omitted (n = 117 streams). Finally, 700 streams in two catchment size-classes (15 to 50 km² and 50 to 250 km²) were randomly selected, resulting in 350 streams in each size-class. Macroinvertebrate samples were taken from 696 of the 700 randomly selected streams (Fig. 16.1). However, due to sampling error, sites situated in the county of Västernorrland were omitted from data analysis, resulting in 658 streams (Wilander, Johnson *et al.* 1998).

Similarly, 700 lakes were randomly selected for sampling wind-exposed (hard-bottom) littoral habitats. In contrast to the selection of streams, a number of criteria or considerations were implemented in the selection of lakes. Data from previous surveys were used to determine the minimum number of sites needed to demonstrate change in selected indicator metrics and critical loads of sulphur and nitrogen. It was also decided that the final sample size should be 1% <X <8%, and that the proportion according to lake size-classes (of surface area) should be 1:1:4:8 for the size-classes 0.04 to 0.1, 0.1 to 1, 1 to 10, 10 to 100 and all lakes >100 km². Due to an early winter (ice-cover occurred in many places at the end of October), samples were taken from only 538 lakes (or n = 519 after omitting lakes in the county of Västernorrland).

Several measures were taken to reduce the often confounding natural or operator-induced variability of the biological (macroinvertebrate) dataset (Johnson *et al.* 1995). Firstly, macroinvertebrate sampling was stratified temporally (autumn samples) and spatially (riffle or exposed littoral habitats). Secondly, samples were collected using standardised kick-sampling,

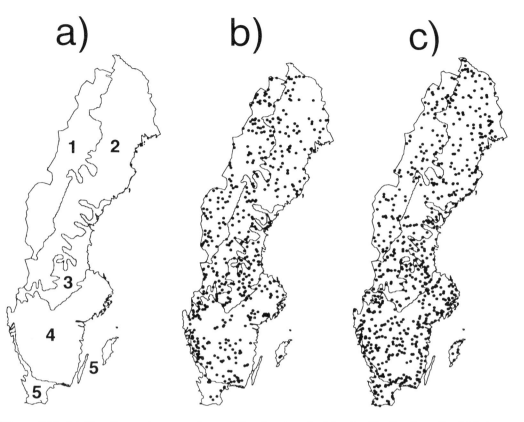

Figure 16.1. (a) The five major ecoregions of Sweden described by the Nordic Council of Ministers (Anonymous 1984), (b) the distribution of lakes (n = 538) and (c) streams (n = 696) sampled in the 1995 national survey. Ecoregion numbers in (a) refer to the alpine/subalpine and northern boreal (1), the middle boreal (2), the southern boreal (3), the boreo-nemoral (4), and the nemoral (5) zones.

using a handnet with a 0.5 mm mesh size (BS EN 27828 (1994)); five kick-samples (1 min and 1 m) were taken from each site and pooled to give one sample for analysis. Thirdly, taxonomic identification was done to a pre-determined list of some 500 operable taxonomic units decided by expert opinion. An additional 10-minute qualitative sample (search sample) was taken at each site by collecting invertebrates from the shoreline and different substrata at the sampling site (i.e. vegetation, stones, branches, logs). All macroinvertebrate samples were sorted at the Department of Environmental Assessment, according to quality control and assurance schemes (Wilander, Johnson *et al.* 1998). Taxonomic identification was done by six experienced biologists, and an intercalibration of the frequency of misidentified or counted taxa was performed (Wilander, Johnson *et al.* 1998). In addition to collecting macroinvertebrate samples, water samples were taken for physico-chemical analyses (see Henriksen, Skjelvåle *et al.* 1998), habitats were classified according to type of the substratum, and the riparian zone and catchments were classified according to vegetation type and land use (Table 16.1).

Table 16.1. *Physico-chemical, habitat, riparian and catchment-scale metrics included in the sampling protocol for the 1995 national survey of lakes and streams in Sweden.*

(1) Ecoregions and sub-ecoregions according to the Nordic Council of Ministers (Anonymous 1984).

(2) Habitat classification of substratum into seven classes: block/boulders, cobbles, pebbles, gravel, sand, silt/clay, fine and coarse detritus.

(3) Habitat classification of vegetation into eight classes: total coverage (%), emergent, floating-leaved, isoetids, elodeids (fine- and broad-leaved submerged), *Fontinalis,* other mosses, filamentous algae.

(4) Riparian classification into ten classes: coniferous forest, deciduous forest, mixed forest, clear-cut, heath/grassland, arable land, wetland, alpine, urban/construction, shading.

(5) Catchment classification, as for riparian classification but also including the percentage of surface water in the catchment and size of the catchment.

(6) Other = metrics measured for streams but not for lakes: slope, velocity, channel width and depth. Sites were also recorded if affected by liming or point-source pollution.

Geographic	Habitat/Riparian/Catchment	Water Chemistry/Other[6]
Latitude	Substratum[2]	Nutrients
Longitude	Vegetation[3]	pH/alkalinity/exceedence
Altitude	Riparian[4]	Water colour
Ecoregion[1]	Catchment[5]	Metals
Sub-ecoregion[1]		

Analyses using simple indicator metrics

The dataset was analysed using simple indicator metrics and also more advanced multivariate analyses (see below). The five metrics considered here are density, taxon richness (of a pre-established list of some 500 taxa), diversity (Simpson 1949), acidity index (Lingdell, Engblom *et al.* unpublished), Saprobien index (Moog 1995), and average score per taxon (ASPT) (Armitage, Moss *et al.* 1983).

The acidity index relies on the presence/absence and tolerance to pH of 146 indicator taxa. Five quality classes are recognised: 0 (no indicator taxa were recorded), 1 (pH <4.0), 2 ($4.0 \leq$ pH <4.5), 3 ($4.5 \leq$ pH <5.0), 4 ($5.0 \leq$ pH <5.5) and 5 (pH ≥ 5.5). Classes 1 to 3 indicate very acid conditions, Class 4 indicates moderately acid conditions, and Class 5 indicates there is no effect of acid stress.

The Austrian Saprobien index of Moog (1995) has five categories: xenosaprobic (Class 0, fully clean water), oligosaprobic (Class 1, little or no influence), ß-mesosaprobic (Class 2, moderately polluted), α-mesosaprobic (Class 3, heavily polluted) and polysaprobic (Class 4, extremely polluted).

Indicator metrics relying on measures of abundance (density, diversity, and the Saprobien index) were calculated using the results of the five kick-samples, while taxon richness, the acidity index and ASPT were calculated using information from both the five kick-samples and the 10-minute search sample.

Analyses using multivariate statistics

Multivariate statistics were used to analyse the relationships between species distribution patterns and environmental variables (Ter Braak 1987, 1990). Detrended correspondence analysis (DCA) showed a biological turnover (gradient length) of >3 standard deviation units, indicating a unimodal species distribution along the main, unconstrained environmental gradient. Hence, canonical correspondence analysis (CCA), a form of direct gradient analysis (otherwise known as constrained ordination), was run using forward selection of environmental variables. Constrained ordination allows parallel comparisons of species distribution patterns and environmental factors. The significance of each environmental variable in explaining biological variability was tested using 99 Monte Carlo permutations. Densities were square-root transformed and downweighting of rare taxa was selected in CCA but not in DCA. In CCA, sites affected by point-sources or liming were run as passive (i.e. these sites are included but do not influence the ordination).

Due to the large influence of latitude on community structure, analyses were also done for relatively large but biogeographically similar regions. The five major ecoregions of Sweden, described by the Nordic Council of Ministers (Anonymous 1984), were used for the regional approach in data evaluation (Fig. 16.1a). One modification was made by combining the arctic, alpine, subalpine and northern boreal zones to form the northernmost ecoregion, here referred to as the alpine/subalpine and northern boreal zone. The five ecoregions range from the nemoral zone in the south, characterised by mixed forests, mean annual temperatures greater than 6°C and a relatively long growth period (180 to 210 days), to the alpine regions in the north, characterised by sparse coniferous and birch forests, mean annual temperatures ranging from –1 to 5°C and short growth periods (*ca* 140 days).

Data usually were not normally distributed and consequently they were evaluated using Wilcoxon/Kruskal–Wallis pairwise comparison tests and Spearman (rho) correlations.

Results and discussion

Spatial variability of selected indicator metrics

Stream communities (riffle habitats) were more taxon-rich and had higher abundances than lake (littoral) macroinvertebrate communities (p <0.0001) (Fig. 16.2). Densities averaged 1591±95 numbers per unit effort (NPUE mean ±1 standard error) for streams, compared with 696±44 NPUE for littoral communities. On average, seven more taxa were found in streams than in lakes. Also, diversity was significantly (p <0.0001) higher for streams (0.724±0.007) than for lakes (0.621±0.009). These discrepancies between biodiversity of lake and stream communities probably reflect differences in environmental variability. In general, lotic communities will experience a larger degree of environmental variation (fluctuations in stream velocity, water chemistry, temperature) than lentic communities. A higher degree of disturbance in streams may also impede the competitive elimination of species, in accordance with the intermediate disturbance hypothesis (e.g. Connell 1978). For example, Townsend *et al.* (1997) showed that richness of highly mobile and relatively sedentary taxa conformed to bell-shaped curve predictions of the intermediate disturbance hypothesis.

Mean acidity index values for lakes were slightly lower (p <0.0001) than for streams (4.26±0.05 and 4.71±0.03, respectively). However, 25% of the lakes (n = 132) and only 7% of the streams (n = 49) had index values indicating very acid conditions (values ≤3, indicating pH below 5.0). Most of these lakes (n = 95 or 18%) and streams (n = 25 or 3.8%) are situated in the northern parts of the country (Fig. 2), areas that are not strongly affected by acid deposition of NO_x and SO_4. This indicates that the acidity index may not be a reliable indicator of acid

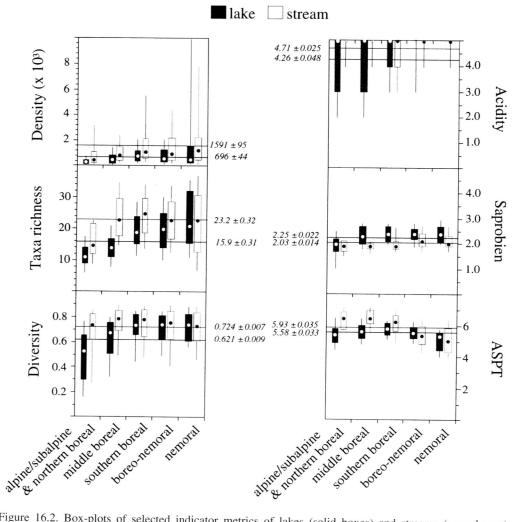

Figure 16.2. Box-plots of selected indicator metrics of lakes (solid boxes) and streams (open boxes) sampled in the 1995 national survey of Sweden. Circles denote median values, boxes show 25 and 75 percentiles and the vertical lines give the 10 and 90 percentiles. Horizontal lines and adjacent numbers show overall mean (±1 SE) values. Index values are given for the five major ecoregions of Sweden (see the text).

stress in these parts of the country. Possibly, the high humic contents (colour and TOC) of the surface waters in this region (Wilander, Johnson *et al.* 1998) may confound the assessment of acid stress using biological indicators (see Lonergan & Rasmussen 1996). In the boreo-nemoral zone, the frequency of lakes and streams with an acidity index ≤3 was 4.7% (n = 25) for lakes, and 2.2% (n = 14) for streams. In contrast to northern Sweden, this region has been strongly affected by acidification. The surprisingly low number of sites with acidity index values ≤3 presumably is due to the fact that a large number of sites have been limed in the boreo-nemoral zone (i.e. the random sampling design used in the 1995 national survey probably has underestimated the effects of acidification in this region). For example, 33% of the lakes (n = 50) and 20% of the streams (n = 52) situated in the boreo-nemoral zone were recorded as being affected by liming. Assuming that limed lakes and streams previously might have had index values ≤ 3, an estimated 50% of the lakes and 26% of the streams are affected by acidification.

Lakes had slightly higher (p <0.0001) Saprobien index values than streams (2.25±0.022 and 2.03±0.014, respectively), indicating either anthropogenic effects or naturally occurring nutrient-rich conditions (Fig. 16.2). For example, 79% of the lakes and 57% of the streams had values ≥ 2, indicating ß-mesosaprobic or moderately polluted conditions. Only one lake situated in the nemoral zone had a Saprobien index value of 3, classified as α-mesosaprobic or heavily polluted. However, as with the evaluation of acidity, the Saprobien scores and interpretation of organic pollution impact are confounded by the relatively large amounts of humic matter that characterise many Swedish inland waters. The 10-percentiles for total organic carbon (TOC) were 2.28 mg l^{-1} for lakes and 2.70 mg l^{-1} for streams. This conjecture was further supported by significant correlations between TOC and Saprobien scores (p <0.0001 for both lakes and streams) and the observation that 40% of the lakes and streams with a Saprobien index ≥ 2 were situated in forest-dominated counties that are relatively unaffected by organic loading from anthropogenic sources (the counties of Kopparberg, Jämtland, Västerbotten, and Norrbotten). ASPT values were higher (p <0.0001) in streams than in lakes, 5.93±0.035 and 5.58±0.033 respectively, thereby confirming the results of the Saprobien index.

Several of the indicator metrics differed among the five major ecoregions, and many were significantly correlated with latitude, longitude and altitude. With the exception of diversity and acidity of streams, and the ASPT score of lakes, all indicator metrics were significantly correlated with latitude (Table 16.2). In contrast, significant correlations of the indicator metrics with longitude were less frequent. Macroinvertebrate densities, taxon richness and the Saprobien index of lakes, as well as richness and diversity of stream communities, were significantly correlated with longitude. These results probably reflect the differences in geographical extension of Sweden along latitudinal and longitudinal gradients, and the stronger climatic gradient in the south to north direction. Littoral communities of lakes, in particular,

Table 16.2. *Correlation coefficients (Spearman rho) for biological indicator metrics and latitude, longitude, and altitude for streams and lakes in Sweden.*

Asterisks give the level of significance: * p ≤ 0.05, ** p ≤ 0.01, *** p ≤ 0.001, **** p ≤ 0.0001.

Indicator	Habitat	Latitude	Longitude	Altitude
Density	Streams	−0.154****	−0.073	−0.018
	Lakes	−0.371****	−0.147***	−0.397****
Taxon richnes	Streams	−0.077*	−0.126***	0.048
	Lakes	−0.472****	−0.107*	−0.478****
Diversity	Streams	0.020	−0.091*	0.125***
	Lakes	−0.366****	−0.078	−0.365****
Acidity	Streams	0.065	0.031	0.004
	Lakes	−0.169****	−0.014	−0.203****
Saprobien	Streams	−0.296****	−0.071	−0.251****
	Lakes	−0.206****	0.139**	−0.355****
ASPT	Streams	0.461****	0.018	0.498****
	Lakes	−0.080	−0.073	−0.094*

seemed to be influenced by the relatively large latitudinal gradient stretching from the nemoral zone in southern Sweden to the alpine regions in the north-west. For example, taxon richness was higher in the three southern regions (19–23 taxa) than in the alpine/subalpine and northern boreal zone (mean = 11 taxa) and middle boreal zone (14 taxa) (Fig. 16.2). Also, diversity decreased along the same latitudinal gradient, from values >0.70 for the nemoral to southern boreal ecoregions, to 0.49 for the alpine/subalpine and northern boreal zone. Stream riffle communities in the alpine/subalpine and northern boreal zone had relatively low richness (mean = 16 taxa). However, taxon richness of the middle boreal zone (24 taxa) did not differ from that of the more southern regions; taxon richness for the remaining regions ranged from 23 (nemoral zone) to 25 (southern boreal zone). In contrast to the diversity of lake macroinvertebrate communities, diversity of stream habitats did not vary significantly among the five ecoregions (p = 0.057).

In some instances, rather strong and highly significant correlations were found between metrics for lake communities (density, richness and the acidity index) and altitude. However, the same indicator metrics for stream communities were only poorly correlated with altitude. Correlations of indicator metrics with geographic variables indicate that geographic position, as well as anthropogenic factors, influence the indicator metrics, and support the conjecture that data analyses should be done using a regional (ecoregion) approach to partition the expected natural variability.

Table 16.3. *The ten most common taxa occurring in 538 lake (exposed littoral) and 696 stream (riffle) habitats sampled in the 1995 national survey in Sweden.*

Numbers in the table indicate the number of sites where each taxon was recorded.

Oligochaeta and Chironomidae are not included; these two groups occurred in >85% of all sites.

* Feeding guilds according to Moog (1995).

Taxon	Lakes	Streams	Feeding guilds*
Leptophlebia spp. (Ephemeroptera)	376	360	Detritivore
Sphaeriidae (Pelecypoda)	323	359	Grazer
Asellus aquaticus L. (Isopoda)	273	353	Shredder/grazer/detritivore
Agrypnia spp. (Trichoptera)	227	—	Predator
Heptagenia fuscogrisea Retz. (Ephemeroptera)	189	—	Grazer/detritivore
Limnephilus spp. (Trichoptera)	167	—	Shredder/grazer/detritivore
Caenis horaria L. (Ephemeroptera)	161	—	Detritivore
Sialis lutaria group (Megaloptera)	160	—	Predator
Cyrnus flavidus McL. (Trichoptera)	156	—	Predator/filtrator
Hydracarina	148	—	Predator
Baetis rhodani Pictet (Ephemeroptera)	—	404	Grazer/detritivore
Nemoura spp. (Plecoptera)	—	373	Shredder/detritivore
Baetis niger-digitatus (Ephemeroptera)	—	307	Grazer/detritivore
Leuctra spp. group (Plecoptera)	—	296	Shredder/grazer/detritivore
Polycentropus flavomaculatus Pictet (Trichoptera)	—	293	Predator/filtrator
Elmis aenea (Müller) (Coleoptera)	—	274	Grazer
Isoperla spp. (Plecoptera)	—	253	Predator

Table 16.4. *Number of lakes and streams containing Red Data Book species, from the 1995 national survey in Sweden.*

Threat categories refer to vulnerable (2), rare (3), and care-demanding (4) species.

Net = standardised kick-sampling with a handnet; Search = 10 minute qualitative search (see sampling methods).

Taxon	Threat category	Lakes Net	Search	Streams Net	Search
Mollusca					
Valvata macrostoma Mörch	3	3	1	1	0
Valvata piscinalis (Müller)	4	5	0	3	4
Valvata sibirica Middendorf	3	0	0	1	0
Marstoniopsis scholtzi (Schmidt)	4	1	1	2	0
Myxas glutinosa (Müller)	3	1	1	2	0
Omphiscola glabra (Müller)	2	2	1	2	1
Segmentina nitida (Müller)	3	4	1	4	2
Gyraulus riparius (Westerlund)	3	0	1	0	0
Gyraulus crista (L.)	4	8	2	6	0
Margaritifera margaritifera (L.)	2	0	0	0	1
Crustacea					
Lepidurus arcticus Kröyer	3	0	1	0	0
Astacus astacus (L.)	4	2	0	5	2
Plecoptera					
Brachyptera braueri (Klapalek)	4	0	0	1	0
Xanthoperla apicalis Newman	3	0	0	5	0
Coleoptera					
Stenelmis canaliculata (Gyllenh)	4	1	0	4	0
Trichoptera					
Hydropsyche saxonica McLachlan	4	0	0	29	3
Hydropsyche contubernalis McLachlan	4	2	1	3	0
Semblis atrata Gmelin	4	0	0	2	0
Ecclisopteryx dalecarlica Kol.	3	0	0	5	0
Molanna albicans Zett.	3	0	1	1	1
Molanna submarginalis McLachlan	3	1	0	0	0
Beraeodes minutus (L.)	4	0	0	1	1
Odontocerum albicorne (Scopoli)	3	0	0	3	0

Community structure and function

Only three of the ten most commonly occurring taxa were found in both lakes and streams, viz. the mayfly *Leptophlebia* spp., a bivalve mollusc (Sphaeriidae) and the isopod *Asellus aquaticus* (Table 16.3). *Leptophlebia* was recorded from 70% of the lakes and 52% of the streams. *Heptagenia fuscogrisea* and *Caenis horaria* were recorded from lakes only, while two *Baetis* species/assemblages (*Baetis rhodani* and *Baetis niger-digitatus*) were found only in streams. In both lakes and streams, mayflies were the three most common taxa. Stoneflies were not ranked among the ten most common taxa for lakes. In contrast, three stonefly species/assemblages were relatively common in streams *(Nemoura* spp., *Leuctra* spp. group, and *Isoperla* spp.). No clear-cut functional differences between stream and littoral communities were found. All functional feeding guilds were present in both habitats (Table 16.3).

A total of 23 species listed in the Red Data Book (RDB) were found at 136 sampling sites (Table 16.4). The majority were classified either as "rare" (11 species) or "care-demanding" (10) whereas only two species were classified as "vulnerable" (Ehnström *et al.* 1993). Fourteen

RDB species were found in lake samples and 20 in stream samples. The caddisfly *Hydropsyche saxonica* was the most common RDB species; classified as "care-demanding", it was found in 24% of the samples. In four instances only, search samples contributed additional RDB species, compared with the standardised kick-samples. This finding suggests that the additional search sample was of minor importance for the detection of rare, RDB species.

Community predictors

CCA ordination of lake communities showed that altitude, and a principal component of substratum and vegetation (PC1SV), respectively explained 4.8% and 3.4% of the variability among lakes (Table 16.5). Relatively large differences were found when ordinations were run individually for the respective ecoregions. For example, TOC and conductivity could account for relatively large amounts of the explained variability of lakes situated in the alpine/subalpine and northern boreal zone. Selection of these variables probably can be explained by the strong influence of the alpine to forest gradient in this region, i.e. the transition from conditions of low TOC and low conductivity to conditions of high TOC and higher conductivity. The importance of substratum and vegetation in explaining variability amongst macroinvertebrate communities was indicated by the selection of the principal component axis (PC1SV) in three of the five ecoregions. Similarly, a number of substratum descriptors, such as coarse detritus, filamentous algae and cobbles, accounted for much of the explained variability for lakes situated in the southern boreal zone, while the presence of emergent vegetation could explain 24% of the variability of macroinvertebrate communities in the nemoral zone.

In the ordination of stream communities, chloride concentration ([Cl]) accounted for the largest portion of explained variability (5.1%). The marine influence on water chemistry reflected by [Cl] may covary with the more densely populated coastal areas of Sweden, and thus with a stronger anthropogenic influence. This conjecture was supported by a significant correlation between [Cl] and total phosphorus concentration. Alternatively, [Cl] may indirectly reflect the more advantageous effect of a marine climate (lower amplitude of annual temperatures). Similar to lake communities, substratum type (PC1SV) also explained significant proportions of the variability of stream communities. With the exception of the alpine/subalpine and northern boreal zone, substratum (PC1SV) and pH were important descriptors when streams were partitioned by ecoregion. In addition, similar to lake communities, TOC explained a significant amount of the variability of macroinvertebrate community composition for streams situated in the alpine/subalpine and northern boreal zone. Again, this probably is a consequence of the TOC gradient in this region, encompassing the transition from the northern boreal forests below the tree-line to the alpine areas above it.

On a national scale the additional search sample resulted, on average, in an increase of 2.6±0.31 taxa (mean±1 SE) in streams and 2.4±0.09 taxa in lakes (p <0.05 for both). However, on a regional scale, taxon richness was not affected by the additional search sample for streams situated in the alpine/subalpine and northern boreal and nemoral regions, or for lakes situated in the boreo-nemoral region. Besides affecting overall taxon richness, the additional search sample also affected a number of richness-dependent biological indices of ecological quality (i.e. BMWP, EPT-taxa) both on national and regional scales, while more qualitative indices were not affected (Goedkoop, Johnson *et al.* 1999). The additive effect of the 10-minute search sample may thus provide some additional information about the biodiversity of lakes and streams, but it certainly does not affect data evaluation if qualitative biological indices are used.

Bioassessment using macroinvertebrate indicator metrics is generally considered to be a robust, time-integrating measure of ecological quality (Johnson *et al.* 1993; Rosenberg & Resh

Table 16.5. *The percentage variability of lake and stream macroinvertebrate communities – sampled in the Swedish national survey – that could be explained by environmental variables, using CCA ordination.*

CCA ordinations were done for the whole country and for sites stratified by ecoregion.
Abundances were square-root transformed, rare taxa were downweighted and
CCA was run using forward selection and 99 Monte Carlo permutations.

Ecoregions: ER1 = alpine/subalpine and northern boreal zone, ER2 = middle boreal zone,
ER3 = southern boreal zone, ER4= boreo-nemoral zone, ER5 = nemoral zone.

Variable	Lakes Total	ER1	ER2	ER3	ER4	ER5	Streams Total	ER1	ER2	ER3	ER4	ER5
Altitude	4.8	—	3.1	—	2.5	—	—	—	—	2.8	—	—
PC1SV	3.4	1.3	3.5	—	8.1	—	2.8	—	4.1	9.0	4.0	4.3
pH	1.4	2.6	—	—	—	—	1.5	—	1.3	3.0	1.3	4.7
Chloride	1.1	—	—	—	—	—	5.1	—	1.0	3.5	—	—
Latitude	0.84	1.9	—	—	—	—	1.1	—	2.3	—	1.8	6.1
Longitude	0.56	—	—	—	—	—	0.95	6.7	1.8	—	1.3	5.2
TOC	0.84	4.8	—	—	—	—	0.57	10	—	—	—	5.5
Total phosphorus	0.56	—	—	—	—	—	0.76	—	—	2.5	—	—
Sand	0.56	—	—	—	—	—	—	—	—	—	—	—
Fine detritus	0.56	—	2.1	—	—	—	—	—	—	—	—	—
Fontinalis	0.56	—	—	—	—	—	0.38	—	—	—	—	—
Alpine	0.56	—	—	—	—	—	0.38	5.5	—	—	—	—
Conductivity	—	3.5	—	—	—	—	0.38	—	—	—	2.6	6.5
Block	—	1.9	—	—	—	—	—	—	—	—	—	—
Silt/clay	—	1.3	—	—	—	—	—	4.3	—	—	—	—
Absorbance	—	—	2.4	—	—	—	—	—	—	—	—	—
Alkalinity	—	—	1.7	—	4.6	—	—	—	—	—	—	—
Mire	—	—	1.7	—	—	—	—	4.3	—	—	—	—
Pebbles	—	—	1.7	—	—	—	—	—	—	—	—	—
Floating-leaved veg.	—	—	1.7	—	—	—	0.38	—	—	3.0	—	—
Coarse detritus	—	—	—	7.5	—	—	—	—	—	—	0.88	—
Filamentous algae	—	—	—	5.3	—	—	0.57	—	1.78	—	—	—
Cobbles	—	—	—	4.8	—	—	—	—	—	—	—	—
PC2SV	—	—	—	4.4	—	—	—	—	—	—	—	—
Emergent veg.	—	—	—	—	—	24	—	—	—	2.8	—	—
Depth	—	—	—	—	—	—	0.95	—	—	3.9	1.5	—
Pebbles	—	—	—	—	—	—	—	4.7	—	—	—	—
Velocity	—	—	—	—	—	—	—	—	—	2.3	0.88	4.0
NO_2+NO_3	—	—	—	—	—	—	—	—	—	—	1.1	—
All variables	24.6	15.5	18.0	19.5	15.1	24.1	16.0	15.7	12.2	32.5	15.1	36.4

1993a). In the 1995 national survey, however, a number of factors (e.g. geographical position, water colour, liming) confounded data interpretation, stressing the need for further development and refinement of the biological indices used in Sweden. In particular, metrics need to be modified for the relatively strong influence of latitude and the often high humic content (water colour) of Swedish waters. Partitioning variability by working on finer and more ecologically similar spatial scales (e.g. ecoregions) to some extent may also alleviate this problem.

Acknowledgements

We thank the many people who assisted in sampling and processing the large number of samples collected in the 1995 national lake and stream survey. In particular, we would like to thank Lars Eriksson who was responsible for macroinvertebrate taxonomy and Björn Söderbäck who assisted in the design-phase of RI95.

CHAPTER 17

Typology of macrofaunal assemblages applied to water and nature management: a Dutch approach

PIET F. M. VERDONSCHOT AND REBI C. NIJBOER

Institute for Forestry and Nature Research,
P.O. Box 23, 6700 AA Wageningen, THE NETHERLANDS

Summary

Multivariate analysis of an extensive dataset based on the macroinvertebrate fauna of surface waters in the province of Overijssel (The Netherlands) has resulted in the description of 42 site groups. These include springs, streams, rivers, canals, ditches, pools and lakes. The site groups are recognised on the basis of environmental variables and the abundance of organisms. For each group only a recognisable centroid and a limited range of variation is given; no clear boundaries are described between the groups. These site groups and their environment are defined as cenotypes.

The cenotypes are mutually related in terms of key factors which represent major ecological processes. The cenotypes and their mutual relationships form a web which offers an ecological basis for the daily practice of water and nature management. The web allows the development of water quality objectives, provides a tool for monitoring and assessment, indicates targets and guides the management and restoration of waterbodies.

The web is included in a software package named EKOO. The main modules in this package are (1) the assignment of a newly sampled site to one of the cenotypes, (2) the characterisation of a new sample in terms of diversity and biotic features, and (3) the option to choose a target for a newly sampled site and to establish a set of measures to reach this target.

Introduction

In a densely populated area such as The Netherlands, where human activities strongly affect the surroundings, there is great concern over conservation of the aquatic biota, all of which contribute to the scientific, aesthetic, recreational and sometimes commercial values of the landscape (Armitage & Petts 1992). The lack of information on the biological effects of human activities on aquatic biota led, in the 1970s, to the development of biological water quality assessment systems in The Netherlands (Moller-Pillot 1971; De Lange & De Ruiter 1977). As in other regions, initially the assessment of pollution (usually organic) was the main goal (Hellawell 1978). In the 1980s, more attention was focused on the entire environment, including all physical, chemical and biological conditions (Wright, Moss *et al.* 1984; Verdonschot 1990), in order to provide assessment with an ecological perspective.

Biological communities are well adapted to the environment in which they live and are sensitive to changes in this environment (Odum 1971). To apply community ecology in water management and nature conservation, one needs to relate biological communities to ranges in environmental conditions (Pennak 1971; Hawkes 1975). Historically, biological communities have been considered as classes comprising discrete groups of species (Tansley 1920), as a continuous gradient along which species merge into each other (Whittaker 1978), or as types in which species groups are identified by an "average" state (nucleus or centroid) but which merge into each other (Tuxen 1955).

An ecological approach to water and nature management should combine the pragmatic part of distinguishing classes with the realism of gradients in our environment (Macan 1961; Hawkes 1975). The typological approach meets this requirement to a certain extent. In an ecological typology, communities are described as nuclei/centroids without mutual boundaries. Each type shows a certain range of biotic variation and a certain range of environmental conditions. Furthermore, types grade into one another. Thus, types are seen as loci in a field of variation.

This chapter summarises the development of an ecological typology of surface waters based on a large regional-scale survey of aquatic environments in The Netherlands. The typology is based on the macroinvertebrate fauna as the main structural parameter. A number of arguments for and against the use of macroinvertebrates as indicator species are given, amongst others, by Wright, Armitage *et al.* (1985), Armitage *et al.* (1992) and Rosenberg & Resh (1993b).

Instead of looking at separate species, the study focused on assemblages of species, because they integrate the responses of individual species to the multiple and complex biotic and abiotic environment, and they are more robust and constant than individual species, which are not always present (temporal segregation, stochastic occurrence, contagious distribution).

Data collection and analysis: building a typology

Collection of samples

Samples were collected from 664 sites situated in the province of Overijssel (The Netherlands); 609 sites were visited in one season only and 55 sites were visited in two seasons. The sampling dates were spread over the four seasons as well as over several years (from 1981 to 1985, inclusive). For logistic reasons it was impossible to take all samples in the same season or to sample a site in more than one or two seasons. This is one of the disadvantages of extensive survey studies (Wiens 1981). "Noise" in the dataset, resulting from seasonal factors, can affect the results. Osborne *et al.* (1980) and Furse, Moss *et al.* (1984) argued that even though multiseason sampling is preferable, single season sampling (especially when all sites are sampled in the same season) is justified for certain purposes. Verdonschot (1990) demonstrated that seasonal differences as well as inconsistencies due to sampling technique and sampling frequency were of little significance compared to differences in water types. In this study, sampling effort was standardised for each site. Season was taken into account by defining sampling periods as nominal "environmental" variables within the analysis.

The objective was to capture the majority of species present at a given site, and assess their relative abundances. At each site, major habitats were selected over a 10 to 30 m long stretch of the waterbody and were sampled with the same sampling effort. At shallow sites, habitats with vegetation were sampled by sweeping a pondnet (20x30 cm, mesh size 0.5 mm) through each vegetation type, several times over a length of 0.5 to 1 m. Bottom habitats were sampled by vigorously pushing the pondnet through the upper few centimetres of each type of substratum, over a length of 0.5 to 1 m. The habitat samples were then combined for the site to give a single sample with a standard area of 1.5 m^2 (1.2 m^2 of vegetation and 0.3 m^2 of bottom). At sites lacking vegetation, the standard sampling was confined to the bottom habitats. At deeper sites, five samples from the bottom habitats were taken with an Ekman-Birge sampler. These five grab-samples were equivalent to one 0.5 m pondnet bottom sample. Habitats with vegetation were sampled with a pondnet as described above. Again the total sampling area was standardised as 1.5 m². Verdonschot (1990) showed that this sampling effort met the requirements for constructing a regional water typology. Macroinvertebrate samples were taken to the laboratory, sorted by eye, counted and identified to species level.

A datasheet was used to note a number of abiotic and some biotic variables in the field. Some were measured directly (width, depth, surface area, temperature, transparency, percentage of vegetation cover, percentage of sampled habitat), others (such as regulation, substratum, bank shape) were classified. Field instruments were used to measure oxygen, electrical conductivity, stream velocity and pH. Surface water samples were taken to determine chemical variables. Other parameters, like land use, bottom composition and distance from source, were gathered from additional sources (data from Water Boards and maps). In total, 70 abiotic variables were measured at each site.

Multivariate analysis

Data processing consisted of the following five main steps: (1) preprocessing of data, (2) clustering, (3) ordination and re-ordination, (4) rearrangement, recognition and removal of sites, (5) post processing of data (Fig. 17.1).

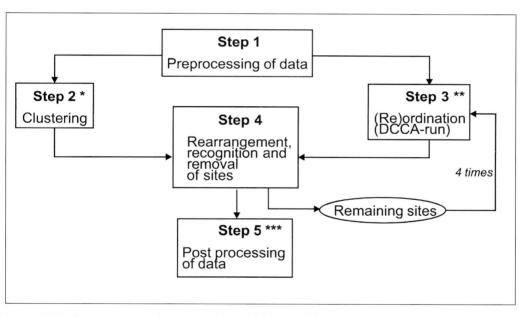

Figure 17.1. Flow-diagram of data processing used for classifying macroinvertebrates into cenotypes in the surface waters of The Netherlands (computer programs used were: FLEXCLUS*, CANOCO** and NODES*** – see the text).

Step (1). The study revealed 853 invertebrate taxa. The macroinvertebrate abundances were transformed into logarithmic classes (Preston 1962; Van der Maarel 1979). Quantitative environmental variables, except pH, were log-transformed because of skewed distributions. All other variables were nominal and dealt with by defining so-called dummy variables.

Step (2). The sites were clustered, based on the macroinvertebrate dataset, by means of the program FLEXCLUS (Van Tongeren 1986), an agglomerative clustering technique. The clustering strategy of FLEXCLUS is based on an initial, non-hierarchical, single linkage clustering, following the algorithm of Sørensen for a site-by-site matrix based on the similarity ratio. This initial clustering is optimised by relocative centroid sorting. Sites are relocated as follows. Each site is compared with each cluster (as it was before relocation of any site) and, if necessary, moved to the cluster to which its resemblance is highest. Before a site is compared with its own cluster, the site is removed from that cluster and the new cluster centroid is computed.

Clusters were accepted if they met a certain homogeneity (>0.4). The homogeneity of a cluster was defined as the average resemblance of its members (based on the similarity ratio) to its centroid.

The resulting clusters were further examined by comparing taxon composition and environmental variables of the sites within a given cluster. Based on biotic and abiotic similarities, in some exceptional cases clusters were divided or fused and/or sites were assigned to other clusters or set apart. The clustering finally resulted in macroinvertebrate site clusters.

Step (3). The sites were ordinated by detrended canonical correspondence analysis (DCCA), using the program CANOCO (Ter Braak 1986, 1987), an ordination (reciprocal averaging) technique which results in an ordination diagram. DCCA is an integration of regression and ordination and shows the response of taxa and sites to environmental variables (Jongman *et al.* 1987). Detrending by fourth-order polynomials was used. These techniques are fully explained by Ter Braak & Verdonschot (1995).

Step (4). Both the results of clustering (step 2) and (re-)ordination (step 3) were combined in ordination diagrams and used to establish site groups. The macroinvertebrate site clusters were projected on to the DCCA ordination diagrams of the first two axes, and sites that caused an overlap of clusters within a diagram were further examined as follows.

Firstly, spatial separation in the third and sometimes the fourth ordination axes were examined. If sites were clearly projected into one of the clusters they were assigned to that cluster. Secondly, comparisons were made of the characteristic and indicative taxa, and also the environmental variables of the site, in relation to the overall composition of characteristic and indicative taxa and ranges of important environmental variables for each of the overlapping clusters. Based on biotic similarity and abiotic correspondence, sites were either assigned to the most similar cluster (>50% identical taxa and all values within the range of the cluster) or set apart.

A site group (cenotype) is established if it is clearly recognisable along an identified environmental gradient and has a distinct macroinvertebrate fauna. Each site group in a diagram is represented by a centroid (indicated by an asterisk) and surrounded by a 90% confidence region (an ellipse) for the mean of the site scores of that group. A contour line around a centroid indicates the total variation of all site scores within the group (for these diagrams see Verdonschot 1990). In addition, groups that show no – or very limited – overlap with other groups and are positioned at the ends of the identified environmental gradients in the diagram, are identified as "cenotypes".

Two techniques were used to select the environmental variables with the highest explanatory power. In the option "forward selection" of CANOCO (version 3.0), the program indicates how well each individual environmental variable "explains" the variation in the species data. First, the program selects the variable with the highest explanatory power. Then it produces a list of how much each variable would contribute extra if that variable was added to the one previously selected. At each addition of a variable, the significance of the contribution of the variable is tested by a Monte Carlo permutation test. This selection is stopped at p <0.10. Additional explanatory environmental variables were selected on the basis of the inter-set correlation

(correlation >0.3) with the axes, i.e. the correlation between a variable and an ordination axis. Both options were applied in each of the (re-)ordinations. All variables selected by these two techniques were used to describe the environment of the cenotypes and were represented in the ordination diagrams. An environmental variable (indicated as an arrow) points in the direction of steepest increase of that variable, and the rate of change is represented by the length of the arrow. This means that the value of an important environmental variable, to a cenotype, is visualised by its perpendicular projection on the environmental arrow or its imaginary extension (in both directions).

When groups of sites (cenotypes) were identified along environmental gradients, and thus a continuum was partitioned, the remaining sites were subsequently re-ordinated. In this way, the impact of the originally observed variable(s) was greatly reduced. This strategy was developed by Peet (1980). After five ordinations all sites were assigned to distinctive groups. The combination of steps (2), (3) and (4) indicate the iterative nature of the analysis.

Step (5). Ordering and weighting of taxa was done by the NODES program (Verdonschot 1990). The cenotypes were used as input. In NODES the typifying weight of a taxon is calculated per cenotype by combining the formulae of constancy, fidelity and concentration of abundance (Boesch 1977; Verdonschot 1984). Taxa were ordered in a taxon-site group matrix according to their typifying weight. Small groups of sites, often composed of aberrant sampling sites (outliers), were excluded from the process of weighting.

The numbers of sites, averages and standard deviations of the quantitative environmental variables, and the relative frequency of the nominal variables per cenotype, were calculated by means of the clustering program FLEXCLUS (Van Tongeren 1986).

Results: a web of cenotypes

The results of clustering (FLEXCLUS) are shown in a hierarchical dendrogram to illustrate the biological similarity between cenotypes (Fig. 17.2). The cenotypes R1, R4, P11, R12, R2 and P8 are quite similar to each other but they differ markedly from the types H5 and H6, which are also completely different from each other (Fig. 17.2). In this way the similarity and differences between all cenotypes can be extracted from this text-figure. In the dendrogram, at the different divisions, the most important variables or complexes of variables related to that division are indicated. Figure 17.3 presents short descriptions of the cenotypes.

In total, five (re-)ordinations were necessary to analyse the entire dataset. Partial results of these analyses are published by Verdonschot & Schot (1987) and Verdonschot (1992a, 1992b, 1992c, 1995). All five ordinations were tested. The first four appeared significant at the 1% level. The fifth run was only significant at the 9% level. By using direct gradient analysis the environmental factors were related to the site groups in two-dimensional space. In fact, species–environmental relationships are multi-dimensional, but here the major patterns are reflected in a two-dimensional diagram.

The graphical result of the first run of the DCCA, i.e. axes 1 and 2, is used as a basis for illustrating the mutual relationships between the cenotypes (Fig. 17.4). The diagram provides a web, which is an integrated description of the cenotypes (based on taxon composition and abundances) versus environmental factors that represent major ecological processes. The contour line indicates the variation in faunal composition and environmental conditions present between the sites. All sites together form a continuum, but the macroinvertebrate site groups are represented as the centroids of the cenotypes (circles with codes) arranged along environmental gradients. Four major key factors, "stream character", acidity, duration of drought and dimensions, represent the environmental gradients that run through the whole diagram (see the inset on Fig. 17.4). Additional significant environmental relations between the

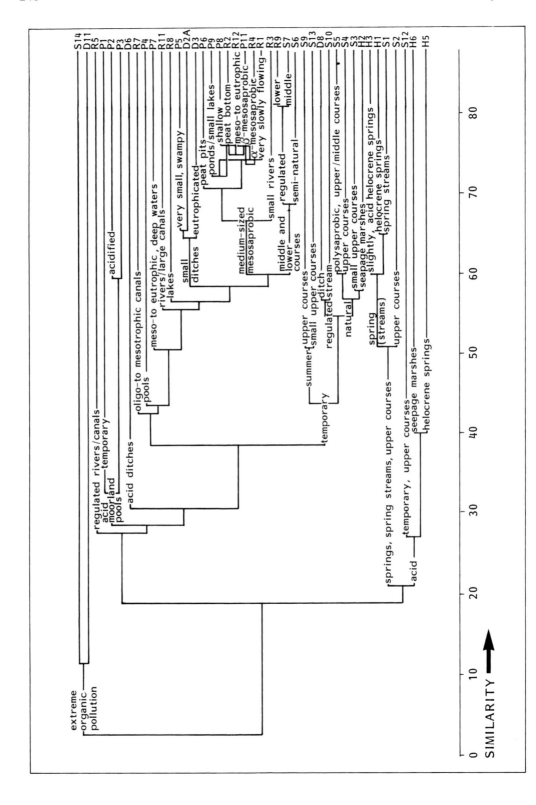

SIMILARITY

Figure 17.2 (*on facing page*). Hierarchical dendrogram of cenotypes found in the surface waters of Overijssel, with factors responsible for the divisions indicated. Codes of cenotypes are explained below in Figure 17.3

Ceno-type	Characterization

Helocrene springs

H1	oligo- to β-mesosaprobic helocrene springs
H2	temporary or desiccating, neutral to slightly acid, β-mesosaprobic seepage marshes
H3	neutral to slightly acid, oligo- to β-mesosaprobic helocrene springs
H5	slightly acid, oligo- to β-mesosaprobic, oligo-ionic helocrene springs
H6	temporary, acid, oligo-ionic, oligo- to β-mesosaprobic seepage marshes

Streams

S1	oligo- to β-mesosaprobic spring streams
S2	permanent, rainwater-fed, β-mesosaprobic upper reaches of natural streams
S3	temporary, α-mesosaprobic, small upper reaches of natural streams
S4	temporary, β-mesosaprobic upper reaches of natural streams
S5	polysaprobic upper and middle reaches of natural and regulated streams
S6	α-mesosaprobic middle reaches of semi-natural streams
S7	α-mesosaprobic middle reaches of regulated streams
S9	the summer aspect with α-meso- to polysaprobic conditions of temporary upper reaches of natural streams or temporary, α-meso- to polysaprobic regulated streams
S10	temporary, α-mesosaprobic, flowing upper reaches of regulated streams or ditches
S12	temporary, slightly acid, α-mesosaprobic upper reaches of regulated streams or ditches
S13	the summer aspect with α-mesosaprobic conditions of temporary, small upper reaches of natural streams

Ditches

D2A	permanent, β-meso- to α-mesosaprobic, small, shallow ditches
D3	permanent, α-mesosaprobic, shallow, small ditches or stagnant regulated streams
D6	acid, oligo-ionic, α-mesosaprobic to polysaprobic small ditches
D8	temporary, very slightly flowing, α-meso-ionic, α-mesosaprobic small ditches

Rivers and canals

R1	β-meso- to α-mesosaprobic, medium-sized to large very slowly flowing lower courses of streams and rivers
R2	β-meso- to α-mesosaprobic, large ditches and small canals on a minerotrophic peat bottom
R3	α-mesosaprobic, medium-sized, slightly meandering, slowly flowing small rivers
R4	α-meso-ionic, β-meso- to α-mesosaprobic, linear shaped small to medium-sized waters
R5	α-mesosaprobic, fairly large regulated rivers or stagnant canals
R7	oligo- to β-mesosaprobic, medium to fairly large stagnant canals
R8	β-mesosaprobic, α-meso-ionic, very large, round to irregularly shaped lakes
R9	α-mesosaprobic, α-mesosaprobic lower reaches of regulated streams or slightly flowing very small rivers
R11	β-meso- to α-mesosaprobic, α-meso-ionic, mesotrophic, large, linear, slightly flowing rivers or stagnant waters
R12	β-meso- to α-mesosaprobic, meso- to eutrophic, large, less deep stagnant waters

Pools and lakes

P1	temporary, acidified, oligo-ionic, α-meso- to polysaprobic, mesotrophic moorland pools
P2	permanent, acid to acidified, oligo-ionic, α-mesosaprobic to polysaprobic, mesotrophic moorland pools
P3	permanent, slightly acid to acid, oligo-ionic, α-mesosaprobic pools
P4	slightly acid to neutral, α-mesosaprobic, vegetation-rich, small, shallow pools
P5	permanent, α-mesosaprobic, eutrophic, very shallow (swampy), small ditches
P6	clear, well oxygenated, β-mesosapobic, meso- to eutrophic waters (peat pits) with a rich vegetation on a minerotrophic peat bottom
P7	β-mesosaprobic, clear, well oxygenated, meso- to eutrophic, medium-sized, deep stagnant waters rich in vegetation
P8	β-meso- to α-mesosaprobic, medium-sized, stagnant shallow waters
P9	α-mesosaprobic, fairly large ponds or small lakes
P11	β-mesosaprobic, medium-sized, deep stagnant waters

Figure 17.3. Characterisation of the site groups (cenotypes) found in the surface waters of Overijssel. Note: cenotypes S14 and D11, which suffer from extreme organic pollution, have been omitted.

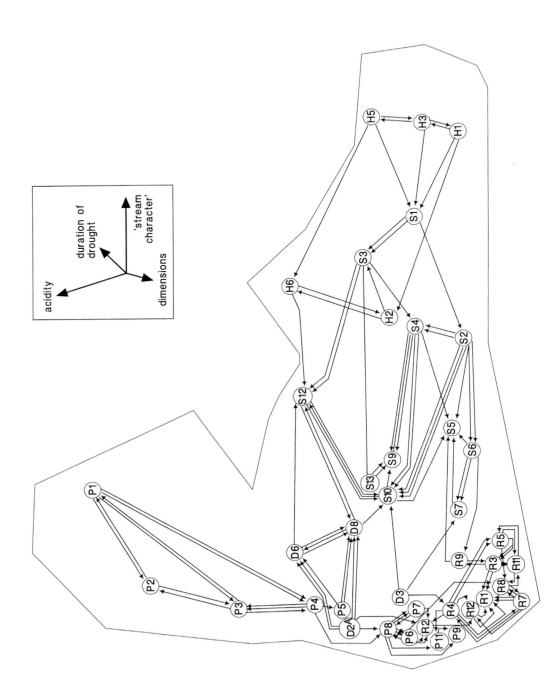

Figure 17.4 (*on facing page*). The web of cenotypes in the surface waters of Overijssel. The contour line describes the total variation present in all site scores. The centroid of each cenotype is indicated by a site group code (Fig. 17.3). The arrows between cenotypes indicate the most important environmental relations (see Figure 11.1 in Verdonschot (1990) for further details). The inset represents the four most important environmental gradients (key factors) in the total dataset. For further explanation see the text.

cenotypes have also been extracted from the environmental characterisation of the cenotypes (for further information see Appendix 2 in Verdonschot 1990). The spatial configuration of cenotypes in Figure 17.4 more or less corresponds to their ecological similarity.

The two most aberrant cenotypes are S14 and D11 (Fig. 17.2). Both types consist of only one extremely organically polluted site, which is reflected in the absence of almost all taxa. The few taxa that are present differ between these two types, and this explains their mutual dissimilarity. Both types were ignored in the ordination as they were outliers.

On the right-hand side of Figure 17.4, the most dissimilar cenotypes were helocrene springs and small streams (spring streams and small upper courses; all indicated respectively by the letter H or S1 to S4). These types were also identified by cluster analysis. They represent an environment inhabited by a characteristic macroinvertebrate fauna, clearly distinct from that of the other water types. All of these sites are situated on the steepest slopes of ice-pushed hill ridges. Their characteristic fauna is probably preserved by this natural physical protection (steep hill ridges) against environmental disturbances mainly caused by agricultural activities.

Further left in Figure 17.4 the cenotypes coded S5 to S13, and R9 and R3, represent larger running waters (middle reaches of streams to rivers). Thus, there is a gradient along the first axis from springs towards rivers, from the right towards the left side of the diagram.

The cenotypes at the top of Figure 17.4 include some acid waters, particularly moorland pools, as indicated by the codes P1 to P4. The upper one is most acidified, whereas P4 is a group of less acid pools. Macroinvertebrate fauna composition in these pools resembles the fauna composition in mesotrophic ditches (like D2A). Lakes (e.g. P8) occur below the pools.

The remaining groups to the left of Figure 17.4 can be separated into temporary versus permanent and running versus stagnant types. The polysaprobic upper and middle reaches of streams such as S5 appear to be similar to temporary upper reaches (i.e. D8 and S10), which can be seen in Figures 17.2 and 17.4. Both desiccation and extreme organic enrichment have, to a certain extent, a corresponding effect upon the fauna.

The similarity between middle and lower reaches of regulated streams, small rivers, ditches and medium-sized, more or less stagnant waters (R1 to P6), is shown both by clustering and ordination. The impoverishment of the macroinvertebrate fauna due to human-induced environmental disturbance can be seen, partly in the variables indicated (Fig. 17.2) and partly in the spatial arrangement of the cenotypes (Fig. 17.4). In particular, the cenotypes in the lower left corner of Figure 17.4 (mostly large waters) have been changed due to human disturbance. These stagnant, hypertrophic, mesosaprobic environments have part of their macroinvertebrate fauna in common. This shows, firstly, the decreasing dominance of current velocity as a key factor in these running waters and, secondly, the decreasing importance of shape, depth and bottom-type in stagnant waters. These trends are due to disturbance and stress induced by human activity (e.g. by regulation of streams, discharge of wastes and agricultural activity in the catchment) and are responsible for the impoverishment of the macroinvertebrate fauna.

It is concluded that there are now almost no truly oligo-mesotrophic waters in the province of Overijssel. For some of the cenotypes this would be a natural condition. The resulting web

(Fig. 17.4) does not distinguish between natural conditions and those that are due to anthropogenic effects; it merely reflects the cenotypes that occur under the present environmental conditions. The number of taxa which typify each cenotype is given in Figure 17.5.

Cenotype	H1	H3	H5	S1	S2	S4	H2	S3	H6	S12	P1	P2	P3	D6	D8	S13	S10	S9	S5	S6	S7
Turbellaria																	2				
Oligochaeta			1	1	4	5	2	2	1	2	1		1				3		4	4	1
Hirudinea				1													2				1
Crustacea	1	1		2	1										1						1
Ephemeroptera					1							1	1								1
Plecoptera			1	1	2		1		1												
Odonata												4	2	1							
Megaloptera				1																	1
Neuroptera																					
Coleoptera	1	2	1	1				1	2	3	11	4	10	15	17	13	4	1			2
Chironomidae	2	8	6	10	4	5	2	2	1	2	4	4	10	3	4		5	4	5	14	3
other Diptera	5	12	2	7	2	5	5	3	1	1	4	3	6	4		1		3		3	1
Trichoptera	4	3	1	5	3	1	4			3		2	2	2						2	4
Heteroptera												3	12		2	2		1			1
Lepidoptera																					
Acarina		1		2	3						1	1	1	1			2			6	4
Mollusca		1					1								2	1	4				1
Average number of taxa	21	28	15	35	38	36	27	19	8	18	23	31	51	33	47	25	39	17	25	46	57

cenotype	R5	R9	P5	D2A	D3	P4	P6	R7	R11	R8	R3	P7	R2	P8	P9	P11	R12	R1	R4	S14	D11
Turbellaria				2	2									1							
Oligochaeta	2	4		1		2	1	8	3	7	3		1	2	2		5	4	2		1
Hirudinea			1	3	2	1	1	1						4	3	1	1	1	1		
Crustacea				1						1	1			1	1			1			
Ephemeroptera			1			1					2	4	1	1			1		2		
Plecoptera																					
Odonata				1		2	2				1	1		2			1		1		
Megaloptera														1			1				
Neuroptera							1														
Coleoptera		13	14	7	17	2	1			1	2	1	5	2		3		1	7		
Chironomidae		5	1	6	2	3	5	1	4	7	11	11	3	7	5	9	10	4	6		
other Diptera		2	2		6	2					1		2		1				3	3	
Trichoptera		1		2		1	6	1	1	1	4	4	1	4	1	3	3	6	3		
Heteroptera			2					8		1	1	5	1	5	3	6		2	4		
Lepidoptera					1																
Acarina		1	1	11	2	4	1	12		5	2	7	6	1		11	4	1	16		
Mollusca		1	5	12	14	3	1	1	2	6	2			2	1	1		1	3		
Average number of taxa	15	58	50	70	64	61	64	42	42	65	68	62	71	78	58	80	70	61	91	3	7

Figure 17.5. The numbers of characteristic taxa in the 42 centoypes of the surface waters in Overijssel, listed by taxonomic groups.

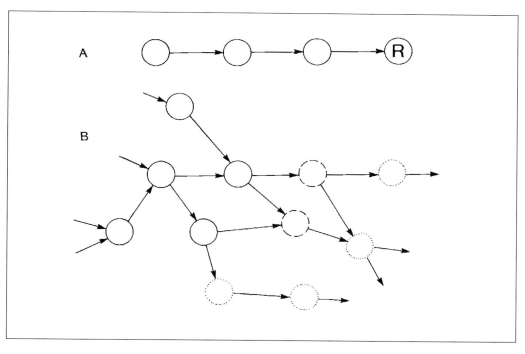

Figure 17.6. Schematic representation of assessment systems applied to surface waters. A represents a univariate system with a fixed end-point (R) and a singular series. B represents a multivariate system with more development stages in different directions (a web) and more or less well defined stages (open and dotted circles).

Web approach

In water assessment, targets are needed for waterbodies. In biological assessment systems these targets are usually unpolluted conditions. Most assessment systems use a singular succession series, with one static end-point as the unpolluted state and thus the optimum in ecosystem development (Fig. 17.6A). However, a static end-point and a singular assessment series is of limited use in water management. This is because target communities of unpolluted sites will differ, depending on the environmental conditions (Verdonschot 1994).

In The Netherlands, a discussion is taking place on the definition of the unpolluted or natural state. Terms such as "unpolluted", "natural", "desired" and "pristine" are all subjective conceptions, and each concept often has different definitions. Four definitions of the target community guide the discussion below. (1) A community in the past: the "former", "historical" (for example the year 1900) or "original" community, known from the literature. (2) A natural community: defined as the community developed under the given climatological, geological, geomorphological and biogeographical circumstances, with or without certain extensive human interference. (3) A present (current) optimal community: the "optimal" community which can be measured, and in which optimal is defined as the condition whereby an ecosystem under the given natural conditions is self-maintaining. (4) A potential community: the "potential optimal" community, taking the present and the future environmental conditions into consideration.

These alternative definitions of the target community are often used arbitrarily without clarification. Sometimes even the most natural or developed stage needs human interference to remain stable (in a dynamic sense). For example, some artificial waters such as ditches and

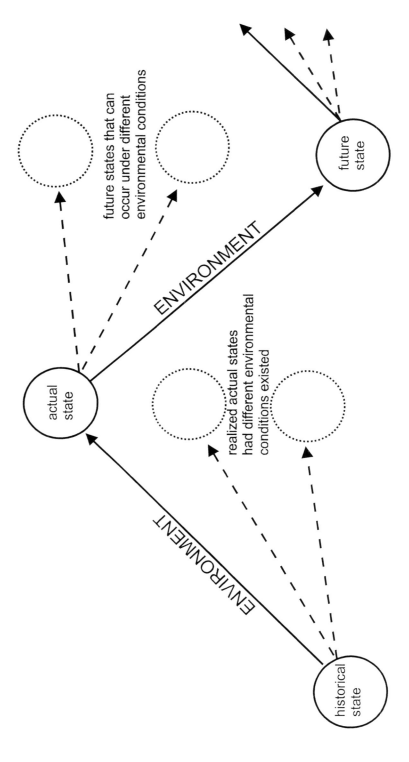

Figure 17.7. The capacity of a biological community (adapted from Warren *et al.* 1979).

canals are constructed by man; these would gradually fill and become shallow or disappear without regular human interference in the form of cleaning and dredging. Their climax would not be aquatic but more or less terrestrial, and would conflict with the objectives of water and nature management. The meanings of terms like "natural" and "optimal" are subjective and depend on the objectives being pursued. There are a number of arguments against a theoretical definition of the target as the most natural state of an ecosystem on an assessment scale. The target will depend on aspects of naturalness, information from the past, variability of the optimum and unfamiliarity with future circumstances. It is clearly impossible to give objective criteria for the definition of a target as a static end-point.

Therefore, we chose a more pragmatic approach. The target should be a condition that indicates a direction of improvement with respect to the objectives of the water manager. In addition, the target must fit within the ecological potential of the respective waterbody. This directional process is described as ecosystem development (Verdonschot 1991). The degree of ecosystem development indicates the stage of the aquatic ecosystem and its potential direction of development. The choices which determine the direction of improvement are made by the water and nature manager, and depend upon important ecological processes. The web of cenotypes offers a basis for deciding which potential developmental directions are possible and what environmental processes should be steered by means of management measures.

In Figure 17.6B a web of more and less well-defined states and their relationships is illustrated. It is an abstraction of the web of cenotypes (Fig. 17.4). Within this web it is possible to indicate different potential developmental directions, from actual states towards ecologically more optimal states. Such a web can serve as a reference framework. New samples can be referred to this framework because it contains both clean and more or less disturbed types. The stage, and the potential directions (targets) in ecosystem development of a waterbody, further depend on the intrinsic character of each waterbody. For a description of this intrinsic character it is important to obtain knowledge of the former conditions and their development towards the actual state, knowledge of the present conditions in terms of abiotic and biotic parameters, knowledge of the potential ecological conditions and processes related to water type (e.g. succession, production and decomposition), and knowledge of the feasibility of change with respect to management, policies and developments in society.

To describe the intrinsic character of a waterbody, a list of abiotic conditions is even more important than a list of rare and/or characteristic species.

To describe the potential of a waterbody, knowledge is needed on the relevant processes. According to Warren *et al.* (1979) only the structure of a community can be measured; its functioning can only be represented indirectly and incompletely. This is true for our web. The parameters that relate cenotypes in our web are extracted from structural community characteristics. However, they reflect underlying processes, such as the relation between profile shape and the processes of erosion and deposition, or phosphorus and nitrogen content in relation to eutrophication. The actual state and the ecosystem's potential capacity is given in Figure 17.7. The potential capacity is the predetermination of all possible states and structures which can evolve from the actual system. The interaction of system capacity and the state of the environment determine the system structure realised at any moment (the realised capacity). If the environment had been different, another sequence of realised capacities would have been the result (Warren *et al.* 1979). This hypothesis is applicable to our web. In practice, management should focus on processes.

Example of the use of the web

The web is best explained by means of a simple example. Figure 17.8 and Tables 17.1 and 17.2 show a small part of the web. Cenotype S5 represents polysaprobic upper and middle reaches of natural and regulated streams. Organically polluted streams are indicated in the transverse profile by black substratum. The relationships between this type and both cenotypes S7 and S6 are illustrated by the arrows indicating organic material. Cenotype S7 represents α-mesosaprobic middle reaches of regulated streams, and is related to cenotype S6 (α-mesosaprobic middle reaches of semi-natural streams) by two parameters: transverse profile shape and nutrient concentration. The first parameter is related to morphology and hydrology of the stream, and the second is related to the agricultural activities in the catchment. A general feature in this region is the combination of intensive agricultural activity and increased discharge by stream canalisation and land drainage. Through these human activities, streams belonging to cenotype S6 shift towards those of S7. The construction of a sewage treatment plant which discharges into a stream belonging to cenotype S6 or S7 will cause a shift towards cenotype S5.

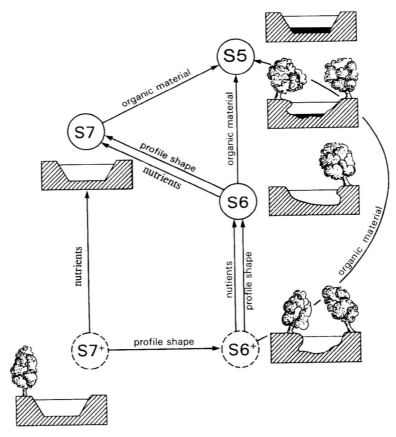

Figure 17.8. A small part of the web of cenotypes (Verdonschot 1990) with three actual cenotypes (closed circles), two potential cenotypes (dotted circles), the most important environmental relationships (the arrows) and some profile shapes. For further explanation see the text.

In this study, none of these cenotypes represent pristine conditions, in the sense that they are unaffected by human activities. Nevertheless, we need stages in development towards more ecologically optimal conditions.

Table 17.1. *Some biotic characteristics of the cenotypes for sites in Overijssel, used in Figure 17.8.*

Cenotype	Number of typifying taxa	Dominant taxonomic group(s)
S5	9	Oligochaeta
S7	21	Coleoptera
		Megaloptera
S7+	30–40	Trichoptera
		Odonata
S6	29	Trichoptera
		Chironomidae
		Acarina
S6+	30–35	Ephemeroptera
		Plecoptera
		Trichoptera

Table 17.2. *Some abiotic characteristics of the cenotypes for sites in Overijssel, used in Figure 17.8*

Parameters	Cenotypes S5	S7	S7+	S6	S6+
pH	7.1–7.7	7.1–7.7	5.5–7.0	6.7–8.3	5.5–7.0
Conductivity ($\mu S\ cm^{-1}$)	205–595	334–550	<200	226–626	<200
NH_4 (mg N l^{-1})	1.6–11.8	0–5.9	0–0.4	0–4.8	0–0.4
NO_3 (mg N l^{-1})	3.0–8.6	2.4–8.6	<1	2.1–7.7	<1
Total P (mg P l^{-1})	0.63–4.43	0–2.03	0.01–0.04	0–3.37	0.01–0.04
Silt (cm)	0–27	0–24	0–5	0–2	0
Width (m)	1.4–4.8	0–9.0	0–9.0	1.7–4.5	1.7–4.5
Depth (cm)	12–54	1–107	1–107	12–64	12–64
Slope (m km^{-1})	0.4–3.8	0.3–25	0.3–2.5	0.2–2.4	0.2–2.4
% Vegetation cover	0–34	0–44	50–80	0–41	<40

Our example of part of the web (cenotypes S5, S6 and S7) is extended with two developmental stages towards an ecological optimum (Fig. 17.8). These stages were not included in the web of cenotypes (Fig. 17.4) and are indicated by plus signs. Knowledge of type-related processes, and present and historical data on comparable waters, were used to describe these potential developmental stages (Tables 17.1 and 17.2). The potential cenotype S6+, β-mesosaprobic middle reaches of natural streams, and S7+, β-mesosaprobic middle reaches of regulated streams, are shown. The relationship between cenotype S6 and S6+ is mainly due to four parameters: profile shape, morphology, hydrology and nutrient concentration. The latter is also important between cenotypes S7 and S7+. Streams that belong to cenotype S6 or S7 can be managed in the direction of more optimal stages S6+ and S7+, respectively. This web and its extension can also be used for assessment and valuation by adding a valuation scale to the different cenotypes, including their developmental stages, or by relating the observed assemblage to the expected one (the chosen target for a site).

Application of the web in management

Ecological typology aggregates the variability in species combinations, and the variability in environmental conditions, into discrete units. Therefore, ecological typology can serve as a basis for water and nature management in fresh waters, in lowland regions. Nowadays, assessment is not enough to carry out management. Ecological typology offers more possibilities, and is a basis for the development of tools to describe and monitor, evaluate and assess, set standards, formulate and assign ecological objectives/targets, predict and test, and advise on management measures.

To use these tools, it is necessary to compare a waterbody with the communities present in other waterbodies with similar major environmental conditions (key factors) as well as under less disturbed conditions. This requires a specification of the present and potential conditions of the waterbody under study. The ideal is the use of a web of reference conditions with which the present condition can be compared and from which potential development can be extracted. This web of reference conditions should include "dead" or "barren" water as well as all intermediate conditions towards and including ecologically pristine conditions.

To use the web of cenotypes as a reference framework, a new sample should first be assigned to a position or type within the web. A software package was developed to undertake this task. Next, it is necessary to establish the target (reference condition) for a certain site. The distance between the present and target stage, and the processes to be steered by management, finally determine the management measures to be taken.

Software development to support ecological management

The database of the web of 42 cenotypes contains lists of species, associated typifying weights and abundances, and environmental variables for each cenotype. These data constitute the basis of a software package entitled EKOO. This software package contains three main modules (Table 17.3). These modules are (1) arithmetic assignment of a newly sampled site to a cenotype, based on the macroinvertebrate fauna composition, (2) characterisation (diversity and biotic description of all species) of a newly sampled site, based on macroinvertebrate fauna composition, and (3) choice of a direction of ecological development and advice on measures to be taken.

Each of these modules will be described and illustrated by a case example, based on a sample of macroinvertebrate fauna from the middle reach of the small Springendalse stream, situated in the eastern part of the province of Overijssel.

Case example 1 (Module 1)

Three techniques are used to assign macroinvertebrate samples to cenotypes. These are passive DCCA (Ter Braak 1987), similarity indices (Hellawell 1978) and weighting, a method which uses typifying weights of species (Verdonschot 1990). Each of these three techniques comprises two different methods (Tables 17.4 and 17.5). The web of cenotypes was constructed on the basis of mathematically transformed abundances; the assignment of samples is therefore also based on transformed data.

All samples used to construct the web of cenotypes were used to test the internal consistency of the program. The percentage of correct assignments was a measure of internal consistency. Table 17.5 shows that the highest consistency (85%) was obtained by using the Czekanowski coefficient. However, by using a combination of the results from both passive analysis techniques, both similarity indices, and weighting on all taxa, the best assignment results were

Table 17.3. *Modules in the program package EKOO.*

SOFTWARE PACKAGE EKOO			
NEW SAMPLE => WEB OF CENOTYPES (sample oriented)			
Module:	1	2	3
Organisation level:	Assemblage	Taxon	Cenotype
Program type:	Arithmetic	Arithmetic	Expert system
Technique:	Passive analysis Weighting Similarity	Diversity Biotic description	Set target Select measures

Table 17.4. *Arithmetic assignment of newly collected macroinvertebrate fauna samples to the web of cenotypes, using two methods (columns down) for each of three different techniques (columns across).*

Techniques are based on: similarity indices (Hellawell 1978), weighting (Verdonschot 1990) and passive DCCA (Ter Braak 1987).

Similarity ratios	Weighting	Passive andysis (DCCA)
Czekanowski coefficient (Czekanowski 1913)	Including all taxa	Mahanalobis distance (Mahanalobis 1936)
Squared Euclidean distance (Jongman *et al.* 1987)	Typifying weight >3	Euclidean distance (Gauch 1982)

Table 17.5. *Internal consistency of sample assignment to cenotypes, using the original dataset and applying six methods and two combinations of methods.*

Methods	Correct assignment (%)
(1) Mahanalobis distance	81.6
(2) Euclidean distance	79.0
(3) Weighting all taxa	66.1
(4) Weighting typifying taxa >3	61.5
(5) Czekanowski coefficient	85.0
(6) Squared Euclidean distance	77.0
(7) Methods (3), (5) and (6)	88.0
(8) Methods (1–3), (5) and (6)	93.0

obtained (93% for methods (1), (2), (3), (5) and (6), Table 17.5). By using the program to assign a new sample, the final result of the combination of these five methods is then presented to the user. The results of assignment in the case example are given in Table 17.6.

Table 17.6. *Arithmetic assignment of a new sample from the Springendalse stream in Overijssel*

Method of assignment	Assigned cenotype
Mahanalobis distance	R9
Euclidean distance	S7
Czekanowski index	S7
Squared Euclidean distance	S7
Weighting on all taxa	S6
Weighting on typifying taxa only	S6
Overall assignment	S7

Table 17.7. *Diversity of a new sample (see Table 17.6) from the Springendalse stream in Overijssel, compared with the mean, range and standard deviation of three indices applied to cenotype S7.*

Diversity indices are from: Shannon & Weaver (1949), Simpson (1949) and Alatalo (1981).

| Parameters of the indices | Diversity index values | | |
	Shannon	Reciprocal Simpson	Alatalo
Mean for S7	0.086	52.1	587
Minimum for S7	0.067	35.3	334
Maximum for S7	0.102	60.8	863
SD for S7	0.011	9.6	166
New sample	0.106	51.3	450.3

Case example 2 (Module 2)

Two types of sample characterisation, "diversity" and "biotic description", are available to describe the biotic status of a new sample. Three diversity measures are included, namely Shannon index (Shannon & Weaver 1949), reciprocal Simpson index (Simpson 1949) and Alatalo index (Alatalo 1981). Table 17.7 gives the diversity measures obtained for a new sample from the Springendalse stream, in relation to the mean and range of values obtained for cenotype S7.

Each taxon is indicative of a number of features of a waterbody. In the option "biotic description", metrics that are indicative of the following features are calculated using the fauna in the new sample: geomorphological water type, habitat, saprobic level, current velocity class, frequency of occurrence (or rarity), higher taxonomic group (order/class), trophic level, functional feeding group, behavioural habit and extreme biotic conditions. Each of these features is classified into about six classes, according to the percentage of taxa indicative of each class.

"Diversity" and "biotic description" measures can be compared only within a cenotype or with other samples from the same waterbody, because taxon richness differs due to differences in the natural environment. It is also essential to keep in mind any differences due to sampling effort and difficulty of sampling. Therefore, it is important to use the standard procedures

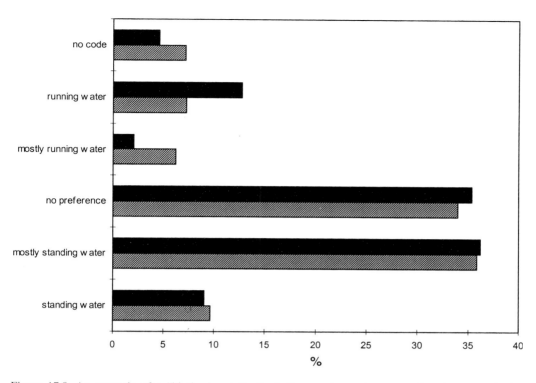

Figure 17.9. An example of a "biotic description" of all macroinvertebrate taxa found at a particular sampling site in relation to an abiotic parameter. In the example, taxa are classed in terms of their known preferences for current velocity, ranging from standing to running water; taxa included in the "no code" category have not been classified for current velocity preferences. Horizontal bars show the proportions (%) of taxa in each of six categories (classes); shaded bars represent cenotype S7 for comparison with the new sample (solid bars).

described in the section on collection of samples. For example, stagnant mesotrophic waters are inhabited by many more taxa than are found in streams (Verdonschot 1990). However, comparison of these diversity and biotic description measures can be useful in monitoring and evaluating the development of a waterbody.

An example of diversity measures for a new sample from the Springendalse stream has been given in Table 17.7. Figure 17.9 shows the biotic description (relation to rheophily) of the same sample. Note that the distribution of species over the classes in the new sample closely follows type S7.

Case example 3 (Module 3)

To be able to choose the developmental direction of a newly sampled site, one has to know the cenotype and its characteristics. The cenotype is calculated by arithmetic assignment and, together with a knowledge of potential characteristics, the manager has to choose a target cenotype. A part of the web of cenotypes is shown in Figure 17.8. After choosing a target, the manager is offered a number of questions in an expert system. These questions relate to the environmental parameters that indicate the processes relevant to the present and target cenotypes. The questionnaire leads the manager through all potential management options and assists in selecting the measures to be taken to reach the target. Relevant questions and measures are listed by the program.

In the case of the Springendalse stream, the overall cenotype assigned was S7. The target direction chosen was from S7 through S6 to S6+; in other words the target cenotype was S6+. The target direction and final target cenotype imply an improvement in the following factors: regulation, organic matter and nutrients, i.e. improvement in the processes of morphology and eutrophication (saprobication). The questionnaire is summarised below, but includes only those questions which lead to action. Disturbances that are not relevant at this specific site are excluded from the list.

Questionnaire on morphology

Question: Is profile consolidation present?
Advice: Remove the profile consolidation or replace it with natural materials. If necessary, use gravel or stones on vulnerable spots. Include migration (water to land) facilities for fauna.

Question: Has the longitudinal profile been changed?
Advice: Induce spontaneous meandering, rehabilitate old meanders or dig a new meandering profile. When this is not possible, insert objects in the stream (e.g. tree-trunks or stones).

Question: Has the transverse profile been straightened?
Advice: Heighten the bottom of the stream-bed, narrow the stream width for low flows and create berms to take high flows.

Question: Are the stream banks morphologically affected?
Advice: Vary the bank profile by creating deposition zones and overhanging or steep banks (create/induce an asymmetric profile shape).

Question: Is a weir present?
Advice: Remove the weir and dig an extension of the longitudinal profile of the stream at this site or construct a cascade or fish ladder.

Questionnaire on eutrophication (saprobication)

Question: Does manuring or fertilisation take place in the up-stream catchment?
Advice: Prevent over-fertilisation by legislation and control. Reduce it further by buying adjacent land, stimulating the development of buffer strips, or inducing a change of land use (such as afforestation).

Question: Does surface and subsurface runoff take place?
Advice: Fill up side streams and drainage ditches, remove drain pipes, create buffer strips or horseshoe-shaped wetlands, plant adjacent woodland and create stream-bank elevations.

Question: Is the adjacent land over-fertilised?
Advice: Decrease the amount of nutrients by mowing and removing the vegetation or remove the upper layer in the infiltration zone without affecting the natural bottom profile.

Conclusions and future developments

Many early works on the classification of surface waters were restricted to a limited number of running waters (Illies & Botosaneanu 1963; Hawkes 1975), stagnant waters (Margalef 1958; Brinkhurst 1974) or both (Thienemann 1955). Most of these works were purely descriptive. More recently, with the introduction of automated data processing techniques, larger classifications have been made of running waters (Braukmann 1984; Wright, Moss *et al.* 1984) and stagnant waters (Kansanen *et al.* 1984; Johnson & Wiederholm 1989). All used indirect gradient analysis techniques to derive their classes but were still limited to certain water types.

The ecological typology presented in this study is based on direct gradient analysis techniques and includes a wide range of water types. As expected, differences were found between waterbodies such as helocrene springs, streams, ditches and ponds. During the study, the relationships between these types were visualised and intermediate types were recognised. Furthermore, a number of types within each of these major categories were described (e.g. five types within helocrene springs, eleven types within streams, and four types within ditches). In general, this means that ecological water types are more than (either) visually, physically, chemically or biologically recognised entities. Of course the number of types also depends on the sampling methods and analysis techniques used. Sampling methods, in terms of sample size, effort and level of identification, were shown to be representative for sites. During the analysis, options were standardised and results were tested statistically, resulting in non-stochastic, reproducible results.

In water management, easily recognisable parameters are often used as simple and practical criteria to distinguish water types. As a result, only some of the features of the ecosystem are taken into account. For the assessment and evaluation of a waterbody, community composition as well as environmental conditions should be used. In the present ecological water typology, each cenotype is the result of its specific biological and environmental complex. By using direct gradient analysis, biota and environmental conditions are directly related to each other. This typological approach offers a method that combines the advantages of using tables incorporating complex data into a relatively simple diagrammatic presentation.

The web of cenotypes can be used as a practical tool in water management. In analysing a waterbody, first the key factors should be distinguished, followed by the other less important environmental factors. All of these factors are responsible for the actual state of the system. Second, a direction of improvement should be chosen. Third, one should distinguish those processes that are responsible for potential improvement and look for related factors that are manageable. Typology can be used to solve water management problems if they are considered together with the appropriate ecological concepts and if the user is aware of the uniqueness of each individual waterbody.

Management also needs to predict the effects of intended measures. May (1984) stated that it is doubtful whether any community is sufficiently well understood for confident predictions to be made about its response to particular disturbances. Hawkes (1975), Resh & Unzicker (1975), Maitland (1979) and Persoone (1979) have all stressed the predictive value of the results of an ecological survey, despite the fact that it is based on conceptual ideas and correlation of data, rather than on causal proof. A comprehensive ecological survey of sites in a given region has a descriptive value and the results can, with caution, be used to predict effects of management measures. In this way, the relationships described in the web are being harnessed.

In conclusion, the web of cenotypes offers a basis for the daily practice of regional water and nature management. It has been developed at the small-scale level of regional water types and can be used from the bottom (small scale) up (large scale = national water and nature management and policies). This means that the web can be used at a larger-scale level by aggregation. The web supports the development of water quality objectives and standards in terms of cenotypes, and supports the methods used to monitor and assess waters. It indicates the potential of waters and can be used to predict and further inform about the management and restoration of waters.

In future the following parts of the package need further development: assignment of new samples based on biotic and abiotic parameters considered together; target selection supported by an expert system to optimise the choices; prediction of the probability of a new site belonging to a particular cenotype, based on known environmental parameters; the arithmetic assignment of a newly sampled site to a particular cenotype, based only on environmental parameters. Furthermore, webs will be developed for different regions as well as for different major physico-geomorphological water types on a national scale.

CHAPTER 18

New approaches to river quality classification based upon Artificial Intelligence

WILLIAM J. WALLEY AND VALENTINE N. FONTAMA

School of Computing, Staffordshire University,
The Octagon, Beaconside, Stafford, ST18 0DG, UK

Summary

This chapter describes the application of Artificial Intelligence (AI) techniques to the biological classification of river quality[1]. The essential characteristics of the data and its interpretation are examined. Uncertainty in the meaning of the data is shown to be central to the interpretation task. It is argued that experts handle this by a combination of "probabilistic" knowledge-based reasoning and pattern recognition. Two AI techniques, Bayesian reasoning and neural networks, are shown to be well suited to the modelling of these processes. Three examples are given: two based on neural networks and one on Bayesian inference. The AI and RIVPACS approaches are compared, and it is shown that the AI approach takes a holistic view of the biology of polluted and unpolluted waters, whereas RIVPACS is based on a single reference state. The future of the AI approach is briefly discussed.

Introduction

The work described in this chapter stems from a chance discussion in 1989 between W. J. Walley, an engineer seeking a practical application for his Artificial Intelligence (AI) skills, and H. A. Hawkes, a former member of the Biological Monitoring Working Party (BMWP), who was concerned about the way in which the BMWP system was being applied in practice (Hawkes 1998). The two agreed to collaborate on the development of AI methods of interpreting benthic data into river quality terms. Their aim was to model the mental processes used by experts when interpreting such data directly (i.e. without reference to any man-made system). These processes were found to involve knowledge-based reasoning and pattern recognition. Thus the project developed along two parallel strands of research, one based upon knowledge-based systems (Boyd 1995) and the other on pattern recognition using neural networks (Ruck 1995). Those wishing to follow the initial development of this approach in more detail are referred to Walley *et al.* (1992a, 1992b), Walley (1994) and Walley & Džeroski (1995).

---

[1] The term "river quality" is used throughout to mean the quality of the river as reflected by its biological community. Various terms and definitions have been used by others for this rather ill-defined concept. Although there is a need for a more robust definition, this complex issue lies outside the scope of this chapter.

Characteristics of the problem

The first stage in the development of any knowledge-based expert system is the elicitation of knowledge from an acknowledged expert in the field. In this case, H. A. Hawkes was the ideal expert, since he had been a pioneer of biomonitoring in Britain and had considerable experience of interpreting benthic data prior to the introduction of the BMWP and RIVPACS systems. Several meetings were held with him to elicit and document his expertise. In some of these he was asked: (a) to classify the river quality of various sites based upon their biological data; and (b) to explain the basis of his classification. These sessions, together with insights gained during the development and testing of prototype systems, highlighted some important characteristics of the problem.

The nature of expert interpretation

It was observed that Hawkes classified sites using a combination of two different, but complementary, processes. He used his knowledge and understanding of river ecology to interpret the data in scientific terms, and used his experience of former cases to recognise patterns in the data that he had come to associate with certain river conditions. His final conclusions seemed to evolve from a subconscious balancing of the two approaches. Discussions with other experts, in river ecology and other fields, have confirmed this observation. Thus, from an AI perspective, the key to effective data interpretation lies in our ability to model these two processes.

Initial attempts at modelling the reasoning processes used by Hawkes were based upon rules, but this approach was soon abandoned when it was realised that his reasoning was not exact but probabilistic in nature. That is, the relationships he used to interpret the data were inherently uncertain, and had to be weighed against each other to draw a "balanced" conclusion. This uncertainty in the meaning of data is a key characteristic of the interpretation task, and has important implications for the types of model that can be considered suitable for use. Any method that eliminates this uncertainty through the use of averages, e.g. the BMWP system (Hawkes 1998) and saprobic systems (Hellawell 1978), or exact rules, e.g. the Trent Biotic Index (Woodiwiss 1964), is bound to result in the loss of valuable information.

Principal factors influencing community composition

The principal factors influencing community composition are river quality, environmental factors (other than river quality), seasonal variation, spatial isolation and intermittent temporal effects. Since our objective is to classify river quality from community data, it is vital that the effects of the other factors are accounted for in our models.

Moss, Furse *et al.* (1987) demonstrated how environmental data could be used to predict the macroinvertebrate fauna at unpolluted running-water sites in Great Britain. Their system (RIVPACS) provides the means of accounting for environmental effects on community composition at unpolluted sites, and defines river quality by means of Ecological Quality Indices (EQIs) (Sweeting, Lowson *et al.* 1992; see also Chapter 4) based on the difference between the observed community and the predicted "unpolluted" community. The weakness of the system lies in the inability of EQIs to adequately represent the complex relationships between community composition and river quality. Alternative ways of representing these relationships are discussed later.

The effects of seasonal variation and spatial isolation can be removed simply by developing separate models for each season or spatially isolated region. It also may be necessary to develop separate models for sub-areas of a single ecoregion if differences in community

CHAPTER 19

The multimetric approach to bioassessment, as used in the United States of America

MICHAEL T. BARBOUR[1] AND CHRIS O. YODER[2]

[1]*Tetra Tech, Inc., 10045 Red Run Blvd,*
Suite 110, Owings Mills, Maryland 21117, USA
[2]*Ohio Environmental Protection Agency,*
1685 Westbelt Drive, Columbus, Ohio 43228, USA

Summary

The multimetric approach to bioassessment is the technique most frequently used by the state water resource agencies in the USA, because it provides a means of integrating ecological information relating to the elements and processes of naturally functioning aquatic assemblages and our current knowledge about those relationships. The detection and evaluation of impairment from the various pollutant sources and other impacts attributable to human activities has required a technique that is (1) applicable to all waterbody types and different aquatic assemblages, (2) readily adaptable to state water resource protection programs, and (3) easily translatable to non-technical managers and the general public. The multimetric approach has been developed, to varying degrees, for streams, rivers, lakes, estuaries and wetlands, and for the periphyton, benthic macroinvertebrate and fish assemblages. It has been most universally applied to streams in the USA. More than 90% of the state water resource agencies use a multimetric approach. The translation of biological data into meaningful results and the subsequent communication to a non-technical audience have been enhanced by the use of multimetrics. Both the USEPA and several states have developed technical guidance for the development and implementation of a multimetric approach to bioassessment. While further development and refinement of multimetric strategies are warranted, this approach has been successfully implemented in the USA.

Introduction

To understand the underpinnings of ecosystem assessment and protection in the USA, one must first be informed of the regulatory statutes behind the development of environmental protection programs. State water pollution control agencies function as custodians of water quality management under the Federal Water Pollution Control Act (Yoder & Rankin 1998), which has become known in later amendments as the Clean Water Act (CWA). This role is delegated by the United States Environmental Protection Agency (USEPA) to qualifying states, which then have the obligation to develop and maintain water quality standards, issue permits to wastewater discharges, lead in the development of basin-wide water quality management plans, and monitor the effectiveness of the overall water quality management program (Yoder & Rankin 1998). Yoder and Rankin state that it is in fulfillment of this latter function that the development of environmental indicators, which include biological monitoring and assessment tools and criteria, have recently received renewed attention in the USA.

A principal objective of the CWA is to restore and maintain the physical, chemical and biological integrity of the nation's surface waters (Clean Water Act Section 101 [a][2]). This goal is fundamentally ecological, and the restoration and protection of the surface waters in the USA is based upon the CWA objective of "biological integrity" (Davis & Simon 1995). The two key concepts here are "surface waters" and "biological integrity". The USA and individual states are responsible for the restoration and the protection of all surface waters, which include streams and rivers, lakes and reservoirs, wetlands, and estuaries and near-coastal areas. Monitoring and assessment programs, whilst being tailored to specific waterbody types, should have similar goals and approaches. The USEPA has provided guidance for establishing biological criteria in regulatory programs (USEPA 1990) and technical guidance for assessing the condition of streams and small rivers (Gibson, Barbour *et al.* 1996), lakes and reservoirs (Gerritsen, Carlson *et al.* 1997), and estuaries and near-coastal areas (Gibson, Bowman *et al.* 1997). The agency is currently developing similar guidance for wetlands and large, navigable rivers. The technical resources that are needed to assess all of these surface waters are substantial. If we consider streams alone, more than 80% of the states have more than 33,000 kilometres of streams (Davis, Snyder *et al.* 1996), the monitoring of which is a daunting undertaking for any agency.

The second key concept, biological integrity (and its broader concept of ecosystem integrity), has been subjected to much debate in the USA, as well as internationally (Scrimgeour & Wicklum 1996). Since its origin in the early version of the CWA, biological integrity has been considered relative to: (1) conditions that existed prior to European settlement of the USA, (2) the protection and propagation of balanced, indigenous populations of aquatic organisms, and (3) ecosystems that are unperturbed by human activities (Yoder & Rankin 1998). These criteria (especially (1) and (3)) are idealistic and probably exist in only a few ecosystems in the conterminous USA. Efforts to construct a workable, practical definition of biological integrity have provided the supporting theory that necessarily precedes the development of standardized measurement frameworks, techniques, and criteria for determining compliance with that goal (Yoder & Rankin 1998). Biological integrity has been defined as the ability of an aquatic ecosystem to support and maintain a balanced, integrated, adaptive community of organisms having a species composition, diversity, and functional organization comparable to that of the natural habitats of a region (Karr & Dudley 1981). Biological integrity means more than achieving a high level of species diversity. By definition, the maintenance of an aquatic community that is balanced and integrative with respect to composition and biomass, survival and propagation, is crucial to biological integrity. Therefore, the USA biological programs are based on measurements of attributes that represent the various components of biological integrity.

A well designed monitoring and assessment program is inherently anticipatory in that it will provide information for needs not yet determined (Yoder & Rankin 1998). Thus, implementation of a program must be a proactive exercise, because once the opportunity passes it is impossible to generate the needed data and information after the fact. State agencies are realizing that biological assessment provides a substantive advantage to programs charged with a multitude of objectives. Degradation of our water resources is caused by more than chemical contamination alone, which is the primary focus of conventional water quality programs (Karr 1995). The cumulative impacts of human actions go well beyond chemical contamination and these impacts influence one or more of five primary classes of variables (i.e. water quality, habitat structure, flow regime, energy source and biotic interactions), with potentially devastating and often undetected effects on the quality of the water resource (Karr 1991). Biological communities integrate the effects of different stressors, such as excess nutrients, toxic chemicals, increased temperature, excessive sediment loading and habitat degradation –

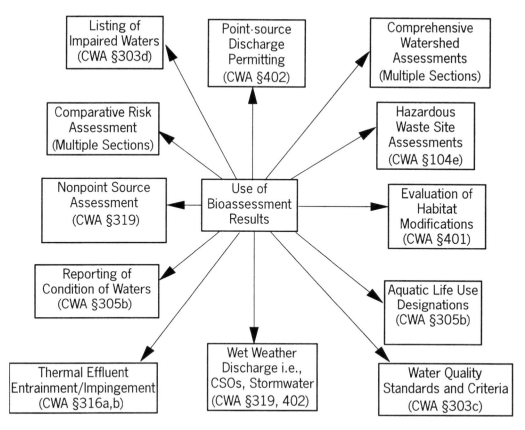

Figure 19.1. Applications of bioassessment data to water resource management programs in the USA. CSO = Combined sewage overflow; CWA = Clean Water Act (see the text).

and thus provide an overall measure of the aggregate impact of the stressors (Barbour *et al.* 1996).

Several sections of the CWA call for the implementation of assessment and monitoring activities, all of which benefit from the incorporation of biological surveys. The water resource programs in the USA have multiple objectives related to these sections of the CWA (Fig. 19.1). States are faced with the challenge of developing monitoring tools that are both appropriate and cost-effective, and that will provide comprehensive coverage of their water resources (Barbour 1997). For making sound management decisions regarding the protection, restoration and maintenance of its water resources, a state must obtain reliable data in a relatively expedient fashion. In addition, results from biological surveys (as with any scientific data) must be translated easily to the public and managers who are making decisions regarding water resources (Barbour 1997).

A National Water Quality Report is required to be submitted to the United States Congress on a periodic basis (every 5 years). Under this mandate, states, territories, some Indian tribes and certain River Basin Commissions have developed programs to monitor surface and ground waters and to report the current status of water quality to the USEPA (Barbour, Gerritsen *et al.* 1999). The Watershed Protection Approach (WPA), which entails comprehensive assessments of entire watersheds (i.e. catchments) in rotation so that all state waters are assessed over a period of time (*ca* 5 years), is becoming the framework for meeting the nation's water resource challenges (USEPA 1997). With this approach, state monitoring and assessment programs will be redirected, in order to more effectively target waters receiving inputs from both point and nonpoint sources, and to identify problems, prioritize mitigation and protection efforts, and provide updated information on a periodic basis. The use of biological assessment in these National Water Quality Reports helps to define an understandable end-point of relevance to society. However, for this to occur, technical data and results must be transformed to conclusions expeditiously after the survey, and translated to a generally non-technical audience (managers and the public) so that they can make informed decisions regarding the water resource.

The multimetric concept

The accurate assessment of biological condition requires a method that integrates biotic examination of patterns and processes from individual to ecosystem levels (Karr, Fausch *et al.* 1986). The primary approach in the USA is to define an array of measures or metrics that individually provide information on diverse biological attributes and, when integrated, provide an overall indication of biological condition (Barbour *et al.* 1995). A metric is a calculated term or enumeration representing some aspect of biological assemblage structure, function or other measurable characteristic that changes in a predictable way with increased human influence (Fausch, Lyons *et al.* 1990; Gibson, Barbour *et al.* 1996). For the broad range of human impacts on aquatic ecosystems, a comprehensive, multiple metric approach has been found to be an effective assessment tool in the USA (Barbour *et al.* 1995; Davis, Snyder *et al.* 1996). The multimetric concept was conceived with the Index of Biotic Integrity (IBI), which was first developed for fish assemblages (Karr 1981). The IBI aggregates various elements and surrogate measures of process into a meaningful assessment of biological condition. Karr (1981) and Karr, Fausch *et al.* (1986) demonstrated that combinations of these attributes or metrics provide a valuable synthesis for assessing the status of water resources. The Ohio Environmental Protection Agency was among the first state water resource agencies to implement the multimetric approach for their statewide monitoring and assessment program (Yoder & Rankin 1995a) and to develop concurrent multimetric indices for both fish and benthic macroinvertebrate assemblages (Ohio EPA 1987). The USEPA broadened this approach to a national guidance known as the Rapid Bioassessment Protocols (RBPs) (Plafkin, Barbour *et al.* 1989; Barbour, Gerritsen *et al.* 1999).

Perhaps the greatest challenge to water resource agencies is to identify an approach that will work in different types of water (i.e. streams, rivers, lakes, estuaries, wetlands) and among different assemblages. Although the multimetric approach has not been rigorously tested in all cases, multimetric indices have been developed for regional application for a variety of waterbody/assemblage assessments. The stream literature is best known and several relevant papers have been cited throughout this chapter. Additional literature on multimetric indices relevant to other waterbody types and assemblages include fish in "great" (large, navigable) rivers (Emery & Simon 1998), fish in lakes (Dionne & Karr 1992; Hughes, Whittier *et al.* 1992; Hughes, Johnson *et al.* 1993; Thoma 1998), benthos in lakes (Dycus & Meinert 1993; Gerritsen & White 1997), fish in estuaries (Thompson & Fitzhugh 1986; Jordan *et al.* 1992) and benthos in estuaries (Farrell 1993; Engle *et al.* 1994). The relevance of most of these papers is discussed in USEPA's technical guidance for lakes and reservoirs (Gerritsen, Carlson *et al.* 1997) and estuaries and near-coastal areas (Gibson, Bowman *et al.* 1997).

Model for development and aggregation of metrics

The diverse geomorphological land-forms of the USA underscore the importance of regional specificity in faunal distributions and composition. However, the basic premise of a multimetric approach to bioassessment remains similar across the country and among assemblages. Therefore, state and local water resource agencies, either in collaboration or independently, are developing multimetric approaches within the framework established for biological criteria (Davis & Simon 1995; Gibson, Barbour *et al.* 1996; Davis, Snyder *et al.* 1996). The conceptual process for developing a bioassessment program based on a multimetric approach for streams was described by Barbour *et al.* (1995), Gibson, Barbour *et al.* (1996), and Barbour, Gerritsen *et al.* (1999), and is illustrated in Figure 19.2.

In the first step, stream classes are determined that partition the natural variability of biological data for reference or minimally disturbed sites into homogeneous "bioregions". Although these bioregions are derived using different procedures from those employed in the British and Australian predictive models (Wright *et al.* 1993; Norris 1995) they are, nevertheless, based on the biological data from reference sites prior to calculation of metrics. Ideally, the bioregions will be the same for all assemblages. Ohio EPA (1987) found that partitioning the surface waters in Ohio by ecoregions (see Omernik 1995; Gibson, Barbour *et al.* 1996; or Omernik & Bailey 1997, for an explanation of ecoregions) was effective for assessing biological condition using both fish and benthic macroinvertebrates (DeShon 1995; Yoder & Rankin 1995a). However, it is plausible that bioregions may differ among faunal and floral assemblages.

The basis of site classification may vary in different regions of the USA. For instance, Ohio uses ecoregions as the basis for classification (Ohio EPA 1997). In Arizona, elevation was found to be a more important classification factor than ecoregions (Spindler 1996). Florida's bioregions were derived from aggregating sub-ecoregions into homogeneous areas of the state (Barbour, Gerritsen *et al.* 1996). In all of these cases, streams were grouped into homogeneous classes to ensure comparable biological assessments. Lyons *et al.* (1996) developed a multimetric index for coldwater streams that was distinctly different from the index used in warmwater streams.

Step 2 of the developmental phase is to identify ecologically relevant metrics for the assemblage and region under study (Fig. 19.2). Candidate metrics that have been found to be informative in the USA for streams, with respect to periphyton, benthic macroinvertebrates and fish, are presented in Table 19.1. Potential metrics represent four central components of the elements and processes of a naturally functioning assemblage. Those that are redundant in their contribution are eliminated from the core set. For a metric to be useful in assessment, it must be (1) ecologically relevant to the biological assemblage under study and to the specified program objectives, and (2) sensitive to stressors and provide a response that can be discriminated from natural variation (Barbour, Gerritsen *et al.* 1999). The range in values of the metrics within the reference sites in each site class is evaluated to obtain the most appropriate metrics for assessment. Step 3 is to reduce the number of potential metrics for each assemblage to those that are core for an integrated assessment (Fig. 19.2). The most appropriate metrics have value ranges for reference conditions that differ from impaired sites, thus providing the discrimination that is crucial for assessment.

All of the core metrics can be aggregated into an index, as in step 4, by transforming the value ranges to scores. Metrics vary in their scale – they can be integers, percentages or dimensionless numbers; it is necessary to standardize core metrics via a transformation to unitless scores for aggregation into an index (Barbour, Gerritsen *et al.* 1999). Aggregation of metric scores simplifies management and decision-making because a single index value is used

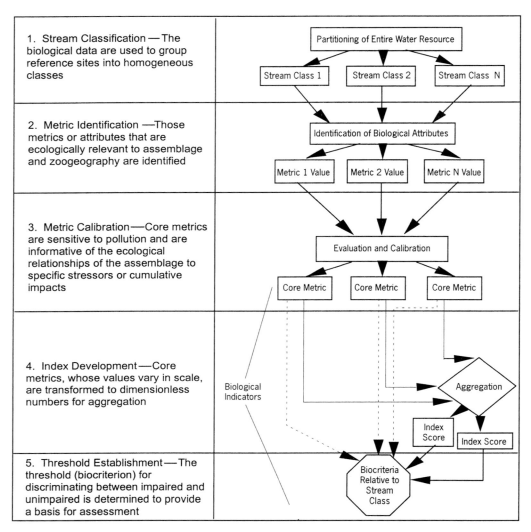

1. Stream Classification — The biological data are used to group reference sites into homogeneous classes	Partitioning of Entire Water Resource Stream Class 1 · Stream Class 2 · Stream Class N
2. Metric Identification —Those metrics or attributes that are ecologically relevant to assemblage and zoogeography are identified	Identification of Biological Attributes Metric 1 Value · Metric 2 Value · Metric N Value
3. Metric Calibration—Core metrics are sensitive to pollution and are informative of the ecological relationships of the assemblage to specific stressors or cumulative impacts	Evaluation and Calibration Core Metric · Core Metric · Core Metric
4. Index Development—Core metrics, whose values vary in scale, are transformed to dimensionless numbers for aggregation	Biological Indicators · Aggregation · Index Score · Index Score
5. Threshold Establishment—The threshold (biocriterion) for discriminating between impaired and unimpaired is determined to provide a basis for assessment	Biocriteria Relative to Stream Class

Figure 19.2. Process for developing assessment thresholds for the multimetric approach in the USA. (Taken from Barbour, Gerritsen *et al.* 1999).

to determine whether action is needed (Fig. 19.2). However, the exact nature of the action needed (e.g., restoration, mitigation, or pollution enforcement) is not determined by the index value, but by analyses of the component metrics and the raw data (Barbour, Gerritsen *et al.* 1999). Therefore, the index score is not the sole determinant of impairment and diagnostics, but when used in concert with the component information, it strengthens the assessment (Barbour *et al.* 1996).

The multimetric index value for a site is a summation of the scores of the metrics and has a finite range within each stream class and index period, depending on the maximum possible scores of the metrics (Barbour, Gerritsen *et al.* 1996). Thresholds (Step 5) are established for the index value, below which a site might be judged to be impaired (or not attaining its expected biological condition). These thresholds, when incorporated into water quality standards for regulatory programs, are termed biocriteria. Usually, a "margin of safety" is applied to the threshold, whereby a site having an index score within a given range of values of the threshold is not judged to be impaired with an appropriate level of confidence (Yoder & Rankin 1995a; Barbour, Gerritsen *et al.* 1996).

Table 19.1. *Some potential metrics for periphyton, benthic macroinvertebrates and fish that could be considered for streams in the USA (from Barbour, Gerritsen* et al. *1999).*

Redundancy of metrics can be evaluated during the calibration phase, to eliminate overlapping metrics.

* EPT taxa = Ephemeroptera, Plecoptera and Trichoptera combined.

Group/Richness	Composition	Tolerance	Trophic/habitat
Periphyton			
Total no. of taxa	% community similarity	% tolerant diatoms	% motile taxa
No. of common	% live diatoms	% sensitive taxa	Chlorophyll-*a*
non-diatom taxa	Diatom (Shannon)	% aberrant diatoms	% saprobiontic taxa
No. of diatom taxa	diversity index	% acidobiontic taxa	% eutrophic taxa
		% alkalibiontic taxa	
		% halobiontic taxa	
Benthic macroinvertebrates			
Total no. of taxa	% EPT	Hilsenhoff biotic index	% filterers
No. of EPT taxa*	% Ephemeroptera	% tolerant organisms	% scrapers
No. of Ephemeroptera taxa	% Chironomidae	No. of intolerant taxa	No. of clinger taxa
No. of Plecoptera taxa		% dominant taxon	% clingers
No. of Trichoptera taxa			
Fish			
Total no. of native	% pioneering species	No. and identity of	% omnivores
fish species	No. of fish per unit	intolerant species	% insectivores
No. and identity of	of sampling effort	% individuals as	% representation of
darter species	related to the	tolerant species	reproductive guilds
No. and identity of	drainage area	% individuals as hybrids	
sunfish species		% individuals with disease,	
No. and identity of		tumours, fin damage,	
sucker species		skeletal anomalies	

The multimetric approach in state water resource programs

From the many state water resource programs that are greatly enhanced through implementing bioassessment (Fig. 19.1), three primary functions or uses can be identified: (1) screening or initial assessment of conditions; (2) characterization of impairment and diagnosis; (3) trend monitoring to evaluate improvements or further degradation. We use examples here from Ohio to illustrate these three aspects of assessment and monitoring as they apply to streams and rivers.

Screening assessments

Performing screening assessments to identify impairment is a major challenge for state water resource agencies. Only 11 out of 50 states can legitimately claim that more than 60% of their stream-miles have been assessed (Davis, Snyder *et al.* 1996). Methods that rely on a multimetric approach, and can be conducted speedily to facilitate decision-making, are now beginning to be developed to improve the "waters assessed" in each state. Hence, the Rapid Bioassessment Protocols of the USEPA have proved to be an effective screening tool (Plafkin, Barbour *et al.* 1989; Barbour, Gerritsen *et al.* 1999). In Ohio, an attempt was made to develop a long-term database that would address the shortfall in assessed waters (Yoder & Rankin

1995a). As part of a 1994 Ohio Water Resource Inventory, a cumulative frequency diagram was used to show changes in the fish multimetric index (Index of Biotic Integrity, IBI) and that of the benthic macroinvertebrates (Invertebrate Community Index, ICI) on a statewide basis. Although the sampling design was not random, 789 sites composed the fish database and 358 sites the benthos, which provided a relatively comprehensive coverage of the streams and rivers in Ohio (Yoder & Rankin 1995a). Results of this analysis show that the conditions of both fish and benthic assemblages have improved since the pre-1988 levels, but a relatively high percentage of Ohio's streams still do not meet attainable goals (Fig. 19.3).

Diagnosing impairment

In cases where impairment is known or suspected, the goal is to obtain more detailed data on the causes and sources of impairment. The diagnostic capability of biological information has not been demonstrated on a widespread basis, although specific examples of biological relationships to individual stressors have been discussed by others (Plafkin, Barbour *et al.* 1989; Eagleson, Lenat *et al.* 1990; Yoder & Rankin 1995b). Discernable patterns in the response of aquatic community attributes (metrics) were first described using Ohio EPA data from more than 250 sites in 25 different streams and rivers, and were termed "biological response signatures" (Yoder 1991). These proved valuable to Ohio EPA in delineating the predominant causes and sources of impairments in the many basin and sub-basin assessments made each year by the agency.

As an example of the diagnostic capabilities of a multimetric index and its component metrics, Ohio EPA examined the biological relationship to nine types or causes of impact: (1) complex toxic contamination from the combination and interactions of major municipal wastewater treatment plants and industrial point-sources that constitute a significant fraction of the summer baseflow of the receiving stream; (2) conventional municipal and industrial impacts that are primarily due to conventional substances, which may not dominate stream flows; (3) combined sewer overflows (CSOs) and urban impacts of a generally non-toxic nature that are in close proximity to sampling sites; (4) channelization, which affects the habitat suitability and constitutes extensive, large-scale channel modification, where little or no habitat recovery has taken place; (5) chemical contamination from agricultural nonpoint sources (NPS), principally runoff from row-crop agriculture; (6) flow alteration, including controlled flow releases downstream from major reservoirs, or areas where water abstraction is the predominant hydrological impact; (7) impoundment effects, which are river segments that have been artificially impounded by low-head dams or by flood control and water supply reservoirs; (8) combined sewer overflows and toxic urban impacts, which usually include municipal sewer systems with significant pre-treatment programs and sources of industrial contributions to the sewer system; (9) habitat degradation from livestock pasturing where the animals have unrestricted access to the stream (Yoder & Rankin 1995b). Some highlights of this analysis were that the index values for both the fish and macroinvertebrate assemblages were the lowest (greatest response) for the complex toxic and CSO toxic impacts, and the responses of the benthic and fish assemblages were generally similar for a given cause of impact, although fish assemblage data were lacking for livestock impacts, and benthic assemblage data were lacking for impoundments (Fig. 19.4).

Figure 19.3 (*on facing page*). Cumulative frequency diagrams for the Index of Biotic Integrity (IBI; upper) and the Invertebrate Community Index (ICI; lower) comparing the pre-1988 and post-1988 status on a statewide basis for Ohio, USA. In each case, estimated attainable level of future performance is indicated. (The Warm Water Habitat (WWH) and Exceptional Warm Water Habitat (EWH) biological thresholds are given for each index).

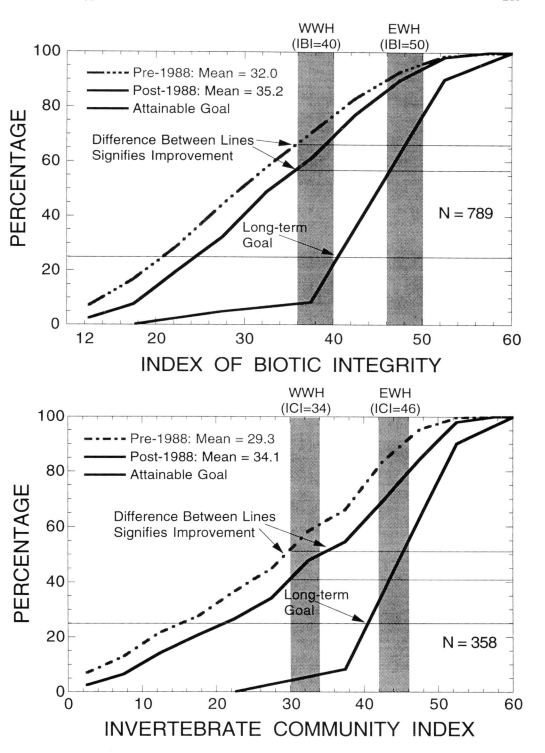

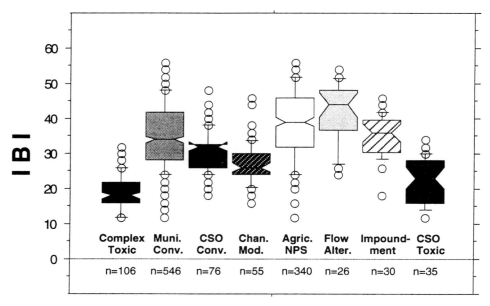

CAUSES OF IMPACT

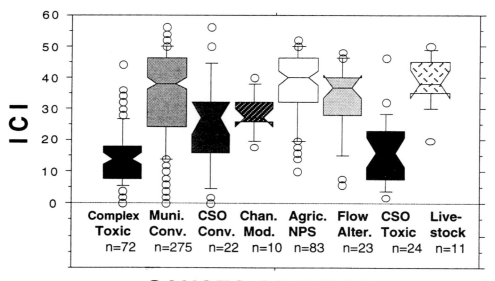

CAUSES OF IMPACT

Figure 19.4. Notched box-and-whisker plots of the Index of Biotic Integrity (upper) and the Invertebrate Community Index (lower) resulting from different types or causes of impact in Ohio, USA. (Taken from Yoder & Rankin 1995b). (Further details are given in the text).

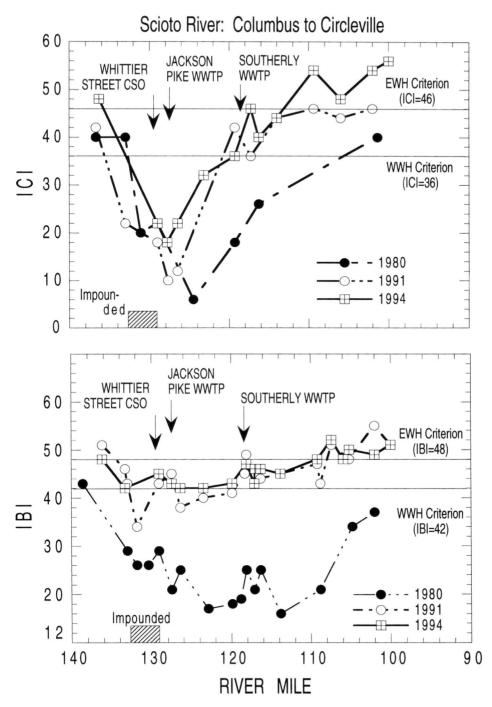

Figure 19.5. Longitudinal profile of the Invertebrate Community Index (upper) and the Index of Biotic Integrity (lower) in the Scioto River between Columbus and Circleville, Ohio (USA) during 1980 (solid circles), 1991 (open circles), and 1994 (squares). (The Warm Water Habitat (WWH) and Exceptional Warm Water Habitat (EWH) biological thresholds are given for each index. CSO = combined sewer overflow; WWTP = Waste Water Treatment Plant).

   Although not presented here, Yoder & Rankin (1995b) also discuss the responses of the individual metrics that comprise the multimetric indices for the nine causes of impact. Various metrics responded differently for the nine causes of impact. An example of a response signature that combined the index and component metrics was for toxic impact: (a) very low scores for an Index of Biotic Integrity (IBI) and high percentage incidence of DELT (disease, erosion, lesion, tumours on fish) anomalies, and (b) very low scores for an Invertebrate Community Index (ICI) and high proportional composition of the chironomid *Cricotopus* (Yoder & Rankin 1995b). While more research is needed on the diagnostic capabilities of these metrics and the aggregated indices, it is evident that the potential for determining causes of impacts is greatly enhanced from data that represent various attributes of the aquatic community.

Spatial and temporal trend analysis

One of the best proven uses for biosurvey data is for spatial and temporal trend analysis (Yoder & Rankin 1995b). Multimetric biological indices integrate chemical, biological and physical impacts to aquatic systems, and portray both condition and status in terms of the attainment or non-attainment of acceptable or desired biological condition. Ohio EPA has multiple years of biological sampling to provide a trend analysis of improvements in their rivers, resulting from pollution mitigation (Ohio EPA 1997). In a specific example from the Scioto River, both spatial and temporal trends in biological condition are evident (Fig. 19.5). The Scioto River downstream from Columbus has been monitored frequently since 1979, over a distance of *ca* 40 miles (67 km). This section of the river receives discharges from two wastewater treatment plants (WWTP) and a major combined sewer overflow. Two low-head dams form sizeable impoundments, and the city of Columbus withdraws water for drinking purposes. The spatial trend of biological condition, based on multimetric indices, illustrates a severe impact in 1980 downstream of the various insults for both assemblages. Improvements in the treatment processes at the two WWTPs, and continued protection of the habitat along the river, has resulted in a much improved biological condition for the fish, and to a lesser extent the benthic macroinvertebrates, since 1991 (Fig. 19.5).

   In conclusion, the Scioto River represents one of the best success stories of any river or stream in Ohio (Yoder & Rankin 1995b). The monitoring of this river system, and others, has allowed Ohio EPA to document the improvements in water quality resulting from both the upgrading of water treatment processes and mitigation of habitat alteration, and to prioritize their management activities.

CHAPTER 20

The reference condition: problems and solutions

TREFOR B. REYNOLDSON[1] AND JOHN F. WRIGHT[2]

[1]*National Water Research Institute, Environment Canada,
CCIW, 867 Lakeshore Rd., Burlington, Ontario, L7R 4A6, CANADA*

[2]*Institute of Freshwater Ecology, River Laboratory, East Stoke,
Wareham, Dorset, BH20 6BB, UK*

Summary of a workshop based on contributions from Trefor Reynoldson (Chair, Canada), John Wright (Rapporteur, UK), Javier Alba-Tercedor (Spain), Torlief Baekken (Norway), Michael Barbour (USA), Nikolai Friberg (Denmark), Chuck Hawkins (USA), Brian Hemsley-Flint (UK), James Hunt (UK), Jackie King (South Africa), Esa Koskenniem (Finland), Michel Lafont (France), Ursula Schmedtje (Germany) and Nikolas Skoulikidis (Greece).

Summary

Five topics were addressed by the workgroup: (1) definition and selection of reference sites; (2) how and when to sample; (3) levels of taxonomic identification; (4) temporal variability of environmental attributes; (5) reliability of the target fauna. The distinctive feature of the reference condition approach, as used in RIVPACS and similar systems, is the availability of a large set of reference sites, previously classified on their biological attributes, a proportion of which can be selected objectively for comparison with a test site. In RIVPACS, the reference condition is based on invertebrate assemblage structure, but this does not preclude the future use of other taxonomic groups or functional attributes. The population of reference sites must represent the full range of conditions expected to occur naturally at all other sites to be assessed. The selection of reference sites can involve stratification of sites, local knowledge and iterative examination of data. The workgroup also considered the difficulties associated with finding suitable reference sites for large rivers and rare or unique locations. Three approaches were suggested: the use of historical data, the establishment of theoretical reference conditions, and extrapolation based on existing reference site data. The desired level of predictive accuracy in the model must be an important consideration but the number of reference sites to be distributed among the strata will also be influenced by the project budget. To assess predictive capability, it is necessary to test a prediction system on an independent set of high quality reference sites.

When sampling, there are two basic approaches: habitat-specific sampling, or the use of a single composite sample from the available habitats. Both have been used successfully and the decision on the procedure to adopt is dependent on the primary aim(s) of the project. When establishing reference conditions, the frequency with which sites are sampled may have important consequences for model development. The stability of macroinvertebrate assemblages over time, and the circumstances in which lack of stability may pose a problem for model development, was also discussed.

The workgroup took the view that the level of taxonomic identification required to characterise reference sites depends on the objectives of the study, but it should not be assumed that identification at the levels of genus or species is always necessary. However, the choice of taxonomic level has consequences for the future uses of the data. The temporal variability in some environmental attributes used for prediction was also considered, including whether instantaneous or long-term average data were more appropriate for predicting the fauna.

Several strengths of the RIVPACS approach were identified. The methodology uses a standard field and laboratory protocol and then delivers a site-specific target of the fauna to be expected in the absence of environmental stress. The basic output is in the form of probabilities of taxon occurrence but a wide variety of outputs can be requested. Several genuine or perceived weaknesses were also identified. RIVPACS predictions are dependent upon the quality of the reference sites, and the software mechanics and outputs may appear to be complex. However, where adequate financial resources and expertise are available, and suitable reference sites can be found, it was agreed that RIVPACS is to be highly recommended. In addition, the one-time investment for each site provides an historical dataset that can also be used as a source of biological data for species conservation and for the management of individual sites and/or rivers.

Definition and selection of reference sites

The workgroup was asked to consider three related issues: (1) What is meant by the reference condition, (2) how can reference or minimally impaired sites be recognised, and (3) what methods exist for selecting reference sites?

The reference condition

RIVPACS (Chapters 1 to 5), and similar methods for biological quality assessment in Australia and Canada (Chapters 8 to 13), use a small suite of environmental variables to set site-specific targets for the benthic macroinvertebrate fauna to be expected at a site in the absence of environmental stress. The target fauna represents the *reference condition* for the site and is obtained by drawing on biological information from a set of appropriate *reference sites* previously allocated to classification groups based on the fauna. In this way, the RIVPACS approach differs from some alternative methods, such as (1) a two-site comparison involving a control site and a test (experimental) site, and (2) the allocation of reference sites to homogenous regions – usually based on geomorphological and landscape features followed by determination of whether certain biological attributes of the reference sites differ from test sites within the given geographic region.

Hughes (1995) describes several approaches for defining reference conditions. One method is the use of regional reference sites but he also proposes alternative techniques, including the use of historical, paleoecological and experimental laboratory data. In this workshop the focus was on regional reference sites, and the working definition of the reference condition used in discussion was *"the condition that is representative of a group of minimally disturbed sites defined by selected physical, chemical and biological attributes"* (from Reynoldson, Norris *et al.* 1997).

It was agreed that the distinctive feature of the reference condition approach, as used in RIVPACS and similar systems, was the availability of a large dataset of reference sites – previously classified on their biological attributes – a proportion of which could be selected objectively for comparison with a test site. This contrasts with the approach frequently used in the USA, in which a series of carefully chosen reference sites within a given ecoregion (Gibson, Barbour *et al.* 1996) are used to obtain the reference condition. However, Gibson,

Barbour *et al.* (1996) also emphasise that the reference condition establishes the basis for making comparisons and for detecting use impairment.

The workgroup acknowledged that while current usage of the reference condition for RIVPACS is based on invertebrate assemblage structure, this does not preclude the future use of other taxonomic groups (e.g. macrophytes and fish) or other functional attributes (e.g. growth rates and functional groups).

Recognition of reference sites

Methods for recognising reference or minimally impaired sites have been proposed by several authors. Hughes (1995) provides an overview on selecting minimally impaired stream reference sites, whilst Gibson, Barbour *et al.* (1996) provide more detailed guidance on the selection of representative sites for streams and small rivers. This process can use absolute criteria or constraints, or be based on best professional judgement or some combination of these processes. For example, Hawkins, Norris *et al.* (1999) defined reference sites as those locations with <5% logging in the subcatchment. Barbour (personal communication) and others are now developing criteria based on land-use features, and the absence of dams, diversions and discharges. However, in many cases it may be difficult to apply objective criteria, or such criteria may not be useful in identifying unimpaired sites.

Reynoldson & Rosenberg (1996) considered the requirements for both still-water and running-water sites and suggested that the following attributes should be examined when determining the quality of potential reference sites: *viz.* the riparian vegetation, the substratum, the channel or shoreline structure, and the hydrograph or water level.

Selection of reference sites

The workgroup agreed that the population of reference sites must represent the full range of conditions that are expected to occur naturally at all other sites to be assessed. In the case of a prediction system for flowing waters, the particular river types and the range of stream orders should be specified, in addition to the geographical limits of the system.

Once the limits of the study have been defined, a three-stage process can be used to select reference sites (Fig. 20.1). First, a stratification method is necessary to ensure that the full range of conditions is represented. The stratification is usually based on physical attributes of the study universe, such as ecoregion and stream order (running waters) or ecoregion and depth (standing waters).

The second stage in site selection is to incorporate local knowledge, because this can be invaluable in providing information on the degree of impairment that a coarse objective criterion may miss. This knowledge is often best obtained either through small workshops or meetings with local experts. Finally, an examination of the data through an iterative process should be conducted to help in the final selection of reference sites for the database.

The RIVPACS study design followed an essentially similar route, albeit with additional iterations because the current version is the end-product of several developmental steps. In 1977, at the outset of the project, the "universe" of reference sites ranged from mid-sized to large streams and rivers, but excluded small streams within Great Britain. Following a series of meetings with Water Authority (WA) and River Purification Board (RPB) personnel throughout the country, a list of *ca* 100 river systems was compiled that were relatively free from pollution, well-documented physically and chemically, and could be sampled by the relevant WA/RPB (Wright, Moss *et al.* 1984). A series of physical and chemical features were then obtained for each river system, including catchment geology, river length, altitude at source, discharge, mean annual temperature, pH and conductivity. After calculating the number of

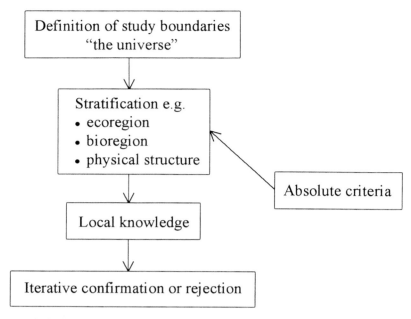

Figure 20.1. Proposed hierarchical strategy for selecting reference sites.

rivers and sites that could be examined during the initial four-year contract, 41 river systems were selected to reflect the range of conditions found in the full set of 100 river systems. Site selection then followed, again in collaboration with local biologists. After sample collection and processing was complete, early analyses indicated that a few sites were extreme outliers (subject to tidal influence or pollution) and these were eliminated because they were outside the specification for the project (Wright, Moss *et al.* 1984). Later phases of the RIVPACS project widened the scope of the reference dataset, but with each enlarged series of reference sites and analyses, more stringent criteria were used for site acceptability. In RIVPACS III, the universe was extended to include Northern Ireland (70 sites as a separate module) and even more stringent criteria were used before 614 sites were accepted for the Great Britain module of the system (see Chapter 1). A description of a more recent site selection exercise for the Fraser River catchment in British Columbia, Canada, is given Chapter 12.

The workgroup also touched on the difficulties associated with finding suitable reference sites for rare or unique locations. This includes the problem of reference sites for very large rivers when no similar rivers can be found. Three possible approaches were suggested: the use of historical data when available, the establishment of theoretical reference conditions, and extrapolation based on existing data or available reference site data.

How and when to sample

The workgroup was asked to address sampling issues that are critical when building a reference database and in particular: (1) how many reference sites are needed; (2) should sampling be habitat-specific or include multiple habitats; (3) how should the sampling programme deal with temporal variability?

How many reference sites?

The number of reference sites is dependent on many factors. For example, Great Britain is geologically very complex and requires more reference sites on its streams and rivers than a geologically simple land mass of similar area. However, the initial decision to exclude small streams from the universe of interest greatly reduced the number of reference sites required. This is because the macroinvertebrate assemblages of small streams tend to change downstream over much smaller spatial scales than those of larger streams and rivers, and therefore small streams need higher representation in the reference dataset.

Although the number of sites to be distributed among the strata will be influenced by the budget for the project, the desired level of accuracy in the predictive model must remain an important consideration. The success of the prediction system is also heavily dependent on the strength of the relationship between the biological and environmental attributes of the reference sites, and identification of a relatively small set of environmental attributes with high predictive capability.

To make a satisfactory assessment of predictive capability, it is necessary to test a prediction system on an independent set of high quality reference sites (Chapter 2). In addition, during the development of RIVPACS, a number of trends in the percentage of correct predictions based on internal re-substitution tests (Chapter 1) became apparent, and these should also be borne in mind when interpreting results. First, predictive capability decreases as the number of predictive variables is reduced (Table 20.1). This would be expected and a judgement must be made on the lowest number of easily acquired environmental attributes that will deliver an acceptable prediction. Second, as the number of reference sites and classification groups increases (whilst group size and number of environmental attributes for prediction remain relatively stable), the percentage of sites predicted to the correct classification group decreases (Table 20.2). This result is not intuitive and needs explanation. During the step-by-step development of RIVPACS, the number of classification groups increased, and in successive versions the individual classification groups express finer divisions within the continuum of sites, making it more difficult to assign each site to the "correct" group. However, if a given site is predicted to the wrong group on an internal test (out of the 35 possible groups in RIVPACS III), the "correct" group may be nearby in discriminant space. The RIVPACS prediction procedure gives probabilities of classification group membership (Chapter 1) and when the target faunal assemblage is predicted, it draws on information from many reference sites in a number of relevant classification groups.

Reynoldson & Rosenberg (1996) used a reference database for the North American Great Lakes to examine the effect of number of reference sites on predictive capability and on the interpretation of impairment. The complete database included 234 sites distributed through 20 ecoregions. The number of sites was progressively reduced to 75, 50 and 25% of the original number by randomly selecting sites from each ecoregion in a stratified manner. This resulted in four reference databases of 234, 176, 123 and 63 sites proportionally distributed across ecoregions.

Using between eight and twelve predictor variables selected by stepwise discriminant analysis, there was only a minor decrease in the percentage of sites correctly predicted (Table 20.3) as the number of reference sites increased. This suggests that the models are robust, although the smaller databases were less able to discriminate impairment. The effectiveness of the different databases was compared using nine test sites and determining whether or not they were impaired, based on the full database and reduced databases. A site was defined as impaired if it was located outside the 90% probability ellipse of the corresponding group of reference sites (Reynoldson, Norris *et al.* 1997).

Table 20.1. *Relationship between the number of environmental variables used for prediction and the percentage of sites predicted to the "correct" group, based on an internal test.*

The classification is of 268 running-water sites in Great Britain and has 15 groups. (From Moss, Furse *et al.* 1987).

No. of environmental variables	% of correct predictions
28 Physical/chemical	75.0
11 Physical/chemical	65.7
11 Physical only	61.6
5 Physical/chemical	52.2
5 Physical only	49.6

Table 20.2. *Relationship between the number of reference sites and the percentage of sites predicted to the correct group in successive versions of RIVPACS.*

No. of sites	No. of environmental variables	No. of class groups	Mean no. of sites per group	% correct predictions
268	11 Physical/chemical	15	17.87	65.7
370 (RIVPACS I)	11 Physical/chemical	30	12.33	62.7
438 (RIVPACS II)	12 (Option I)	25	17.52	56.6
614 (RIVPACS III)	12 (Option I)	35	17.54	51.6

Table 20.3. *Effect of the number of reference sites on predictive power, based on data from North American Great Lakes (Reynoldson, Rosenberg et al. 1996).*

No. of sites	No. of predictor variables	No. of biological groups in the reference database	No. of sites correctly predicted
234	10	5	61.5
176	11	5	65.9
123	12	4	65.8
63	8	4	69.8

For four of the sites there was no difference in interpretation with the reduced datasets, demonstrating 100% concordance. Nevertheless, there was a general trend of reduced concordance with the smaller datasets, from 76% (176 reference sites) to 56% (123 and 63 reference sites). The tendency to make Type II errors (false negatives) in the smaller datasets was primarily due to the greater variance and larger probability ellipses in smaller reference groups. Type I errors were due to sites being assigned to the wrong group, and again this is more likely with fewer sites. Note that the issue of Type I and Type II errors is particularly relevant to the BEAST (Chapter 11) where prediction is to a single classification group.

The Northern Ireland module for RIVPACS, based on 70 sites in seven classification groups, had 68.9% of sites predicted to the correct group on an internal test. This is close to the value of 69.8% for the subset of 63 Laurentian Great Lakes sites in just four groups (Table 20.3). As previously indicated, the actual number of sites chosen will depend upon available resources, geographical scale and habitat heterogeneity. A minimum of 60 to 70 sites may be capable of generating a preliminary model, but 175 to 250 sites will produce more reliable assessments of test site status and would be a preferable target for a first model in many regions. Further reference sites can be added later if the number of aquatic community groups suggests that it is necessary. Individual site groups should aim for a minimum of five and preferably at least ten sites (Wright 1995). The mean number of sites per group in both RIVPACS II and III has been *ca* 17–18. This allows a reasonable estimate of variance to be established for the reference state, and is particularly relevant when using the BEAST (Reynoldson, Bailey *et al.* 1995) to determine whether or not a site is impaired.

Sampling protocol

Spatial variability among sites is addressed through the stratification design, but variability within sites also requires consideration. There are two basic approaches: habitat-specific sampling, or the use of a single composite sample from the available habitats. Both techniques have been used successfully and the decision on the procedure to adopt is dependent on the primary aim(s) of the project.

In the original USEPA Rapid Bioassessment Protocols (RBP), Plafkin, Barbour *et al.* (1989) argued for sampling the most productive and dominant benthic habitat, and therefore the riffle habitat was the primary focus of the original RBP studies. More recently, Barbour, Gerritsen *et al.* (1997) discuss single versus multiple habitat sampling and indicate when one strategy is recommended over the other, concluding that the final decision rests on the proportional representation of habitat types in the reference streams typical of the site class.

Prior to the development of RIVPACS, many WA/RPB biologists undertook habitat-specific sampling in riffles because their major concern was organic pollution. In formulating the RIVPACS protocol, members of the team were uneasy at the concept of developing a classification of running-water sites for Great Britain based on samples from one habitat only. Riffles vary from site to site and the proportion of the total site fauna within the riffle is likely to vary with season and with the range of adjacent habitat types. The RIVPACS development team concluded that a procedure, standardised by sampling effort, which included all available habitat types in proportion to their occurrence, would offer the best basis for acquiring a reasonably comprehensive taxon list for use in a classification and prediction system. This protocol would also generate more comprehensive data for assessing biodiversity and detecting rare species of conservation interest. Throughout, the team was mindful that the method had to be simple, flexible and applicable to a wide range of streams and rivers. The option of sampling a series of individual habitats was resisted, because the number of habitats varies with season and site, thereby creating its own problems for data analysis.

In one recent study of the effect of habitat-specific sampling on biological assessment using predictive models, Parsons & Norris (1996) showed that riffle only, edge only or composite samples could each detect impairment, and there was considerable data redundancy by sampling several habitats. However, some species may be lost as a result of human-induced changes in the physical structure of the habitat. Thus changing land use, resulting in soil loss and sedimentation downstream, may reduce the area of riffle habitat over time and if sampling is restricted to riffles, then overall impairment of the site may be recognised too late.

In conclusion, no specific recommendations could be made on sampling multiple versus single habitats, as the final decision is determined primarily by the nature and purpose of the database. In general, databases designed for specific objectives (e.g. water quality assessment, and sediment assessment) can utilise single habitat data, but databases designed for multiple uses (e.g. river quality assessment and conservation) will require information from multiple habitats. The decision must be made very carefully as it will determine the future utility of the information.

Temporal variation in the fauna

Seasonal variation tends to be directional and is related to patterns of weather and the life history adaptations of the organisms. Hence, the seasonal patterns observed in aquatic communities are well known and decisions on the season or seasons for sampling can focus on maximising the information content of the reference dataset. In RIVPACS, it was possible to sample in each of spring, summer and autumn, and the site classification was based on the taxon list available from the three seasons combined. As a consequence, RIVPACS can offer faunal predictions for single seasons, pairs of seasons or three seasons combined (Chapter 1). This approach has always been used, although in some early analyses separate classification and prediction systems were also developed using single season biological data (Furse, Moss *et al.* 1984).

In two Canadian studies on the Laurentian Great Lakes (Reynoldson *et al.* 1997) and the Fraser River (Chapter 12), data collected in a single season (autumn) were examined for their applicability in predicting communities collected in other seasons. In the Great Lakes, autumn data was considered acceptable for predictions for most of the year, with the exception of the extremes of spring and autumn (Reynoldson *et al.* 1997). In the Fraser River, seasonal variation was not considered to be a significant problem at six sites examined by Dymond, Richardson *et al.* (1997). This is not to suggest that seasonal variation is absent, but rather that the variation over the range of sites and stream classes forming the reference condition was greater (> 90%) than the seasonal variation at single sites (<10%) in this study. In contrast, Hawkins, Hogue *et al.* (1997), in a study on Californian streams, found that there was a very strong temporal gradient in assemblage structure, but it was not associated with temperature. Differences in temperature between sites produced added pattern, but the date of sampling was by far the strongest signal.

When establishing reference conditions, several options are available. Reference sites may be sampled seasonally, in which case either seasonal models or a combined seasons model with the flexibility to predict single season assemblages may be developed, as in RIVPACS. Alternatively, subsets of sites, representing the range of environments in the "universe", may be sampled to test the seasonal applicability of models constructed from the single season database. The procedures used in RIVPACS are more conservative, but require greater effort, whereas the last option is less expensive but may turn out to have restricted applicability. Alternatively, reference sites can be sampled through the year and sampling date may be included as a predictor variable (Hawkins, personal communication).

Annual changes in faunal composition are less directional and predictable, and are influenced by larger-scale phenomena such as floods and droughts (see also Chapter 10). To date there are few lotic studies that offer a long time-series of faunal observations related to environmental conditions. The workgroup was less comfortable about the validity of models constructed from reference sites where collections are from a narrow window of time, and recommended the repeat sampling of a subset of reference sites to examine temporal change. The longest period over which reference site data have been collected and used in predictive models is in RIVPACS, where progressively larger datasets were assembled and analysed over 15 years. The strong relationship between the macroinvertebrate fauna at reference sites and site environmental attributes implies that assemblages are reasonably stable over time. However, it would be unwise to be complacent about variation in community structure over time, particularly in geographical areas subject to climatic extremes and in smaller streams which are more subject to stochastic events (Wright 1995).

What level of taxonomic identification is required?

There is debate over the level of taxonomic identification required to characterise reference sites and the consequences this has on the future uses of the data. The conservative view is that identification to genus and/or species is preferable for bioassessment (Resh & Unzicker 1975), the underlying philosophy being that even closely related species respond differently to given environmental stressors. In addition, reference sites with data at genus/species level form a more valuable historical dataset, with greater potential for assessing conservation interest (Wright, Blackburn *et al.* 1996). Where data at genus/species level are available for reference sites, target assemblages can be predicted at this taxonomic level or at other taxonomic levels (e.g. family level) as demonstrated in RIVPACS (Chapter 1). However, both freshwater biologists (Brooker 1984) and marine biologists (Ellis 1985) have argued that the effort expended should only be appropriate to the objectives of the study. Warwick (1988a, b) showed that in marine systems, identifications to phylum were sufficient to detect impairment, whilst Bowman & Bailey (1997), who examined ten datasets for freshwater macroinvertebrates, found that genus level did not provide a strikingly different description of community pattern when compared with identifications made to the level of families or orders. The workgroup concluded that the decision will largely depend on the objectives of the study, but it should not be assumed that identification to genus/species level is always necessary (see also Chapter 15).

Temporal variability in some environmental variables

On this topic, the debate considered temporal variation in some environmental attributes of sites and whether instantaneous measures or long-term average data would be better predictors of faunal composition. To address this problem, it is useful to consider the variables and the way in which the prediction system generates the target fauna. In RIVPACS, environmental variables that indicate geographical location, some attributes of catchment geology, position downstream and basic site characteristics, are used for prediction. Many of these variables are fixed, but some site features vary with time. The prediction draws on information from many reference sites and is therefore a statement of the typical fauna to be expected at a site with the given attributes. Some catchments may exhibit stable environmental characteristics and biotic assemblages, whilst others may be prone to environmental variability (e.g. floods). Such events may be necessary for maintaining the characteristic assemblages but occasionally they may result in catastrophic (but temporary) changes in the assemblages. Floods may be viewed as natural stresses which, like man-induced stresses, will be recorded as departures – by the observed fauna – from the expected target fauna. With this view of the system, there is merit in attempting to obtain long-term fixed values for all environmental variables in order to generate a fixed target fauna for a site, rather than one which varies slightly from year to year, depending on the values of the environmental variables used. This means that the model is "static" and is not designed to offer predictions of how the fauna responds to minor changes in flow regime, substratum, width or depth (see Chapter 7). It was recognised that average values will underestimate the importance of some events, and that extremes or thresholds require further consideration in some river systems.

Reliability of the target fauna

Strengths and weaknesses of the RIVPACS approach

Several strengths of the RIVPACS approach were identified. The methodology uses a standard field and laboratory protocol and then delivers a site-specific target of the fauna to be expected at the site in the absence of environmental stress. The basic output is in the form of probabilities of taxon occurrence but a wide variety of outputs can be requested. For example, in RIVPACS III (Chapter 1) predictions can be requested for different seasons, different taxonomic levels, presence/absence or $\log_{10}$ categories of abundance (family level only), and for the various indices of the BMWP system. The various outputs are used to compare the fauna observed (O) with the expected (E) fauna in the form of O/E ratios, to detect environmental stress (low O/E ratios) or, alternatively, unusually species-rich sites (O/E ratios well above unity).

Several genuine or perceived weaknesses were also identified by the workgroup. RIVPACS predictions are dependent upon the quality of the reference sites, and every effort should be made to acquire high quality sites for the range of conditions across which the system is to apply. This may not always be possible, examples being deep sites on large lowland rivers, or regions where the underlying geology makes streams subject to acidification. Those favouring the multimetric approach took the view that RIVPACS relies on just one or two measures (metrics) of community structure (i.e. the use of O/E ratios). The workgroup suggested that the RIVPACS approach should consider additional outputs to the existing range of O/E ratios, including functional and other measures which could be derived from the observed fauna and expected probabilities of taxon occurrence. To some, the software mechanics and variety of outputs seemed complex. They expressed the view that by making the system more user-friendly, biologists would be able to present their results to managers more effectively.

In summary, the workgroup was extremely supportive of this approach to biological assessment and, where it was feasible to use this technique, considered that it was probably the most useful method for conducting biological assessment.

Alternatives to the use of reference sites

The workgroup also discussed alternatives when suitable reference sites were unavailable. Where no minimally impacted sites exist, including countries where all lotic systems are heavily influenced by man (e.g. The Netherlands) or geographical areas are badly affected by acidification (e.g. parts of Scandinavia), alternative approaches are required. Suggestions included the use of stress trajectories or establishing dose-response gradients. The concept of incorporating stressed sites into the reference database has been used in The Netherlands (Chapter 17) and offers a valuable technique for river management and conservation.

Summary and recommendations

The workgroup was very supportive of the RIVPACS approach. Where adequate financial resources and expertise were available, and suitable reference sites could be found, it was agreed that this technique was to be highly recommended. In fact, the issue of cost is somewhat spurious, because an initial one-time investment for each site provides an historical dataset that can be utilised over a long period of time, not only in the prediction system, but as a source of biological data for species conservation (Wright, Blackburn *et al.* 1996) and for the management of individual sites and rivers.

The workgroup made some specific recommendations, enumerated below.

(1). Current usage of the reference condition is based on invertebrate community structure, but this does not preclude the use of other taxonomic groups (e.g macrophytes, fish) or functional attributes (e.g. growth rates, functional groups) in the future.

(2). It is important to define the "universe" of reference sites. This crucial step may be influenced by physical, geographical or institutional factors, or a combination of these factors.

(3). A more formal process should be adopted for the selection of reference sites. It was acknowledged that the recognition of high quality sites is not always straightforward and that an iterative process is often required. Sometimes, it may be necessary to increase the number of reference sites in stages, as funding allows, or if the universe of sites is extended.

(4). No specific recommendations could be made on the question of composite versus single habitat samples because the decision must be based on the primary objective(s) of the project. The decision must be made with care because it determines the future utility of the dataset.

(5). There was strong support for the view that subsets of reference sites should be sampled annually to establish the sensitivity of the prediction procedure and document annual variation.

(6). The workgroup could not recommend one taxonomic level for identification of the fauna. Identifications at species and generic level require more financial resources and expertise, but provide greater flexibility to prediction outputs and a more valuable historical dataset with greater potential for conservation studies. A system based on identifications at family level is cheaper to develop and implement, and may be capable of detecting sites suffering from a range of environmental stresses (but see Chapter 15).

(7). Site classification groups should aim for a minimum of five and preferably ten sites. This allows for a reasonable estimate of variance for the given reference state.

(8). The use of long-term mean values for prediction, as advocated by the RIVPACS team, rather than short-term or seasonal measures of environmental attributes, needs further research.

(9). Further consideration should be given to possible alternatives to O/E ratios when evaluating abundance and functional measures of communities.

Acknowledgements

The authors would like to thank everyone in the workgroup for contributing to the discussions that helped to mould this chapter. Thanks are also extended to those who commented on early drafts of the text and, in particular, to Chuck Hawkins who offered many helpful suggestions.

CHAPTER 21

Summarising, presenting and interpreting outputs from RIVPACS and AUSRIVAS

RICHARD H. NORRIS

Cooperative Research Centre for Freshwater Ecology,
University of Canberra, Canberra 2601, AUSTRALIA

Summary of a workshop based on contributions from Richard Norris (Chair, Australia), Bob Dines (Rapporteur, UK), Cristina Cappelletti (Italy), Ralph Clarke (UK), Nicki Mitchell (Australia), Catia Monauni (Italy), Ilse Stubauer (Austria) and Roger Sweeting (UK).

Summary

RIVPACS and AUSRIVAS empirical models must serve management and scientific purposes. Familiarity with the outputs from RIVPACS and AUSRIVAS is crucial to their use and this can be achieved by: consistency in outputs; accurate and defensible outputs; help with common text for reporting, possibly included in the program; graphical outputs; defensible banding systems. Whether indices of biological quality or quality banding systems are used, they should also include error estimates so that change can be properly assessed.

The average score per taxon (ASPT) is seen as a useful measure and is less subject to sampling bias than other indices. ASPT is more robust than the BMWP score and its continued use is encouraged over the latter. The Australian SIGNAL index (equivalent to ASPT) has so far proved to be insensitive to water quality but requires additional work to achieve full benefit from it. Observed to expected ratios (O/E) for number of taxa, ASPT and SIGNAL are useful indices and fundamental to the success of RIVPACS and AUSRIVAS. Many other indices have been proposed, including some that use abundance and purport to measure community structure and trophic function. Some of these could be investigated for inclusion in RIVPACS and AUSRIVAS. Additionally, habitat assessment and indices representing habitat condition may provide the basis for more accurate and meaningful interpretations of site conditions with regard to the interplay between habitat and water quality.

Differing viewpoints of scientists and managers are briefly discussed. Users would benefit from additional support when reporting outputs and this could be programmed into the existing programs, to provide some kind of expert system. The ancillary site information, also useful for site assessment, is currently little used and programming should be included to ensure easy access to these data.

RIVPACS and AUSRIVAS are probably sufficiently developed to be marketed commercially, possibly offsetting the cost of maintaining and developing the packages while concurrently enhancing water quality assessment.

Introduction

RIVPACS, and similar empirical models for the assessment of water quality such as AUSRIVAS, will have most impact if they are able to serve management, as well as scientific, purposes. To achieve these aims, model outputs representing complex biological data need to be simplified so that they can be used accurately by non-specialists, while also being scientifically defensible (Wright 1995).

Outputs from RIVPACS and AUSRIVAS include: the probability of a test site belonging to the environmental types (groups) of reference sites used in the model; the expected or "target" probabilities of taxa collected at reference sites occurring at a test site, weighted for the site characteristics; the number of taxa expected; the number of taxa observed; the observed to expected taxa ratio.

In the UK, the Biological Monitoring Working Party (BMWP) system uses family-level identifications, and assigns pollution sensitivity scores to each family to create the BMWP index (Armitage, Moss *et al.* 1983). The average score per taxon (ASPT), i.e. the BMWP score divided by the number of scoring taxa, is also used for assessing sites (Armitage, Moss *et al.* 1983; Wright 1995). In Australia, an index similar to ASPT, the stream invertebrate grade number average level (SIGNAL, Chessman 1995) is used for assessment. The expected value of this score is weighted by the probabilities of taxon occurrence at the site before the calculation of observed to expected (O/E) ratios. In general the O/E ratios for taxa, the BMWP score and the ASPT or SIGNAL, probably are of greatest value when interpreting the condition of a site.

Decisions on desirable outputs from RIVPACS and AUSRIVAS models will be based on their purpose. This is seen as assessing the quality of a river site and whether or not the site has changed since previous sampling. The level of output also may be dependent on the audience – both their level of understanding and willingness to understand. If the customers are biologists, outputs can be more complex and may require more expertise to understand. Regardless of which outputs are agreed on, they must have scientific validity, and if they are accepted nationally, and internationally, that is a great advantage. Managers must be able to rely on the outputs and decisions based on them must be defensible.

This chapter reports on a workshop that considered the scientific and practical consequences when summarising, presenting and interpreting RIVPACS and AUSRIVAS outputs. The aim is to guide future developments so that information derived from such methods is presented in a form that is comprehensible to water managers and aids their decisions, while retaining scientific validity and adequate information content.

Presentation

Where should the balance lie between accessibility/simplification and scientific content? It is desirable to have outputs from systems such as RIVPACS and AUSRIVAS that are straightforward and easy to understand. This will often mean that complex biological data must be simplified. Simplification itself may be a misleading word in this context because carefully thought out and applied outputs from RIVPACS and AUSRIVAS can increase the information content, especially for non-specialists. Familiarity is basic to the successful use of outputs from RIVPACS and AUSRIVAS models for assessment of river condition. This can be achieved in several ways, summarised below.

(1). Consistency in the outputs and their meaning. Special care should be taken with education of users if changes are made to established outputs, so that errors with interpretation and comparisons are avoided.

(2). The information must be accurate and defensible so that users have a clear basis from which to argue interpretations and decisions.

(3). Outputs from RIVPACS and AUSRIVAS will often be used for reporting, and the addition of non-technical, common text associated with the reports would aid understanding by those receiving them. Given the electronic nature of the programs, standardised reporting text could be available automatically and would be less subject to accidental variation than if transferred from a hard copy.

(4). Graphical outputs, which are not currently used, would also aid interpretation and understanding.

(5). Banding or grading systems (Chapters 3 and 4) provide a basis for understanding how good or bad a site's biological condition may be. Such systems should be encouraged to help users to understand the outputs.

Scientists and managers or planners often have different views of the role of science and its use. The following points are relevant and may need to be addressed if liaison is to be satisfactory (Cullen 1990). Scientists seem to have difficulty in coming to an agreed conclusion on generally imperfect data; they have difficulty in communicating the results of their work; many have a lack of motivation to participate wholeheartedly in the planning/management process; they are often driven by the need to publish and may be less interested in the application of their ideas. On the other hand, planners and managers may be seen by scientists as inadequately trained to interpret complex data; as not knowing where and how to find information; they may know so little of biological sciences that they have difficulty in realising what they do not know. These tensions lead scientists to feel isolated and under-utilised. Also, amongst scientists there is a feeling that planners/managers need to improve their communication about the facts surrounding an issue and the thinking framework used to look at a problem (Cullen 1990). These are all issues that RIVPACS and AUSRIVAS are addressing, either in the nature of the outputs, or in the supporting information. More could be done in this area to ensure more and better use is made of them.

Indices

The observed to expected ratio of taxa (O/E taxa) has proved to be a powerful tool for assessing river condition, and is commonly used and well understood by users (Wright 1995). ASPT (see above and Chapter 1), also implemented within RIVPACS, has been shown to be less affected by sampling effort than O/E taxa. Therefore, it may be more robust in some circumstances. For this reason the workshop recommended continued use of the index. The SIGNAL index used in AUSRIVAS models is similar to ASPT, but the former has proved to be insensitive in Australia so far, although this may result from the way in which it has been implemented in Australia (see Chapter 9). In view of the success of ASPT in Britain, further evaluation of the SIGNAL index in Australia seems warranted.

The BMWP score implemented in RIVPACS is widely used for biological assessment of rivers in Britain (Sweeting, Lowson *et al.* 1992). Members of the workshop with experience in the use of the BMWP score felt strongly that it was over-used and that much information valuable for river assessment was lost or disregarded. It was felt that ASPT was more robust and that use of the BMWP score should be discouraged in favour of the use of O/E taxa and O/E ASPT.

RIVPACS and AUSRIVAS currently predict taxon presence and absence, although some $\log_{10}$ abundance predictions have been built into RIVPACS (Chapter 1). Measures of abundance have long been incorporated into methods for the biological assessment of water quality (e.g. Barbour, Plafkin *et al.* 1992; Kerans *et al.* 1992, Kerans & Karr 1994; Reynoldson, Bailey *et al.* 1995). In some circumstances (e.g. mild organic pollution) presence and absence data may not detect impacts. In such cases community structure data may be

Table 21.1. *Indices used in the Benthic Index of Biotic Integrity (Kerans & Karr 1994)*
that could be investigated with regard to possible use in RIVPACS and AUSRIVAS.

Attribute	Hypothesised effect of impact
Community structure and composition	
Total taxa richness	Decline
Number of intolerant snail and mussel species	Decline
Ephemeropteran taxa richness	Decline
Trichopteran taxa richness	Decline
Plecopteran taxa richness	Decline
Sediment-surface taxa richness	Decline
Proportion of individuals as *Corbicula*	Increase
Proportion of individuals as oligochaetes	Increase
Proportion of individuals as chironomids	Increase
Proportion of individuals as the two most abundant taxa	Increase
Processes	
Proportion of individuals as omnivores and scavengers	Increase
Proportion of individuals as detritivores	Increase
Proportion of individuals as shredders	Decline
Proportion of individuals as collectors-gatherers	Increase
Proportion of individuals as collectors-filterers	Increase
Proportion of individuals as grazers-scrapers	Decline
Proportion of individuals as strict predators (excluding chironomids and flatworms)	Decline
Total abundance	Decline

important and this will need measures that are based on abundances. Research work is needed to look at the most useful measures, which may involve the use of absolute, rank or logarithmic scales of abundance, or alternatively, variable groups of relative abundance (1, 2–5, 6–10, 11–20 etc.). Additionally, many other indices used by the United States Environmental Protection Agency (USEPA) have proved useful in the USA but have received little attention in connection with RIVPACS and AUSRIVAS (Table 21.1).

Habitat condition will affect the biota present at a site. The USEPA (Plafkin, Barbour *et al.* 1989) has advocated assessment of stream habitat and an initial determination of whether it will support aquatic biota. If habitat is assessed as non-supporting, outputs from models should not be interpreted only in terms of water quality. This area has been neglected in RIVPACS and AUSRIVAS, but recent work (e.g. Raven, Fox *et al.* 1997) may provide the basis for assessing habitat condition and linking this to other model outputs.

The computerised nature of RIVPACS and AUSRIVAS empirical models provides the possibility for developing standardised reporting formats, including ancillary site data that currently seem to be largely neglected by users. Such data include group membership probabilities, pollution sensitivity of taxa, probabilities of taxon occurrence and site assessment information. It would be possible to develop a question system to ensure that the full and correct information is recorded and reported.

Banding

There seem to be no scientific advantages to the banding systems provided in RIVPACS and AUSRIVAS but there are advantages to science! The banding systems help non-expert users to understand outputs and to set targets that drive investment for rehabilitation. Normally, the bands will be used in conjunction with other measures to manage a river in order to achieve the rehabilitation targets (e.g. chemistry and ecotoxicology). Managers must also consider whether a change in state is significant before action is taken (see Chapter 3), i.e. they must have confidence in the assessment.

The width and number of bands should be based on credible scientific and/or mathematical criteria. There is always a danger of constructing bands within which sites/sampling occasions cannot be separated sensibly because of the size of the associated errors relative to the width of the bands (Chapter 3). Such a situation would make the allocation and use of bands meaningless. The use of standardised criteria for determining band widths has the added advantage of maintaining the confidence that can be placed in different indices.

Whether the bands or the original index values are used for assessing changes in the biotic condition of sites, confidence of change (error levels) is required (Chapter 3). The user may determine the level of detail required.

Commercial applications

RIVPACS and AUSRIVAS-type packages for the biological assessment of water quality include the associated methods and training requirements for data collection, analysis and interpretation. As indicated above, more needs to be added to the packages to enhance their ease of use and value, but they have already proven to be useful tools. In Australia, frequent requests are received from environmental consultants wishing to use the packages to assess water quality, and it is also planned to develop them for use by community groups. It is expected that the pressure to make the packages generally available will grow in Australia and in the UK. In fact, a prototype release of the Great Britain section of RIVPACS III, as used in the 1995 General Quality Assessment (GQA) survey in England, Wales and Scotland, has been available for purchase since January 1997. In due course, it is anticipated that additional versions, optimised for the commercial and educational market, will be developed. Training requirements will be similar in both the UK and Australia, but distribution and management may be different. At present, RIVPACS is distributed on disks as a stand-alone system while AUSRIVAS runs on the internet and access is controlled by password. There are several advantages to the internet approach (Chapter 9), one being that short-term access can be granted and rescinded via the password control. This approach is useful for organisations requiring only limited use and not wishing to pay a full purchase price for the complete long-term use of the package.

Sampling reference sites, updating models and software all consume considerable resources and these costs will need to be offset. Commercial availability of the packages will serve to reduce the financial burden on the organisations currently funding RIVPACS and AUSRIVAS.

Acknowledgements

The author would like to thank all those whose contributions have helped in preparing this chapter, and to apologise for any inadvertent misrepresentation of their views.

CHAPTER 22

Using RIVPACS as a modelling tool to predict the impacts of environmental changes

NIELS DE PAUW

University of Ghent, Department of Applied Ecology and Environmental Biology, I. Plateaustraet 22, B–9000, Gent, BELGIUM

Summary of a workshop based on contributions from Niels De Pauw (Chair, Belgium), John Murray-Bligh (Rapporteur, UK), Karl-Jan Aanes (Norway), Patrick Armitage (UK), Ian Boothroyd (New Zealand), Ulrich Braukmann (Germany), John Hilton (UK), Otto Moog (Austria), Ana Pujante (Spain), Vincent Resh (USA), David Rosenberg (Canada), Nick Schofield (Australia), Gloria Tapia (Spain).

Summary

RIVPACS predicts the macroinvertebrate fauna to be expected in the absence of environmental stress, but it cannot predict faunal response to an environmental stressor. The workshop considered how this development could be approached and whether it would be appropriate to modify RIVPACS for this new role.

The question

RIVPACS was developed to classify macroinvertebrate community types and to predict the fauna expected to occur in different types of watercourses, based on a small number of environmental variables. The prediction is essentially a static "target" of the fauna to be expected at a site with stated environmental features, in the absence of environmental stress. A model that offered a prediction of faunal response to changes in environmental features (e.g. changes in the discharge regime, dissolved oxygen level, etc.) would be of considerable value for river management. For example, a water quality manager may have the task of convincing an industrial organisation that heavy investment is required to clean up an effluent. This task will be simpler if a reliable model demonstrates that by modifying certain environmental variables through investment, the desired biological improvement will be achieved. An associated but different problem is the inverse question: what is causing an observed effect on the fauna?

So far, no comprehensive model has been developed to predict either a change in the biological community resulting from change in a stressor, or to identify the stressor from community change. The aim of this workshop was to consider how this application should be developed or could be approached.

The strengths and limitations of RIVPACS

The RIVPACS approach is currently one of the best available for assessing the biological quality of running waters because it offers the ability to use environmental variables to predict the species that are expected to occur at a site if it is unstressed. The expected fauna is then compared with the observed community of macroinvertebrates in order to assess river quality.

However, biological communities are dynamic and the nature of RIVPACS would need to be altered in order to predict a change in faunal composition in response to new environmental conditions at a given site. Although predictive dynamic modelling has been successful in hydrology, sediment transport and hydrochemistry, it is necessary to undertake this modelling with care, using good field data for calibration and validation. The development of predictive models describing the occurrence (presence/absence) of freshwater invertebrates is relatively new, and the extent to which a deterministic or a stochastic approach would be successful is still unknown (Armitage 1994). Recent applications of chaos theory to population dynamics are of interest in this context (Hastings, Hom *et al.* 1993; Rohani & Miramontes 1996). Dynamic modelling of biotic systems requires the solution of time-dependent equations, and models have to be structured accordingly. Future models will require high quality data and knowledge of both the rates of development of polluting effects and the rates and mechanisms of recolonisation when the stress has ceased.

Can RIVPACS be modified to predict change in the macroinvertebrate fauna?

Long-term studies are required to obtain information for predicting changes in fauna. Predictions could address either the events following short-term acute stress with no recolonisation, or (semi-) continuous stress in which the community has reached an equilibrium point.

In the medium term, synergistic effects are likely to be difficult to deal with and it will be necessary to concentrate on the effects of individual stresses. A preliminary list of the most important stressors would include: organic pollution, eutrophication, chemical pollution, acidification, thermal pollution and physical manipulation (e.g. flow regulation, channel modification). Interactions between these stressors could have major effects (Hellawell 1986) and ultimately they would need to be taken into account (e.g. the interaction between thermal and organic pollution).

In its present form, RIVPACS predicts the macroinvertebrate fauna expected at any location within its geographical region and range of river types. The prediction for a given site may vary slightly from one year to the next if the measured environmental variables for the site show between-year variation. The ideal situation is for the values of the required environmental variables to be long-term averages which provide stable predictions of the typical fauna to be expected at the site with the stated environmental features. This reinforces the fact that the current version of RIVPACS contains no dynamic component. One possible way to add a dynamic component might be to generate a new classification and prediction system based on a much larger dataset including sites that demonstrate the impact of a stressor, in order to predict the effect of different levels of stress (i.e. different concentrations of a given pollutant) on the fauna.

In Great Britain, the fauna expected at a given site with stated environmental features is predicted by RIVPACS from a small set of environmental variables: altitude, distance from source of the river, mean air temperature, annual air temperature range, latitude, longitude, slope, alkalinity, mean width, mean depth, mean size of substratum particles (phi units), and discharge category (see Chapter 1). From these twelve variables, prediction of the expected fauna is obtained and then compared statistically with that found (observed) at the site. Two facts become apparent from the variables used: (1) except in the most extreme conditions, the first seven predictors are unlikely to change within the lifetime of the RIVPACS system, and (2) the predictive power of the twelve predictors varies. Some are very powerful (e.g alkalinity) and others are weaker because not all of the RIVPACS predictors are independent (e.g. distance from source and discharge are correlated, as are substratum and slope). Therefore, the effect of varying a particular variable will depend upon which one is selected (see also Chapter 7).

The predictions are based on information obtained from a set of reference sites, and therefore a large number of additional sites will be required if the effect of a pollutant is to be included in the prediction. Even if only two different concentrations of a single pollutant are to be included, a large number of additional classification groups would be needed within the model. Therefore, RIVPACS in its present form is impractical as a predictive tool for solving time-dependent problems.

Alternative predictor models will be needed for stresses that affect parameters in the predictor set, particularly width, depth, substratum and discharge. One possibility would be to use computer simulation of the physical habitat (Physical HABitat SIMulation, PHABSIM; Bovee 1995) to predict the proportion of different habitat types at a location. However, such an approach requires expansion to be dynamic and predict a range of parameters. If faunal communities were shown to be effectively constant in a given type of habitat, the probability of occurrence of particular species could then be predicted, although some chemical or geographical modifier might be needed to predict the "correct" community according to river type (Armitage *et al.* 1995). Work is required to assess the hypothesis that communities are effectively constant in a given type of habitat, and to identify the number of habitat types that need to be considered. For assessing the effects of physical manipulations in different types of rivers, such as changes in hydraulic conditions, it is reasonable to assume that a predictive model could be developed soon.

However, for chemical pollutants an alternative approach may be found in the combination of bioassessment and bioassay. The addition of a pollutant at a site does not change the expected community at that site, as predicted by RIVPACS. It cannot be assumed that the effect of a given pollutant on a given species would be the same everywhere, because changes in chemical conditions (hardness, in particular for heavy metals), hydraulic flow conditions and site characteristics (e.g. riffle or pool) may each have a significant effect upon the impact of the pollutant. Hence, it may be possible to use a combination of field sites with a single, known pollutant or bioassay experiment where, for example, sediment from a site is removed with its fauna, and exposed to known concentrations of the pollutant in a mesocosm. A comparison of the expected species/community with the observed species/community after a period of exposure to a pollutant, to determine whether the animals are alive or dead, would allow a sensitivity curve to be developed for most species, thus enabling predictions to be made of the likely effect of a change in pollutant concentration on the community. This approach uses the information content of both the dead animals and the live ones. Ideally a wider range of effects might be considered, related to alterations in life-history end-points such as growth and reproduction, but mortality should be considered initially.

Conclusion

In its present form, RIVPACS is unsuitable for predicting the fauna to be expected at a site after the impact of specific environmental changes. Therefore an alternative procedure is required. A first step in developing a dynamic predictive system is to develop a diagnostic tool. This requires the analysis of information from databases of observed communities at impacted sites. These data would then be linked to specific types of stressors to produce a model that would enable the nature (as well as the severity) of environmental stress to be diagnosed. Developing the dynamic aspects will be more difficult because it cannot be based on existing data. Collecting information on the rates of impact and recovery will require considerable research effort. The RIVPACS approach may not be the best for this. Appropriate information could be fed into an expert system, with decision trees based on the use of neural networks or other artificial intelligence techniques. The need for this work will become more urgent with the introduction of environmental quality standards and objectives based on biological criteria, as proposed in the Water Framework Directive. To ensure that biological targets are met on time, environmental managers will need to identify the stress causing poor biological quality and the extent to which it must be reduced. The modelling tools outlined above would be very relevant to this problem.

Acknowledgements

The author would like to thank all those whose contributions have helped in preparing this chapter, and to apologise for any inadvertent misrepresentation of their views.

CHAPTER 23

Using RIVPACS for
studies on conservation and biodiversity

PHILIP J. BOON

Scottish Natural Heritage, 2 Anderson Place, Edinburgh, EH6 5NP, UK

Summary of a workshop based on contributions from Philip Boon (Chair, UK), Paul Logan (Rapporteur, UK), Wojciech Fialkowski (Poland), Konstantinos Gritzalis (Greece), Iain Gunn (UK), Peter Hale (UK), Ray Martin (UK), Jay O'Keeffe (South Africa), John Steel (UK) and Gerardo Vina-Vizcaino (Colombia).

Summary

Invertebrate conservation relies not only on public support and political will, but also on possessing an adequate understanding of the distribution and ecology of invertebrate species and communities. In the UK, RIVPACS is making an important contribution to assessing the conservation importance of river invertebrate assemblages. So far, work has largely centred on using RIVPACS as an integral part of SERCON (System for Evaluating Rivers for Conservation), in which data collected using the standard RIVPACS method are interpreted with reference to conservation criteria such as species richness and representativeness. Applications of RIVPACS to other areas of conservation – whether providing information on the ecological requirements of rare species, monitoring the success of river restoration projects, or making broader assessments of sustainability – are probably more limited, but merit further examination. It is important to develop closer links between RIVPACS and techniques such as SERCON and RHS (River Habitat Survey) in order to maximise the benefit each can bring to studies on conservation and biodiversity. It should also be recognised that there are limitations in transferring such systems to other countries where approaches to nature conservation may be very different.

Introduction

Until recently, strategies aimed at conserving biodiversity have centred largely on vertebrates (Hafernik 1992). This general neglect of invertebrates in conservation programmes reflects both a lack of knowledge of invertebrate species ecology and limited public enthusiasm for less visible, and aesthetically less attractive, species. Public perception is now beginning to change (Bratton 1991), and there is a growing awareness that invertebrates are important intrinsic components of biological communities and of ecological processes, and provide resources of direct human benefit (Wells *et al.* 1983). The problem of inadequate information, especially an understanding of the species ecology of such a large and diverse group of organisms, is likely to present the more serious barrier to greater efforts in conserving invertebrates.

Nonetheless, over the past five to ten years, national and international conventions and statutes have begun to address the conservation needs of invertebrates. For example, the EC Directive on the conservation of natural habitats and of wild fauna and flora (otherwise known as the Habitats Directive) lists 59 invertebrates out of 625 species *(ca* 10%) of plants and animals on Annex II (whose conservation requires the designation of Special Areas of Conservation). In the UK, the Biodiversity Action Plan (BAP) (Biodiversity Steering Group, 1995) contains 638 invertebrate species out of a total of 1659 *(ca* 38%) species of plants and animals described as "globally threatened" or "declining", some of which will have BAPs produced in response to the agreements reached at the international Rio Convention in 1992.

Nevertheless, despite the higher profile of invertebrates in initiatives such as these, relatively few species associated with rivers in the UK are afforded special protection or are the subject of BAPs. For example, in Great Britain (separate legislation covers Northern Ireland) only four riverine invertebrates (Atlantic stream crayfish or white-clawed crayfish *Austropotamobius pallipes,* freshwater pearl mussel *Margaritifera margaritifera,* southern damselfly *Coenagrion mercuriale,* and glutinous snail *Myxas glutinosa)* are statutorily protected under the Wildlife and Countryside Act 1981.

This chapter is not principally concerned with the *mechanisms* for protecting rivers and their invertebrate communities, nor with the problem of *public perception* of invertebrates and their conservation. Rather, it seeks to explore the information requirements and evaluation techniques needed to underpin conservation action, and the particular role that RIVPACS can play in helping to meet those needs.

Discussion topics

Evaluating sites

The relative merit of focusing river conservation efforts on habitats rather than on species is an area of lively debate. There are persuasive arguments for viewing habitat conservation as the most cost-effective means of protecting populations of individual species or entire communities: indeed, an approach which divorces species from their habitats is to some extent artificial and less likely to succeed.

In Britain, some rivers are protected under the Wildlife and Countryside Act as Sites of Special Scientific Interest (Boon 1991, 1995), most of which are selected not for the presence of a single rare species, but rather for a wider range of biological features (Nature Conservancy Council 1989). In recent years, increasing attention has been given to the way in which the conservation value of rivers is assessed, across the full spectrum of river "quality". This has led to the development of SERCON (System for Evaluating Rivers for Conservation) which aims to provide a more rigorous and repeatable method for river conservation evaluations (Boon, Holmes *et al.* 1996, 1997). SERCON is essentially a scoring system, and requires information both on physical habitat features (derived from River Habitat Survey (RHS): Raven, Fox *et al.* 1997; Raven, Holmes *et al.* 1998), and on a wide range of biological data, to produce a comprehensive assessment of conservation value in terms of accepted criteria such as naturalness, species richness, representativeness and rarity (Ratcliffe 1977). At present, RIVPACS is used in two ways to assist SERCON evaluations.

First, the taxon list in RIVPACS III (Wright, Blackburn *et al.* 1996) provides a standard reference against which to assess the criterion of species richness, although caution is needed in evaluations of this type. The high profile of biodiversity issues has led, perhaps, to an undue focus on species richness, under the misapprehension that the word "biodiversity" is synonymous with "species richness", and that rivers with high species richness are therefore necessarily important for conservation (and *vice versa).* Relatively natural rivers in some locations (e.g. on resistant geology, and with harsh flow regimes) will invariably be species-poor, yet may be important for conservation for other reasons; conversely, species richness may sometimes increase as a consequence of human impact (e.g. through nutrient enrichment). In other words, assessments of species richness for the purposes of conservation evaluation must always be interpreted in the light of the naturalness and representativeness (or typicalness) of the system. Nevertheless, rivers that harbour a wide diversity of species are likely to be considered more valuable than those of a similar type with fewer species, and this basic descriptor of river invertebrate communities will continue to feature in most conservation evaluation systems.

   This raises the fundamental question of the taxonomic level at which evaluations should be carried out. In SERCON, assessments of invertebrate species richness derived from family-level data are given a lower weighting than those based on species-level data (Boon *et al.* 1996). In RIVPACS, data at species level and at family level are used to generate predictions of the probability of occurrence, although site classification using RIVPACS operates satisfactorily only with data at species level. Herein lies a dilemma: the concept of conserving *invertebrate families* is comparatively meaningless, yet the time and expense of gathering data at the species level is often prohibitive – at least for an extensive programme. One approach is to explore the relationship between invertebrate family richness and species richness to see whether the former might act as a surrogate for the latter. Recent work by the Institute of Freshwater Ecology (Wright *et al.* 1998b) has shown a close correlation between family richness and species richness, and between BMWP family richness and species richness (Fig. 23.1). This opens up the possibility of carrying out extensive invertebrate surveys at the family (or BMWP family) level, and using them as a means of targeting more intensive, species-level surveys for rivers shown to be family-rich. Moreover, careful preservation of samples identified to family level provides future opportunities for species-level identification should resources (time, money, identification keys) become available.

   The second application of RIVPACS in SERCON evaluations concerns the criterion of "representativeness". Assessments of invertebrate representativeness in SERCON (which are more complex than those of species richness) aim to assess whether a site is a good example of its "type", and thereby deemed to be of conservation value (Boon, Holmes *et al.* 1996). A list of predicted BMWP families is generated for each site, and divided into four groups falling within four bands of probability of occurrence. A composite list of taxa is compiled for the site from samples taken in three seasons (spring, summer, autumn) following the standard RIVPACS protocol. The similarity of the observed and expected fauna is compared using a chi-squared test, with higher chi-squared values indicating extremely unrepresentative sites. The unit of evaluation in SERCON is a river reach (usually 10–30 km long) termed an Evaluated Catchment Section (ECS); thus, representativeness scores for all sampling sites within an ECS are summed and the final assessment is given by the mean.

   Of course, in other ways the *unrepresentativeness* of a site or a stretch of river may be considered an important conservation feature, provided that the unusual or atypical variant is not a reflection of human impact. Such rare or unusual habitat types may require a particular type of management to ensure their conservation. These sites may be identified using RIVPACS, by first discarding any with high O/E ratios caused by human impact (e.g. nutrient-poor streams subject to minor effluent input, resulting in a modest increase in taxon richness), and then trying to establish what it is that makes the remaining sites atypical.

   As river evaluation methods such as SERCON and RHS are further refined, it is important to strengthen existing links with RIVPACS, and to develop new approaches. For example, some of the assumptions in RHS concerning the importance of physical habitat features for invertebrates merit further testing, and an integration of RHS and RIVPACS data from the same sites would be a useful step forward. Setting RIVPACS alongside other systems for habitat assessment or more general conservation assessment may also assist river management decisions. For example, are there correlations between rivers in the highest class for biological

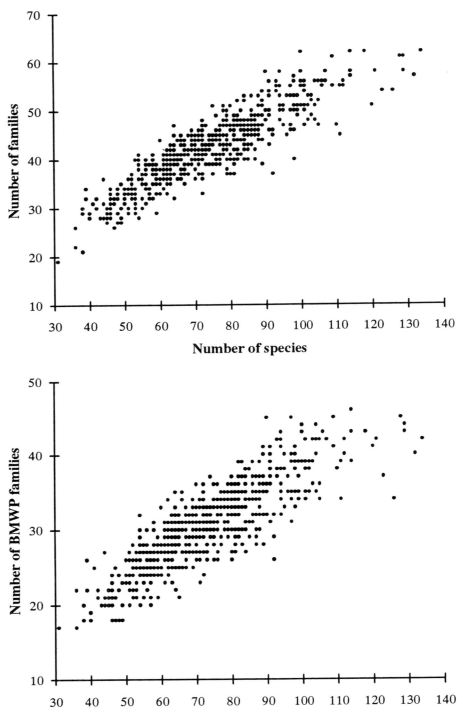

Figure 23.1. Relationships between the number of families (and BMWP families) and the number of "species" of macroinvertebrates at 614 sites. Correlation coefficient $r = 0.890$ for families and 0.854 for BMWP families. (Reproduced from Wright *et al*. 1998b, with permission of the publishers).

quality (assessed by RIVPACS) and those in the highest class in terms of habitat quality (assessed by RHS) or for overall conservation value (assessed by SERCON)? Whilst correlations might be expected in some cases, it is likely that in others the distinctiveness in outputs from each assessment system will help to determine priorities for river management by highlighting different aspects of "quality" within the same river (Boon & Howell 1997a).

Despite the fact that RIVPACS was not created as a conservation tool for site evaluation, both the RIVPACS *method* and the RIVPACS *dataset* could be applied in other ways to make full use of their potential in conservation assessment. For example, recording the range of RIVPACS classification end-groups in a river might add another dimension to assessments of invertebrate "richness", and this could be supplemented by a similar procedure for aquatic macrophyte communities, using the botanical classification of British rivers (Holmes 1989; Holmes *et al.* 1998). Evaluations of "rarity" might be extended by noting the presence, within a river, of particular RIVPACS end-groups less commonly encountered within the entire RIVPACS database.

Evaluation procedures are needed not only for high quality rivers important for conservation, but also for those which are degraded and have the potential for rehabilitation or restoration (Boon 1992). As developed countries have succeeded in tackling the worst excesses of water pollution, so attention is now being given to restoring some of the physical habitat features lost through past engineering practices (Iversen, Kronvang *et al.* 1993; Nielsen 1996; Hansen, Boon *et al.* 1998). Many such schemes have as their objective the restoration of semi-natural animal and plant communities, and several have included surveys of river invertebrates (e.g. Biggs, Corfield *et al.* 1998 (UK); Friberg, Kronvang *et al.* 1998 (Denmark); Laasonen *et al.* 1998 (Finland)). However, most studies tend to concentrate on recording changes in species composition, species richness and abundance following restoration (or in restored and control sections), but they rely on inference from the observed species complement rather than using a predictive approach such as RIVPACS to compare observed (O) and expected (E) species assemblages. In fact, RIVPACS may prove to be of limited value for predicting the impact of restoration on invertebrates, as some of the environmental variables used in prediction (e.g. altitude, longitude, latitude, distance from source, etc.) will remain unchanged following restoration. Nevertheless, restoration schemes for degraded rivers could at present have the general aim of seeking to increase low O/E values, with the longer-term objective of expanding the reference database of RIVPACS to include a range of sites degraded through physical habitat destruction, as well as those suffering impaired water quality.

Evaluating species distribution, biodiversity, and sustainability

Despite the artificial distinction already discussed between habitat and species conservation, it may be instructive to consider the role of RIVPACS in work specifically targeted at invertebrate species and assemblages. How can RIVPACS be used, for example, in studies on rare species' distribution, ecological requirements of invertebrates, or broader assessments of biodiversity and sustainability?

Initiatives in river conservation, and studies on riverine biodiversity, inevitably require at least some information at the species level. Whilst it is possible to use surrogates such as family richness for species richness, or family/generic level invertebrate indicators to assess water quality, information is still needed on the distribution, abundance and ecology both of rare and common species. The RIVPACS database has an important role to play in this, although its limitations must be recognised. Species data are only routinely available for the RIVPACS reference sites, and while the degree of accuracy of species identifications in the reference site database was extremely high, the same level of standardisation in sampling methods was not achieved. Moreover, rare species are likely to feature only rarely in the database, so using RIVPACS to learn more about their ecological requirements may not necessarily be fruitful, especially when the standard technique of "pooling" samples from habitats representative of the reach makes it more difficult to determine microhabitat preferences.

For species that are generally believed to be rare, the RIVPACS database can assist in providing useful data on locations where those species have been recorded. However, Wright, Furse *et al.* (1992) emphasised that whereas a high frequency of occurrence may confirm that a taxon is common, a low frequency, though of interest, cannot be assumed to indicate a scarce taxon. The authors also pointed out that RIVPACS II (the version then in use, containing 438 sites) included very few headwaters or small streams. This gave an inaccurate picture of the relative rarity of species recorded in the database, some of which may be common in headwaters but uncommon elsewhere. RIVPACS III contains a better representation of small sites but, despite this, there is a strong argument for the development of a separate module for headwater streams (Chapter 6). The overall conclusion by Wright, Furse *et al.* (1992) was that the RIVPACS database could offer a valuable indication of the common and less common taxa found over the range of sites sampled, but could not be used to generate Red Data Book (RDB) or other formally defined rarity categories for taxa.

Wright, Blackburn *et al.* (1996) discuss in more detail the use of the RIVPACS III database (containing 614 reference sites), and again describe its use as complementary to, but separate from, the red list threat categories designated in the RDBs for invertebrates (Shirt 1987; Bratton 1991). Of the 637 "standardised" taxa in RIVPACS III, 369 occur at less than 5% of sites, and 15 of these species are accorded RDB status. However, the same analysis also indicates that species within certain rarity categories are in fact more widely distributed than previously thought.

The broader concept of "biodiversity" is rapidly gaining popular appeal, although when the word is used in the restricted sense of "species richness" many important aspects of its meaning are lost. The definition of biodiversity derived from the 1992 Rio Convention went some way to capturing its complexity: *"The variability among living organisms from all sources including,* inter alia, *terrestrial, marine and other aquatic ecosystems and the ecological complexes of which they are part; this includes diversity within species, between species and of ecosystems"* (Department of the Environment *et al.* 1994). According to Noss (1990), however, even broad definitions such as this may be insufficient, and he suggests that a "characterisation" of biodiversity that identifies the major components at several levels of organisation is probably more useful than a definition. The characterisation proposed (developed from Franklin 1988) incorporates "composition" (including, e.g., species lists), "structure" (including, e.g., habitat complexity), and "function" (including, e.g., nutrient cycling), each one encompassing multiple levels of organisation from genes to biomes.

As it stands, RIVPACS can contribute to studies on biodiversity principally through providing information on species richness, and on the distribution of particular BAP species, although its usefulness may be enhanced by interpreting RIVPACS outputs in the light of other information, such as on functional feeding guilds. In countries such as the UK, much of the effort on conserving biodiversity is now focused on species and habitat action plans, arising from the Biodiversity Convention in Rio in 1992. Very few UK species listed in the BAP (Department of the Environment *et al.* 1994) are truly riverine, although many are associated with riverine shingle (e.g. *Rhabdomastix hilaris* (a crane-fly) and *Meotica anglica* (a beetle)). Some species that are riverine are less likely to be collected in standard RIVPACS surveys owing to their microhabitat preferences (e.g. *Margaritifera margaritifera* (freshwater pearl mussel) and *Austropotamobius pallipes* (white-clawed crayfish)). Whilst others (such as the stonefly *Brachyptera putata)* have been recorded from time to time in RIVPACS surveys, the application of RIVPACS to work on BAP species may be limited.

Biodiversity Action Plans cover habitats as well as species. In the UK, one of the key habitats within the broad habitat grouping of "running waters" is described as "chalk rivers". RIVPACS III has improved the prediction of fauna expected in rivers of this type (Wright *et al.* 1998a) and can thus add valuable information in describing, comparing, evaluating and monitoring BAP sites.

The applications of RIVPACS to studies under the broad banner of "sustainability", as opposed to rather narrower concerns about biodiversity, are less easy to document. Ecosystem sustainability is intrinsically related to concepts of sustainable development, which by definition are focused on the use that human beings make of ecosystems. For example, the First Principle of the Rio Declaration states that *"Human beings are at the centre of concerns for sustainable development. They are entitled to a healthy and productive life in harmony with nature"*. (Department of the Environment *et al.* 1994). Similar sentiments comprise the IUCN definition of conservation (International Union for Conservation of Nature and Natural Resources 1980), and the philosophy that natural resources should be maintained for handing on to future generations is a principle subscribed to by many individuals, organisations and governments.

Perhaps the main issue of controversy is whether the general notion of freshwater ecosystem sustainability is a valid concept at all, or whether it can only be considered in the context of specific freshwater "uses". In other words, should the question be "Does this river contain a sustainable trout fishery?", or "Is the rate of water abstraction sustainable?", or should it be "Is this river a sustainable ecosystem?" This subject lies outside the bounds of this chapter; further discussion may be found in Boon & Howell (1997a, b).

To what extent, then, can river invertebrates be used in assessing sustainability, and does RIVPACS specifically have a role to play in this? Apart from a few exceptions (e.g. some freshwater shrimps, crayfish, pearl mussel) river invertebrates are not subject to deliberate human exploitation. It is the exploitation of other parts of a river ecosystem that brings about change in invertebrate populations.

One of the problems inherent in assessing sustainability is the determination of an appropriate time-scale for measurement. For example, an apparent downward trend in the population size of a particular invertebrate species might be merely a small part of a long-term trend in population fluctuation in which numbers both increase and decrease. Nevertheless, over a specified time period, it might be feasible to plot RIVPACS-derived O/E ratios against time, and to observe the point on the graph at which a continued downward trend signals an unacceptable reduction in sustainability. This point has been termed the "Threshold of Potential Concern", and is part of an approach that has been used to define the desired state of river systems in South Africa (Rogers & Bestbier 1997). However, for some South African rivers such as the Sabie, changes in habitat features are likely to provide better indicators of sustainability than changes in invertebrate communities (Jay O'Keeffe, University of Grahamstown, personal communication). Invertebrate communities are characteristically resilient, and may often recolonise rivers rapidly after disturbance. Structural changes to habitats are likely to be more important in reducing the long-term sustainability of river systems.

Summary and recommendations

RIVPACS was not designed principally as a conservation tool. Nonetheless, it has already demonstrated that it has the potential to make a valuable contribution to river conservation assessments, although at present these are mainly restricted to SERCON evaluations of species richness and representativeness.

Many national and international initiatives are now focused on conserving "biodiversity". This term should be understood to include more than "species richness", although species richness is an important element. Unfortunately, the routine use of RIVPACS in river quality assessments usually entails identifications only to family level, and thus provides only limited information for biodiversity studies. The close correlations found between family (and BMWP family) richness and species richness may afford one way of targeting resources in future by focusing intensive, species-level surveys on areas found to be family-rich.

In theory, the general "RIVPACS approach" – comparing observed and expected characteristics to produce a quality index – could be extended to other habitat types and to other groups of organisms, provided that taxonomic knowledge is adequate and that sufficient is known about the variables influencing species distribution. Other RIVPACS-related systems are already planned, such as one based on aquatic macrophytes. However, further developments such as these must be monitored carefully to ensure that they fulfil a real need, rather than becoming ends in themselves.

Techniques such as RIVPACS, SERCON and RHS tend to stress the importance of "naturalness" as a criterion for assessing the quality of rivers and their value for conservation. To some extent, this may be perceived as a "first-world" rather than a "third-world" perspective (Wishart, Davies *et al.* 2000). In developing countries, especially those where factors such as climate, topography and land-use put the supply of clean, potable water at a premium, conservation objectives must be set within the wider framework of the human use of river systems. Thus, transferring UK assessment techniques such as RIVPACS, SERCON or RHS to other countries must take account not only of the physical and biological differences, and the availability of environmental information, but also the cultural context in which such systems are developed and used.

Specific recommendations

The present use of RIVPACS as an integral part of the SERCON procedure needs to be re-examined and refined. Refinements might include the use of other information generated by RIVPACS: for example, enhancing the evaluation of "richness" by assessing the diversity of RIVPACS classification end-groups within a river, or modifying assessments of "rarity" and "representativeness" by noting the presence of end-groups that are particularly unusual or uncharacteristic, respectively.

Interpretations of river "quality" using RIVPACS should be compared with outputs from RHS and SERCON. Both the presence and absence of positive correlations between quality indices for the same site may yield valuable insights for conservation management.

Consideration should be given to expanding the RIVPACS reference database to include sites where the physical habitat of the river has been degraded. This would assist in pre- and post-project appraisal of river restoration schemes.

Acknowledgements

The author would like to thank all those whose contributions have helped in the production of this chapter, and to apologise for any inadvertent misrepresentation of their views. PJB is especially grateful to Paul Logan (Environment Agency) who provided transcripts of the workshop discussions. Fig. 23.1 is reproduced from *Verh. internat. Verein. Limnol.* **26**, 1174-78, by kind permission of the publishers.

CHAPTER 24

RIVPACS and alternative statistical modelling techniques: accuracy and soundness of principles

RICHARD K. JOHNSON

Swedish University of Agricultural Sciences,
Department of Environmental Assessment, Box 7050, S-750 07, Uppsala, SWEDEN

Summary of a workshop based on contributions from Richard Johnson (Chair, Sweden), Mike Furse (Rapporteur, UK), Peter Davies (Australia), Alastair Ferguson (UK), Chris Humphrey (Australia), Sandy Milner (UK), Dorian Moss (UK), Leonard Sandin (Sweden), Justen Simpson (Australia), Piet Verdonschot (The Netherlands) and Bill Walley (UK).

Summary

A number of methods, ranging from the use of simple indices to complex algorithms, are currently used for assessing the biological quality of rivers. Two approaches, in particular, are frequently used to estimate the expected conditions in the absence of environmental stress: (1) an ecoregion approach, where a single index or combinations of indices is/are calculated for a predetermined set of regionally representative reference sites, and (2) a site-specific approach, where conditions, indices, or probabilities of taxon occurrences, are predicted. The Institute of Freshwater Ecology (IFE) was a pioneer in developing site-specific predictive algorithms using a suite of multivariate techniques. In brief, classification of reference sites and discriminant function models are used to estimate the weighted average probability of occurrence of individual taxa. The approach developed by the IFE, called RIVPACS, has been modified and used in a number of RIVPACS-type models, a testament to its robust nature. The workgroup discussed a number of factors that might affect classification and prediction, as well as alternative predictive techniques, but found no compelling reason to recommend altering the RIVPACS approach.

Introduction

Benthic ecologists were pioneers in understanding how indicator assemblages relate to ecosystem quality. During the last hundred years, and in particular in the last two decades, a number of biotic indices have been constructed to evaluate the structural and functional integrity of surface waters, using macroinvertebrates (Johnson 1995). In a recent review, Knoben *et al.* (1995) noted that of some 100 different biological methods currently used in freshwater bioassessment, two-thirds were based on macroinvertebrates. Methods range from relatively simple algorithms or biotic indices, to combinations of several indices (the multimetric approach), and to relatively complex, multivariate approaches.

The use of multivariate predictive algorithms, often combined with simple biotic metrics, shows much promise as a diagnostic tool in biomonitoring and assessment studies. For example, predictive modelling of expected taxon occurrences in the absence of stress is increasingly being used to ascertain reference or ecological target conditions. Since the late

1970s, discriminant function analysis has been used by ecologists for predicting community structure, using sets of environmental data (e.g. Green 1979; Wiegleb 1981). The IFE team (Wright, Moss *et al.* 1984; Moss, Furse *et al.* 1987) was the first to develop predictive models of stream macroinvertebrates, using classification and discriminant function analysis. These types of approaches hold much promise, as they de-emphasise the expertise of the individual investigator (Johnson *et al.* 1993). Moreover, the predicted taxon occurrences also may be used to calculate biotic metrics such as BMWP scores (Hawkes 1998) or acidity scores. Currently, this is being done in the UK (e.g. Wright, Armitage *et al.* 1988), where observed BMWP indices are compared with expected indices in national river surveys (Sweeting, Lowson *et al.* 1992).

The RIVPACS approach to predictive modelling consists of three basic steps: (1) the determination of community types, (2) selection and determination of explanatory environmental variables, and (3) prediction of the probabilities of taxon occurrences (Moss, Furse *et al.* 1987) (Fig. 24.1). Group classification of stream macroinvertebrate communities is performed by two-way indicator species analysis (TWINSPAN) (Hill 1979a). Multiple discriminant analysis (MDA) is then used to develop predictive models, which discriminate between groups of sites using environmental data. The probability that new sites are members of established groups is calculated and the probabilities of occurrence of taxa at a new site are derived. The three steps commonly used in RIVPACS-type predictions, mentioned above (clustering, selection of environmental variables, and prediction), together with associated issues and alternative approaches, were the subject of the workshop reported in this chapter, which summarises the comments and suggestions arising from the workshop and incorporates additional review material assembled by the author.

Questions that participants in the workshop were asked to address

Classification – options and evaluation.

Which is the best multivariate classification technique for constructing RIVPACS-type models?

Does the best technique vary according to the structure of the data?

Is classification an essential precursor to predictions?

What criteria are to be used in assessing the merits of different classifications?

Does the number of taxa affect the outcome of the classification, i.e. should rare taxa be excluded?

Prediction – options and evaluation.

Which is the best multivariate prediction technique for constructing RIVPACS-type models?

Should predictions be for individual species rather than faunal assemblages?

Alternatives to multivariate classification and prediction techniques.

What are the comparative merits of multivariate statistics and artificial intelligence techniques for developing predictive models?

What are the comparative merits of multivariate statistics and multimetric procedures for assessing the ecological quality of watercourses?

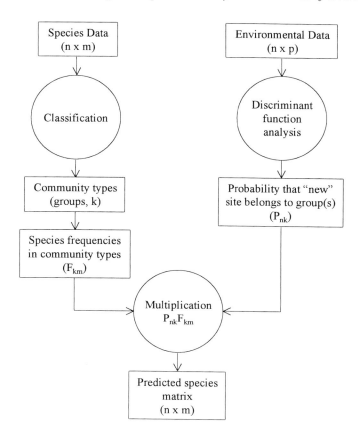

Figure 24.1. Schematic diagram showing the steps used in RIVPACS-type predictions of taxon occurrence.

Classification of community types

Cluster analyses are techniques designed for grouping subjects (sites) into classes so that similar subjects are grouped into the same class. A number of approaches and algorithms are commonly used (Norris & Georges 1993), and include: (i) simple table arrangement, (ii) hierarchic techniques that use the distance of each subject to all other subjects as the method to form groups, either by the process of agglomeration or division — resulting in a dendrogram, (iii) non-hierarchic techniques that involve partitioning or movement of subjects between groups at different stages of the analysis, the process continuing iteratively until stability is achieved with a predetermined number of groups, and (iv) ordination.

The classification method used in RIVPACS is TWINSPAN (Hill 1979a), a polythetic divisive classification technique. The method is based on the first axis of correspondence analysis (reciprocal averaging) (Hirschfeld 1935) (Fig. 24.2), and is considered to be robust when the dataset is complex or noisy (Gauch & Whittaker 1981). TWINSPAN divides the whole set of subjects (sites) into two groups at the first division, and further divides each daughter group into two at each new level of division. In brief, the first correspondence analysis (CA) or reciprocal averaging (RA) axis is divided roughly in the middle, and differential taxa are defined as those showing a preference for sites on one side of the dichotomy. A second ordination of sites is then constructed by assigning weights to the

TWINSPAN

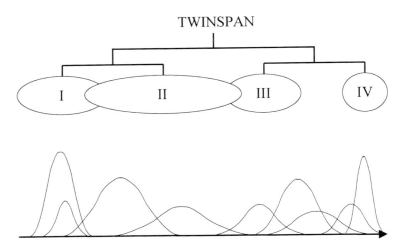

Figure 24.2. Schematic diagram showing the hypothetical distribution of species along the first axis of correspondence analysis (CA) and grouping (I to IV) by two-way indicator species analysis (TWINSPAN).

differential taxa. Taxon weights are summed for each site and the location of the dichotomy is repositioned. In other words, in TWINSPAN classification, emphasis is placed on gradient segmentation as a classification criterion rather than cluster seeking. Hence this technique falls somewhere in between conventional cluster analysis procedures using similarity or dissimilarity indices, and "cluster-free" ordination and re-ordination techniques. Lastly, one of the notable attributes and attractive features of TWINSPAN is the ordered two-way table, which reflects the primary ordination. This is both easily understood and relatively straightforward, and is undoubtedly one of the reasons for TWINSPAN's popularity and widespread use. A search of Biological Abstracts from 1990 to 1996 gave 304 hits for "TWINSPAN" (n = 25, 31, 45, 53, 40, 62 and 48 for 1990 to 1996, respectively).

Given its widespread use, it is surprising that the robustness of the technique has been relatively poorly studied. Two weaknesses of TWINSPAN are that sites can be misclassified along the first CA axis, and the order of placement of sites (the data input file) affected classification or divisions in the early version of TWINSPAN. One method for testing the robustness of a cluster technique is to evaluate how well a method recaptures the structure of a known dataset. Using this approach and simulated "biological" data, Van Groenewoud (1992) showed that CA (the precursor of TWINSPAN classification) was able to recapture the structure of the first gradient, if second or higher order gradients were small. Conversely, when two gradients were of the same length, CA gave poor results for both axes. This artifact of CA and gradient length is supposedly one of the main reasons why TWINSPAN does not perform well with predominant secondary gradients.

Also, Belbin & McDonald (1993) showed that TWINSPAN performed rather poorly in recapturing the structure of a known (hypothetical) dataset. As in Van Groenewoud's study, two problems were noted. Firstly, TWINSPAN performed relatively poorly when more than one gradient was evident in the dataset, i.e. indicating dependence on a predominant primary gradient. Secondly, if the primary gradient is not accurately detected, then the placement of the first dichotomy may be incorrect and, once split, groups cannot be reformed and subsequent divisions will only compound this problem. These inherent problems of TWINSPAN classification are undoubtedly important if the ultimate goal is to classify sites. However, though serious, misclassification is probably of less importance in the penultimate use of

TWINSPAN classification in RIVPACS-type predictions. In RIVPACS, discriminant function analysis (DFA) is used to predict group membership, and sites may be predicted to one or more TWINSPAN groups. Estimates of the probabilities of taxon occurrences, however, may be affected by misclassifications, as this step relies on the frequency of occurrence of the taxa in each TWINSPAN group.

Tausch, Charlet *et al.* (1995) noted that changing the input order of species or sites in a dataset can cause changes in the results of ordinations and classifications done by using particular programs such as CA and detrended correspondence analysis (DCA). Oksanen & Minchin (1997) tested this instability more thoroughly and found a programming error in one of the subroutines. The most serious cases of instability in both CA and DCA occurred when convergence did not occur before the maximum number of iterations was reached. Also, trial runs showed that the scores on the first two axes were much more stable than subsequent axes. However, the authors noted that even the ordinations that had relatively even eigenvalues for the first few axes (e.g. axis 1 and 2, or 2 and 3) might suffer from instability. It was suggested that the reliability of ordinations should be checked using shuffling and comparison software, until the commercial programs using CA and DCA are debugged. RIVPACS uses reciprocal averaging (RA), a form of CA which is affected by this programming error, as part of the TWINSPAN program that is used for classification. The effects of RA (CA) instability on RIVPACS predictions should be assessed. In particular, the TWINSPAN classification should be re-run using the latest version of the program that uses strict convergence criteria in RA ordinations, according to Oksanen & Minchin (1997).

The workgroup discussed a number of the advantages and disadvantages of various clustering techniques. Many algorithms are currently used for cluster analysis, but there is no generally accepted "best" method. Moreover, different algorithms do not necessarily produce the same results on a given set of data (Manly 1994) and usually there is a rather large subjective component in the assessment of results from any particular method. The workgroup considered that at present there is no compelling reason to move away from TWINSPAN. It was considered that all cluster analysis techniques suffer from "misclassifications", so a pragmatic approach should be used with re-allocation of misclassified sites (e.g. using centroid sorting re-allocation).

In addition, alternative approaches that do not rely on classification were also discussed by the workgroup. In particular, methods of ordination and re-ordination, and artificial intelligence (e.g. Bayesian techniques; see Chapter 18) were briefly reviewed. The workgroup considered that these cluster-free approaches deserve greater attention. However, as with conventional non-hierarchical clustering methods, these techniques do not provide structure, an attribute that is considered to be of value both for interpretation of data output as well as for supplying "targets" to be used in conservation.

A species-by-site matrix is often "noisy", with a large number of low abundance or rare species. In addition, species distributions generally do not form discrete communities, but are successively replaced along gradients. Here the discussion focussed on two issues; specifically, should rare taxa be downweighted or removed, and when should clustering be stopped? The workgroup recognised a number of difficulties regarding the use of rare taxa in clustering. Although the information value of removed taxa may be as great or even greater than information provided by more common taxa, the informative value of individual taxa and hence the effect of their removal on the data output is difficult to know beforehand. It is recommended that when using statistical analyses that are sensitive to outliers, the inclusion or exclusion of rare taxa should be evaluated.

The main goal of using a grouping technique is to select groups that reflect real (statistically significant) relationships among the underlying communities, as opposed to groups that are simply the result of random effects. The workgroup discussed a number of methods that can be used to test the robustness of classifying sites, thereby adding more objectivity to the analysis. These included randomisation techniques such as bootstrapping (e.g. Efron & Tibshirani 1993) and Monte Carlo permutations (Hope 1968), and predictive methods such as discriminant function analysis, to study differences between biotic and abiotic classifications.

RIVPACS-type predictions

RIVPACS-type predictions are based on predicting, with environmental data, the probabilities of a site belonging to predetermined groups established using biological data. A number of techniques (e.g. ordination methods) can be used to examine relationships between biotic and abiotic components.

Each species occurs in a characteristic, limited range of habitats within its geographic range, and tends to be most abundant around its particular environmental optimum (e.g. Ter Braak & Prentice 1988). Hence the composition of biotic communities changes along environmental gradients, with successive replacements occurring as a function of the variation in the environment. Ordination methods are frequently used to summarise the main structure in a species-by-site data matrix (dimension reduction) and to relate structure to environmental factors. These include both indirect gradient methods such as CA (and its detrended counterpart DCA; Hill & Gauch 1980) and principal components analysis (PCA) (Hotelling 1933), and direct gradient methods (otherwise known as constrained ordination) such as canonical correspondence analysis (CCA) and redundancy analysis (RDA) (e.g. Ter Braak 1988). A third group of methods that rely on distance-scaling techniques, as opposed to the variance-maximisation methods already mentioned, are also used, e.g. multidimensional scaling (MDS) (Kruskal 1964). This technique has gained much popularity in handling ecological data, often replacing the use of PCA (Norris & Georges 1993).

If the ultimate aim of clustering is to predict community structure (as in RIVPACS-type predictions), then determining the underlying correlative relationships between biological groups and physico-chemical predictors of the groups (e.g. water chemistry and other habitat descriptors) is of principal importance. Although the selection of which ordination method to use is often rather subjective, but hopefully not arbitrary, some thought should be given to the inherent properties of the method and algorithm selected. One of the first and probably most important assumptions that needs to be considered is the expected distribution or species response along one or more environmental gradients. For example, species abundances may seem to change linearly along short sections of a gradient, indicating that a linear response model may be most appropriate. Alternatively, if the underlying gradients are rather broad and a large number of zero values for abundance occur in the dataset, then a unimodal (or Gaussian) response model may give a better fit. Of the ordination methods reviewed above, PCA, MDS and RDA assume monotonic responses of species, while CA, DCA and CCA assume unimodal responses of species. In reality, species response curves are generally more complicated, showing both linear and nonlinear responses, and alternative approaches, such as the use of ß-functions to model species response curves, have been proposed (e.g. Austin, Nicholls *et al.* 1994).

Also, the choice of indirect or direct gradient methods needs to be addressed. Early in the development of RIVPACS, Wright, Moss *et al.* (1984) used DCA and MDA to analyse the underlying environmental gradients of species distribution patterns. In indirect ordination methods, focus is placed first on analysing the major pattern of variation in the dataset (e.g. community composition). Interpretation of the underlying gradients is subsequently done *a posteriori* through correlation of the main axes with another matrix of explanatory variables. Direct gradient methods, on the other hand, enable parallel comparisons of species distribution patterns and environmental factors that may be linked to the underlying gradients. Indirect gradient methods have the advantage that no *a priori* assumptions are needed about what environmental factors are relevant. In contrast, direct gradient analysis enables a simultaneous comparison of relationships in species composition and environmental factors (Ter Braak 1986), but requires both species and environmental datasets. Since the advent of CCA as an ordination technique in the mid-1980s, and the relative ease of access to CCA (and RDA) in the program CANOCO (e.g. Ter Braak 1988), this method has become popular among terrestrial and aquatic ecologists (Ter Braak & Verdonschot 1995). A search of Biological Abstracts from 1990 to 1996 revealed 281 papers using CCA and 50 using RDA. Ultimately, the choice of a multivariate gradient-analysis technique should be based on the aim of the study, and indirect- and direct-gradient methods should be viewed as complementary and not alternative techniques. Økland (1996) argued that indirect methods are appropriate when the emphasis is placed on the generation of hypotheses about species–environmental relationships. Constrained ordination, on the other hand, is considered as a powerful tool for hypothesis testing.

Building on the concept of constrained ordination, Carleton, Stitt *et al.* (1996) proposed a grouping method, constrained-indicator-species-analysis (COINSPAN), where environmental variables form an active constraint on the TWINSPAN divisions. As an extension of the CCA approach, COINSPAN substitutes a CCA axis for the CA axis of TWINSPAN. As a complement to TWINSPAN, this is a new technique that could be used as a form of discriminant analysis to determine the underlying environmental gradients. However, a separate or independent grouping procedure (e.g. TWINSPAN) should be used in RIVPACS-type predictions, to avoid confounding predictions; i.e. there is some circularity in selecting predictor variables which are based on variates that maximise correlation with species distribution patterns.

Although the research upon which RIVPACS is based began twenty years ago, it is still being developed. Even now it is likely that it is not being utilised to its full potential. In biomonitoring studies many assessment systems are developed for predicting and using the probabilities of taxon occurrences at family level. However, the approach is just as easily used for species-level predictions. Predictions made at species level enable the assessment of not only structural but even functional aspects (feeding guilds) of reference and impaired sites. Probability estimates of predictions also are central to understanding and interpreting output files. Here the workgroup considered that more effort should be devoted to partitioning and understanding error estimates, not only of model predictions but also errors intimately associated with sampling *in situ* communities (e.g. sampling and natural variability). In fact, much of this work has been done recently. Clarke (Chapter 3) provides a comprehensive analysis of sources of variation and errors that can affect RIVPACS-type predictions. For example, in a study designed to estimate the effect of sampling variation on RIVPACS predictions, Clarke, Furse *et al.* (1999) found that increasing the number of seasons sampled (from one to three) resulted in lower error estimates or tighter confidence limits around the predicted means. These and other studies recently performed by the IFE team substantially add to our understanding of error estimates associated with RIVPACS predictions.

Other means of reducing error estimates, such as variance partitioning or the choice of better predictor variables (i.e. variables that account for residual variation) might be given greater attention. For example, though the effect of within-year or seasonal variation has been evaluated (Chapter 3), much less is known of the effect that among-year variability has on RIVPACS predictions. Inclusion of predictor variables that explicitly quantify aspects of among-year variability (e.g. degree-days) may increase the predictive power of RIVPACS. Similarly, partitioning large-scale spatial variability may also increase the predictive power of RIVPACS-type predictions. For example, models developed for biogeographically similar regions may be more robust than those developed using national boundaries (see Chapter 16). Lastly, the workgroup considered that greater attention should be devoted to evaluating the use of Geographic Information System (GIS) technology in predictive models (e.g. Guisan *et al.* 1998).

Alternative approaches

An underlying assumption of models using empirical datasets to predict species occurrence is that the fundamental niche of a species can be determined from species distribution maps (Prentice & Helmisaari 1991). Alternatively, when this space is restricted by biotic interactions, the realised niche is more appropriate (e.g. Austin *et al.* 1990). These assumptions are, of course, less valid when factors such as pollution affect and confound the interpretation of species distribution patterns. Discriminant function analysis (DFA) is being used more frequently by ecologists, both as an exploratory tool to study relationships between biological groups and environmental factors, and as a predictive tool to predict the membership of a site or group of taxa in a previously established classification of sites or taxa. Moreover, since the advent of RIVPACS, predictions of taxon occurrences using DFA have increased (e.g. Johnson 1995; Reynoldson, Bailey *et al.* 1995; Simpson, Norris *et al.* 1997).

In RIVPACS-type predictions, DFA is used to predict the probabilities of taxon occurrences (e.g. Moss, Furse *et al.* 1987). Such estimates of probabilities are indirect, as they are based on the frequency of taxon occurrences in the predetermined groups. A number of modelling techniques are available that can be used to predict taxon occurrences directly. For example, in order to predict taxon occurrence, terrestrial and aquatic ecologists have used generalised linear models (e.g. Nicholls 1989), logistic regression (Agresti 1990), Gaussian logistic regression or the more simplified weighted averaging regression (e.g. Ter Braak & Looman 1986), Bayesian models (e.g. Brzeziecki *et al.* 1995), partial least squares regression (Wold 1982), ß-functions (Austin, Nicholls *et al.* 1994), and taxon-specific models (Bio *et al.* 1998). IFE researchers have recently assessed the effects of a number of methods for site classification on RIVPACS predictions (Moss, Wright *et al.* 1999; see also Chapter 2). In addition to clustering approaches, they also evaluated the use of logistic regression to predict taxon occurrence directly. Although the performance of logistic regression generally fell within the range of the other techniques tested, at least two of the indirect methods were deemed to be better (Chapter 2).

Palaeocologists, in particular, have had much success using modelling techniques based on weighted averaging to predict pH (e.g. Dixit *et al.* 1989; Kingston & Birks 1990; Renberg *et al.* 1993), total phosphorus (e.g. Anderson & Odgaard 1994) and temperature (e.g. Walker *et al.* 1991). These workers have used indicator values and species composition to predict environmental variables but, unfortunately, inverting the models to predict taxon occurrences along gradients is not as common. Moreover, the use of single gradient predictions is not as informative as predictions based on several environmental gradients. The RIVPACS-type approach elegantly solves this dilemma, by using discriminant models incorporating more than single environmental gradients. A comparison of more direct modelling approaches (Fig. 24.3) with RIVPACS-type predictions of taxon occurrences (Fig. 24.1) would probably provide a better understanding of the merits of the different approaches.

The majority of predictive models mentioned above are based on the response of species along environmental gradients, and fit either linear (e.g. logistic regression), unimodal (e.g. weighted averaging) or taxon-specific (e.g. ß-functions) models to predict the probability of taxon occurrence. The use of neural networks and Bayesian techniques, otherwise known as artificial intelligence (AI) methods, which do not rely on pre-established species responses for predicting habitat quality, is a relatively new and interesting approach. The workgroup

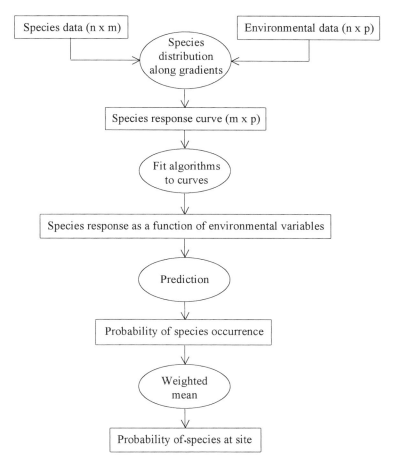

Figure 24.3. Schematic diagram showing the steps used to predict the occurrence of individual species, using a direct modelling approach.

discussed the merits of AI techniques, and concluded that classification and prediction based on AI gave results that are similar to RIVPACS-type approaches. However, AI techniques are able to link levels of expert-derived information, and hence one of the strengths of AI technology is that of diagnostic use. For example, AI methods show much promise in pattern recognition (water quality classification) as they generally remove a great deal of the subjectivity inherent in many of the more traditional approaches (e.g. Walley & Hawkes 1997). The merits of AI techniques and the more traditional classification and prediction methods should be thoroughly appraised.

The workgroup discussed the value of multimetric and more statistically-based multivariate approaches in biomonitoring. Multimetric approaches are characterised by the use of more than one type of measurement or metric, each of which provides independent or unique information, but when integrated provide an overall indication of the condition of the biological community (Chapter 19). In contrast to RIVPACS-type approaches, the integrated metric is compared with pre-established reference values, while multivariate methods often predict the reference condition (expected fauna) using environmental variables that are not affected by anthropogenic stress. The workgroup considered that combining multivariate and multimetric approaches may synergistically enhance the value of these two approaches in biomonitoring, and should be looked upon as complementary and not competing approaches. As with AI techniques, the combined use of multivariate/metric approaches lies in their diagnostic potential.

Concluding remarks of the workgroup

The workgroup concluded that RIVPACS is a robust means of predicting community structure, a fact that is supported by the development and use of similar RIVPACS-type approaches in environmental assessment studies. However, more effort could be placed on using the information of the output file. Predictions at family level or, more interestingly, at species level, could be used in improving our understanding of the linkages between structural and functional aspects of aquatic ecosystems, and their importance for biodiversity and conservation evaluations. RIVPACS is based on relatively static measures (i.e. the environmental variables selected are resilient to change), while communities are responding to dynamic processes acting on temporal scales of days to years. More information is needed concerning the importance of temporal variability on predictions. RIVPACS models might also benefit from periodic validations using, for example, data from national surveys. The relatively long time-period during which RIVPACS has been developed and used (20 years) and the similarities between independent approaches suggest, however, a great deal of confidence in RIVPACS-type predictive models.

Specific recommendations

(1) TWINSPAN classification works well due to the inherent properties of its algorithm (correspondence analysis or reciprocal averaging), and the workgroup found no compelling reason to recommend change. Cluster-free techniques, though interesting, do not provide structure, an attribute that is often of high diagnostic value (e.g. in conservation work).

(2) The early version of TWINSPAN suffered from instability when convergence did not occur before the maximum number of iterations was reached. This effect should be evaluated and TWINSPAN groupings re-done using the revised TWINSPAN program.

(3) The effects of misclassifications of sites in the original RIVPACS classification should be evaluated and re-allocation techniques used to minimise their influence.

(4) A serious limitation of clustering techniques is the subjectivity by which data outputs (e.g. dendrograms) are interpreted. Randomisation techniques such as bootstrapping and Monte Carlo simulation are recommended to test the robustness of groups formed by clustering procedures.

(5) The workgroup discussed a number of prediction methods, but found no compelling reason to justify change to an alternative technique.

Acknowledgments

Many thanks are extended to the "RIVPACS gang" for arranging the workshop and in particular to Dorian Moss and Mike Furse for their input into the "alternative methods" workgroup. Also, thanks to all the other participants of the alternative methods workgroup, including Mike Barbour who kindly participated during the discussion of the merits of multimetric approaches. The comments and suggestions of the workgroup were greatly appreciated. However, RKJ takes sole responsibility for any misinterpretations of their "input files".

REFERENCES

[In this volume, multi–authored publications are cited in the main text and listed below in the following manner. For three authors, all three names are listed below *but only the first is given in the text*; for example, a paper listed below as Alba-Tercedor, J., González, G. & Puig, M. A. (1992) is cited in the text as Alba-Tercedor *et al.* (1992). For four or more authors *only the first two names are listed below and similarly cited in the text*; for example, a paper by Armitage, P. D., Blackburn, J. H., Winder, J. M. & Wright, J. F. (1994) is listed below and also cited in the text as Armitage, Blackburn *et al.* (1994).]

Agresti, A. (1990). *Categorical data analysis*. John Wiley & Sons, New York.

Ahtiainen, M. (1992). The effects of forest clear-cutting and scarification on the water quality of streams. *Hydrobiologia* **243/244**, 465-473.

Alatalo, R. V. (1981). Problems in the measurement of evenness in ecology. *Oikos* **37**, 199-204.

Alba-Tercedor, J. (1996). Los macroinvertebrados acuáticos y la calidad de las aguas de los ríos. *IV Simposio del Agua en Andalucía, Almería* **II**, 203-213.

Alba-Tercedor, J. & Prat, N. (1992). Spanish experience in the use of macroinvertebrates as biological pollution indicators. In *River water quality: ecological assessment and control* (eds P. J. Newman, M. A. Piavaux & R. A. Sweeting), pp. 733-738. Publication EUR 14606 EN-FR. Commission of the European Communities, Luxembourg.

Alba-Tercedor, J. & Sánchez-Ortega, A. (1988). Un método rápido y simple para evaluar la calidad biológica de las aguas corrientes basado en el de Hellawell (1978). *Limnética* **4**, 51-56.

Alba-Tercedor, J., González, G. & Puig, M. A. (1992). Present level of knowledge regarding fluvial macroinvertebrate communities in Spain. *Limnética* **8**, 231-241.

Aldenberg, T. & Peters, J. S. (1990). On relating empirical water quality diagrams and plankton dynamical models: the SAMPLE methodology applied to a drinking water storage reservoir. *Archiv für Hydrobiologie Beiheft. Ergebnisse der Limnologie* **33**, 893-911.

American Society for Testing and Materials (ASTM) (1994). *Standard guide for conducting sediment toxicity tests with freshwater invertebrates*. ASTM. E 1383-94a. Philadelphia, Pennsylvania. 33 pp.

Anderson, N. J. & Odgaard, B. V. (1994). Recent palaeolimnology of three shallow Danish lakes. *Hydrobiologia* **275/276**, 411-422.

Anonymous (1984). *Naturgeografisk regionindelning av Norden*. Nordiska ministerrådet 1984.

ANZECC (Australian and New Zealand Environment and Conservation Council) (1992). *Australian water quality guidelines for fresh and marine waters*. ANZECC, Australian Water Resources Council, Canberra.

Armitage, P. D. (1987). The classification of tailwater sites receiving residual flows from upland reservoirs in Great Britain, using macroinvertebrate data. In *Advances in regulated stream ecology* (eds J. F. Craig & J. B. Kemper), pp. 131-144. Plenum Press, New York.

Armitage, P. D. (1989). The application of a classification and prediction technique based on macroinvertebrates to assess the effects of river regulation. In *Alternatives in regulated river management* (eds J. A. Gore & G. E. Petts), pp. 267-293. CRC Press Inc., Boca Raton, Florida.

Armitage, P. D. (1994). Prediction of biological responses. In *Rivers handbook Volume 2* (eds P. Calow & G. Petts), pp. 254-275. Blackwell Scientific Publications, Oxford.

Armitage, P. D. & Gunn, R. J. M. (1996). Differential response of benthos to natural and anthropogenic disturbances in three lowland streams. *Internationale Revue der Gesamten Hydrobiologie* **81**, 161-181.

Armitage, P. D. & Petts, G. E. (1992). Biotic score and prediction to assess the effects of water abstractions on river macroinvertebrates for conservation purposes. *Aquatic Conservation: Marine and Freshwater Ecosystems* **2**, 1-17.

Armitage, P. D., Cannan, C. A. & Symes, K. L. (1997). *Appraisal of the use of ecological information in the management of low flows in rivers.* Environment Agency R&D Technical Report W72. 97 pp.

Armitage, P. D., Furse, M. T. & Wright, J. F. (1992). Anexo: Calidad medioambiental y valoración biologica en los ríos británicos. Perspectivas de passado y futuro. [Environmental quality and biological assessment in British rivers – past and future perspectives.] In *Caracterizacion Hidrobiologica de la red fluvial de Alava y Gipuzkoa* (ed. Departamento de Economia Planificacíon y Medio Ambiente del Gobierno Vasco), pp. 477-511. Itxaropena, S. A. Zarautz.

Armitage, P. D., Pardo, I. & Brown, A. (1995). Temporal constancy of faunal assemblages in mesohabitats. Application to management. *Archiv für Hydrobiologie* **133**, 367-387.

Armitage, P. D., Blackburn, J. H. *et al.* (1994). Impact of vegetation management on macroinvertebrates in chalk streams. *Aquatic Conservation: Marine and Freshwater Ecosystems* **4**, 95-104.

Armitage, P. D., Gunn, R. J. M. *et al.* (1987). The use of prediction to assess macroinvertebrate response to river regulation. *Hydrobiologia* **144**, 25-32.

Armitage, P. D., Moss, D. *et al.* (1983). The performance of a new biological water quality score system based on macroinvertebrates over a wide range of unpolluted running-water sites. *Water Research* **17**, 333-347.

Armitage, P. D., Pardo, I. *et al.* (1990). Assessment and prediction of biological quality. A demonstration of a British macroinvertebrate-based method in two Spanish rivers. *Limnética* **6**, 147-156.

Arthington, A. H., Hart, B. *et al.* (1993). *National River Management R&D Program. Identification of R&D priorities for biomonitoring.* Consultant report to Land and Water Resources R&D Corporation, Canberra.

Austin, M. P., Nicholls, A. O. & Margules, C. R. (1990). Measurement of the realized qualitative niche: environmental niches of five *Eucalyptus* species. *Ecological Monographs* **60**, 161-177.

Austin, M. P., Nicholls, A. O. *et al.* (1994). Determining species response functions to an environmental gradient by means of a ß-function. *Journal of Vegetation Science* **5**, 215-228.

Australian and New Zealand Environment and Conservation Council (ANZECC) (1992). *Australian water quality guidelines for fresh and marine waters.* ANZECC, Australian Water Resources Council, Canberra.

Balloch, D., Davies, C. E. & Jones, F. H. (1976). Biological assessment of water quality in three British rivers: the North Esk (Scotland), the Ivel (England) and the Taf (Wales). *Water Pollution Control* **75**, 92-110.

Barbour, M. T. (1997). The re-invention of biological assessment in the U.S. *Human and Ecological Risk Assessment* **3**, 933-940.

Barbour, M. T. & Gerritsen, J. (1996). Subsampling of benthic samples: a defense of the fixed-count method. *Journal of the North American Benthological Society* **15**, 386-391.

Barbour, M. T., Diamond, J. M. & Yoder, C. O. (1996). Biological assessment strategies: applications and limitations. In *Whole effluent toxicity testing: an evaluation of methods and prediction of receiving system impacts* (eds D. R. Grothe, K. L. Dickson & D. K. Reed-Judkins), pp. 245-270. SETAC Press, Pensacola, Florida.

Barbour, M. T., Stribling, J. B. & Karr, J. R. (1995). The multimetric approach for establishing biocriteria and measuring biological condition. In *Biological assessment and criteria. Tools for water resource planning and decision making* (eds W. S. Davis & T. P. Simon), pp. 63-77. Lewis Publishers, Boca Raton, Florida.

Barbour, M. T., Gerritsen, J. *et al.* (1996). A framework for biological criteria for Florida streams using benthic macroinvertebrates. *Journal of the North American Benthological Society* **15**, 185-211.

Barbour, M. T., Gerritsen, J. *et al.* (1999). *Rapid bioassessment protocols for use in wadeable streams and rivers: periphyton, benthic macroinvertebrates and fish.* 2nd Edition. EPA 841-B-99-002. USEPA, Office of Water, Washington D.C.

Barbour, M. T., Plafkin, J. L. *et al.* (1992). Evaluation of EPA's rapid bioassessment benthic metrics: metric redundancy and variability among reference stream sites. *Environmental Toxicology and Chemistry* **11**, 437-499.

Barr, C. J., Bunce, R. G. H. *et al.* (1993). *Countryside Survey 1990. Main Report.* Department of the Environment, London. 174 pp.

Bartsch, A. F. & Ingram, W. M. (1966). Biological analysis of water pollution in North America. *Verhandlungen der Internationalen Vereinigung für theoretische und angewandte Limnologie* **16**, 786-800.

Beale, R. & Jackson, T. (1990). *Neural computing: an introduction.* Adam Hilger, Bristol, Philadelphia and New York.

Beckman, R. (1996). Portrait of Australia. In *State of the environment, Australia 1996.* (eds State of the Environment Advisory Council), pp. 2.1-2.32. CSIRO Publishing, Collingwood, Australia.

Bedard, D., Hayton, A. & Persaud, D. (1992). *Ontario Ministry of Environment laboratory sediment biological testing protocol.* Water Resources Branch, Ontario Ministry of Environment, Toronto, Ontario. 26 pp.

Belbin, L. (1991). Semi-strong hybrid scaling, a new ordination algorithm. *Journal of Vegetation Science* **2**, 491-496.

Belbin, L. (1992). *PATN, pattern analysis package.* Division of Wildlife and Ecology, CSIRO, Canberra, Australia.

Belbin, L. & McDonald, C. (1993). Comparing three classification strategies for use in ecology. *Journal of Vegetation Science* **4**, 341-348.

Besser, J. M., Giesy, J. P. *et al.* (1996). Assessment of sediment quality in dredged and undredged areas of the Trenton Channel of the Detroit River, Michigan, USA, using the sediment quality triad. *Journal of Great Lakes Research* **22**, 683-696.

Biggs, J., Corfield, A. *et al.* (1998). Restoration of the rivers Brede, Cole and Skerne: a joint Danish and British EU-LIFE demonstration project. V – Short-term impacts on the conservation value of aquatic macroinvertebrate and macrophyte assemblages. *Aquatic Conservation: Marine and Freshwater Ecosystems* **8**, 241-255.

Bio, A. M. F., Alkemade, R. & Barendregt, A. (1998). Determining alternative models for vegetation response analysis: a non-parametric approach. *Journal of Vegetation Science* **9**, 5-16.

Biodiversity Steering Group (1995). *Biodiversity: the UK steering group report.* HMSO, London.

Biological Monitoring Working Party (1978). *Final report: assessment and presentation of the quality of rivers in Great Britain*. Unpublished report, Department of the Environment, Water Data Unit.

Bishop, C. M. (1995). *Neural networks for pattern recognition*. Oxford University Press, Oxford.

Bishop, J. E. (1973). *Limnology of a small Malayan river Sungai Gombak*. Junk Publishers, The Hague.

Blackburn, J. H. & Forest, M. B. (1995). New records of *Hydropsyche saxonica* McLachlan (Trichopt., Hydropsychidae) from small streams in Great Britain. *Entomologist's Monthly Magazine* **13**, 71-76.

Boesch, D. F. (1977). Application of numerical classification in ecological investigations of water pollution. *Special Scientific Report of Virginia Institute of Marine Science* **77**, 1-114.

Boon, P. J. (1991). The role of Sites of Special Scientific Interest (SSSIs) in the conservation of British rivers. *Freshwater Forum* **1**, 95-108.

Boon, P. J. (1992). Essential elements in the case for river conservation. In *River conservation and management* (eds P. J. Boon, P. Calow & G. E. Petts), pp. 11-33. John Wiley & Sons, Chichester.

Boon, P. J. (1995). The relevance of ecology to the statutory protection of British rivers. In *The ecological basis for river management* (eds D. M. Harper & A. J. D. Ferguson), pp. 239-250. John Wiley & Sons, Chichester.

Boon, P. J. & Howell, D. L. (Editors) (1997a). *Freshwater quality: defining the indefinable?* The Stationery Office, Edinburgh. 552 pp.

Boon, P. J. & Howell, D. L. (1997b). Defining the quality of fresh waters: theme and variations. In *Freshwater quality: defining the indefinable?* (eds P. J. Boon & D. L. Howell), pp. 522-533. The Stationery Office, Edinburgh.

Boon, P. J., Holmes, N. T. H. *et al.* (1996). *SERCON: System for Evaluating Rivers for Conservation. Version 1 manual*. Scottish Natural Heritage Research Survey and Monitoring Report No. 61. Scottish Natural Heritage, Edinburgh.

Boon, P. J., Holmes, N. T. H. *et al.* (1997). A System for Evaluating Rivers for Conservation (SERCON): development, structure and function. In *Freshwater quality: defining the indefinable?* (eds P. J. Boon & D. L. Howell), pp. 299-326. The Stationery Office, Edinburgh.

Borgmann, U., Ralph, K. M. & Norwood, W. P. (1989). Toxicity test procedures for *Hyalella azteca* and chronic toxicity of cadmium and pentachlorophenol to *Hyalella azteca, Gammarus fasciatus* and *Daphnia magna. Archives of Environmental Contamination and Toxicology* **18**, 756-764.

Boulton, A. J. & Lake, P. S. (1992). The ecology of two intermittent streams in Victoria, Australia. III. Temporal changes in faunal composition. *Freshwater Biology* **27**, 123-138.

Bovee, K. D. (1982). *A guide to stream habitat analysis using the instream flow incremental methodology*. United States Fish and Wildlife Service, Instream Flow Information Paper No. 12, FWS/OBS 82/26.

Bovee, K. D. (Editor) (1995). *A comprehensive overview of the instream flow incremental methodology*. National Biological Service, Fort Collins, Colorado.

Bowman, M. R. & Bailey, R. C. (1997). Does taxonomic resolution affect the multivariate description of freshwater benthic macroinvertebrate communities? *Canadian Journal of Fisheries and Aquatic Sciences* **4**, 1802-1807.

Boyd, M. (1995). *The application of methods of uncertain reasoning to the biological classification of river water quality*. Unpublished PhD thesis, Aston University, Birmingham.

Boyd, M., Walley, W. J. & Hawkes, H. A. (1993). Dempster-Shafer reasoning for the biological surveillance of river water quality. In *Water pollution: modelling, measuring and prediction* (eds L. C. Wrobel & C. A. Brebbia), pp. 349-356. Computational Mechanics Publications, June 1993, Southampton.

Bratton, J. H. (1990). *A review of the scarcer Ephemeroptera and Plecoptera of Great Britain.* Research and Survey in Nature Conservation No. **29**. Nature Conservancy Council, Peterborough. 40 pp.

Bratton, J. H. (Editor) (1991). *British red data books. 3. Invertebrates other than insects.* Joint Nature Conservation Committee, Peterborough.

Braukmann, U. (1984). *Biologischer Beitrag zu einer allgemeiner regionalen Bachtypologie.* Thesis, Justus Liebig Universitat, Giessen. 474 pp.

Bravard, J. P., Amoros, C. & Pautou, G. (1986). Impact of civil engineering works on the successions of communities in a fluvial system. *Oikos* **47**, 92-111.

Brinkhurst, R. O. (1974). *The benthos of lakes.* St. Martin's Press, New York. 190 pp.

Brinkhurst, R. O. (1993). Future directions in freshwater biomonitoring using benthic macroinvertebrates. In *Freshwater biomonitoring and benthic macroinvertebrates* (eds D. M. Rosenberg & V. H. Resh), pp. 442-460. Chapman & Hall, New York.

British Columbia Ministry of Environment, Lands and Parks, and Environment Canada (1993). *State of the environment report for British Columbia.* BC Ministry of Environment, Lands and Parks and Environment Canada, Victoria, British Columbia. 127 pp.

Brooker, M. P. (1984). Biological surveillance in Welsh rivers for water quality and conservation assessment. In *Freshwater biological monitoring* (eds D. Pascoe and R. W. Edwards), pp. 25-33. International Association of Water Pollution Research and Control. Pergamon Press, Oxford.

Brooks, A. (1994). River channel change. In *The rivers handbook, Volume 2* (eds P. Calow & G. E. Petts), pp. 55-75. Blackwell Scientific Publications, Oxford.

Brown, A. V. & Brussock, P. P. (1991). Comparison of benthic invertebrates between riffles and pools. *Hydrobiologia* **220**, 99-108.

Bruns, D. A. & Minshall, G. W. (1985). River continuum relationships in an 8th-order river reach: analyses of polar ordination, functional groups, and organic matter parameters. *Hydrobiologia* **127**, 277-285.

Bruns, D. A., Hale, A. B. & Minshall, G. W. (1987). Ecological correlates of species richness in three guilds of lotic macroinvertebrates. *Journal of Freshwater Ecology* **4**, 163-177.

Bruns, D. A., Minshall, G. W. *et al.* (1982). Ordination of functional groups and organic matter parameters from the Middle Fork of Salmon River, Idaho. *Freshwater Invertebrate Biology* **1**, 2-12.

Brzeziecki, B., Kienast, F. & Wildi, O. (1995). Modelling potential impacts of climate change on the spatial distribution of zonal forest communities in Switzerland. *Journal of Vegetation Science* **6**, 257-258.

BS 5700 (1984). *British standards guide to process control using quality control chart methods and cusum techniques.* British Standards Institution, London.

BS EN 27828 (British Standard 1994). *Water quality. Methods for biological testing. Methods of biological sampling: guidance on handnet sampling of aquatic benthic macro-invertebrates.*

Bunn, S. E. (1995). Biological monitoring of water quality in Australia: workshop summary and future directions. *Australian Journal of Ecology* **20**, 220-227.

Cairns, J. Jr & Pratt, J. R. (1993). A history of biological monitoring using benthic macroinvertebrates. In *Freshwater biomonitoring and benthic macroinvertebrates* (eds D. M. Rosenberg & V. H. Resh), pp. 10-27. Chapman & Hall, New York.

Cairns, J. Jr & van der Schalie, W. H. (1980). Biological monitoring. Part 1 – Early warning systems. *Water Research* **14**, 1179-1196.

Canfield, T. J., Dwyer, F. J. *et al.* (1996). Assessing contamination in Great Lakes sediments using benthic invertebrate communities and sediment quality triad approach. *Journal of Great Lakes Research* **22**, 565-583.

Carleton, T. J., Stitt, R. H. & Nieppola, J. (1996). Constrained indicator species analysis (COINSPAN): an extension of TWINSPAN. *Journal of Vegetation Science* **7**, 125-130.

Carpenter, K. E. (1928). *Life in inland waters*. Sidgwick & Jackson, London.

Chandler, J. R. (1970). A biological approach to water quality management. *Water Pollution Control* **69**, 415-422.

Chapman, P. M. (1986). Sediment quality criteria from the sediment quality triad: an example. *Environmental Toxicology and Chemistry* **5**, 957-964.

Chapman, P. M. (1990). The sediment quality triad approach to determining pollution-induced degradation. *Science of the Total Environment* **97/98**, 815-825.

Cheng, J., Bell, D. A. & Liu, W. (1997). An algorithm for Bayesian belief network construction from data. In *Sixth international workshop on AI and statistics* (eds F. Golshani & K. Makki), pp. 325-331. Fort Lauderdale, Florida.

Chessman, B. C. (1995). Rapid assessment of rivers using macroinvertebrates: a procedure based on habitat-specific sampling, family level identification and a biotic index. *Australian Journal of Ecology* **20**, 122-129.

Chong, H. G. & Walley, W. J. (1996). Rule-based versus probabilistic approaches to the diagnosis of faults in wastewater processes. *Artificial Intelligence in Engineering* **10**, 265-273.

Clarke, R. T., Furse, M. T. & Wright, J. F. (1994). *Testing and further development of RIVPACS. Phase II: Aspects of robustness.* IFE interim report (R&D 243/7/Y) to the National Rivers Authority, Bristol. 117 pp.

Clarke, R. T., Cox, R. *et al.* (1997). *RIVPACS III + user manual. (River InVertebrate Prediction And Classification System with error assessments)*. July 1997. The Environment Agency, Bristol. 190 pp.

Clarke, R. T., Furse, M. T. *et al.* (1996). Derivation of a biological quality index for river sites: comparison of the observed with the expected fauna. *Journal of Applied Statistics* **23**, 311-332.

Clenaghan, C., Giller, P. S. *et al.* (1998). Stream macroinvertebrate communities in a conifer afforested catchment in Ireland: relationships to physico-chemical and biotic factors. *Freshwater Biology* **40**, 175-193.

Coffman, W. P. & Ferrington, L. C. J. (1996). Chironomidae. In *An introduction to the aquatic insects of North America, 3rd Edition* (eds R. W. Merritt & K. W. Cummins), pp. 635-754. Kendall/Hunt Publishing Company, Dubuque, Iowa.

Connell, J. H. (1978). Diversity in tropical rain forests and coral reefs. *Science* **199**, 1302-1310.

Cook, D. G. & Johnson, M. G. (1974). Benthic macroinvertebrates of the St. Lawrence Great Lakes. *Journal of the Fisheries Research Board of Canada* **31**, 763-782.

Corkum, L. D. & Currie, D. C. (1987). Distributional patterns of immature Simuliidae (Diptera) in northwestern North America. *Freshwater Biology* **17**, 201-221.

Cornell, H. V. & Lawton, J. H. (1992). Species interactions, local and regional processes, and limits to the richness of ecological communities: a theoretical perspective. *Journal of Animal Ecology* **61**, 1-12.

Council of the European Communities (1992). Council Directive 92/43/EEC of 21 May 1992 on the conservation of natural habitats and of wild fauna and flora. *Official Journal of the European Communities* **L206** (35), 369-385.

Council of the European Communities (1994). *Proposal for a Council Directive establishing the Ecological Quality of Water.* Draft Council Directive 93/C 222/06.DOCE 10-8-94, pp. 6-15.

Council of the European Union (1998). *Amended proposal for a Council Directive establishing a framework for a community action in the field of water policy 9265/98 ADDI.* DGI Interinstitutional File No. 97/0067 (SYN). ENV 258. PRO-COOP 92. Brussels, 9 June 1998. 88 pp.

Cox, R., Furse, M. T. *et al.* (1991). *RIVPACS II. A user manual.* Report to the National Rivers Authority, River Purification Boards and Department of the Environment (Northern Ireland). IFE River Laboratory, Wareham. 100 pp.

Crowder, B. (1995). *The wonders of the weather.* Australian Government Publishing Service. 270 pp.

Crunkilton, R. L. & Duchrow, R. M. (1991). Use of stream order and biological indexes to assess water quality in the Osage and Black River basins of Missouri. *Hydrobiologia* **224**, 155-166.

Cuffney, T. F., Gurtz, M. E. & Meador, M. R. (1993a). *Methods for collecting benthic invertebrate samples as part of the national water-quality assessment program.* United States Geological Survey, Report No. 93-104. 66 pp.

Cuffney, T. F., Gurtz, M. E. & Meador, M. R. (1993b). *Guidelines for the processing and quality assurance of benthic invertebrate samples collected as part of the national water-quality assessment program.* United States Geological Survey, Report No. 93-407. 80 pp.

Cullen, P. (1990). The turbulent boundary between water science and water management. *Freshwater Biology* **24**, 201-209.

Czekanowski, J. (1913). *Zarys metod statystycznych (The principles of statistics).* Warsaw Press, Warsaw. 422 pp.

Dauta, A. (1986). Modélisation du développement du phytoplankton dans une rivière canalisée eutrophe le Lot (France). *Annales de Limnologie* **22**, 119-132.

Davies, P. E. (1994). *River bioassessment manual. Monitoring River Health Initiative.* Department of the Environment, Sport and Territories, Land and Water Resources R&D Corporation, Commonwealth Environment Protection Agency, Canberra. 39 pp.

Davis, W. S. & Simon, T. P. (Editors) (1995). *Biological assessment and criteria. Tools for water resource planning and decision making.* Lewis Publishers, Boca Raton, Florida.

Davis, W. S., Snyder, B. D. *et al.* (1996). *Summary of state biological assessment programs for streams and rivers.* EPA 230-R-96-007. USEPA Office of Planning, Policy and Evaluation, Washington DC.

Day, K. E., Kirby, R. S. & Reynoldson, T. B. (1994). Sexual dimorphism in *Chironomus riparius* (Meigen): impact on interpretation of growth in whole sediment toxicity tests. *Environmental Toxicology and Chemistry* **13**, 35-39.

Dean, J. C. & Cartwright, D. I. (1987). Trichoptera of a Victorian forest stream: species composition and life histories. *Australian Journal of Marine and Freshwater Research* **38**, 845-860.

De Lange, L. & De Ruiter, M. A. (1977). *Biologische waterbeoordeling.* Instituut voor Milieuhygiëne en Gezondheidstechniek TNO, Delft. 251 pp.

Department of the Environment and Welsh Office (1986). *River quality in England and Wales 1985. A report of the 1985 survey.* HMSO, London. 42 pp.

Department of the Environment *et al.* (1994). *Biodiversity: the UK action plan.* Command 2428. HMSO, London. 187 pp.

DeShon, J. E. (1995). Development and application of the invertebrate community index (ICI).

In *Biological assessment and criteria. Tools for water resource planning and decision making* (eds W. S. Davis & T. P. Simon), pp. 217-243. Lewis Publishers, Boca Raton, Florida.

Dionne, M. & Karr, J. R. (1992). Ecological monitoring of fish assemblages in Tennessee River reservoirs. In *Ecological indicators, Volume 1,* (eds D. H. McKenzie, D. E. Hyatt & V. J. McDonald), pp. 259-281. Elsevier Applied Science, New York.

Dixit, S. S., Dixit, A. S. & Smol, J. P. (1989). Lake acidification recovery can be monitored using chrysophycean microfossils. *Canadian Journal of Fisheries and Aquatic Sciences* **46**, 1309-1312.

Docampo, L. (1995). Calidad ecológica del agua. Comparación del indice fisicoquímico de Prati con el índice "E" del estado ambiental de los ríos. *Tecnología del Agua* **144**, 85-97.

Dycus, D. H. & Meinert, D. H. (1993). Monitoring and evaluation of aquatic resource health and use suitability in Tennessee Valley Authority reservoirs. A report on Water Management (TVA/WM-93/15). Tennessee Valley Authority, Chattanooga, Tennessee.

Dymond, P. F. (1998). *Seasonal changes of benthic macroinvertebrate communities in southwestern British Columbia.* MSc thesis, University of British Columbia, Vancouver. 146 pp.

Dymond, P. F., Richardson, J. S. *et al.* (1997). Seasonal changes of benthic macroinvertebrate community structure and the implications for biomonitoring. Abstract of paper presented at the 45th Annual Meeting of the North American Benthological Society, San Marcos, Texas, 26-30 May, 1997. *Bulletin of the North American Benthological Society* **14**, 95.

Dynesius, M. & Nilsson, C. (1994). Fragmentation and flow regulation of river systems in the northern third of the world. *Science* **266**, 753-762.

Džeroski, S., Demšar, D. *et al.* (1997). Learning to infer chemical parameters of river water quality from bioindicator data. *Proceedings of the 6th Electrotechnical and Computer Science Conference ERK '97*, pp. 129-132. Slovenia Section IEEE, Ljubljana.

Džeroski, S., Grobović, J. *et al.* (1996). Using machine learning techniques in the construction of models: II. Data analysis and rule induction. *Ecological Modelling* **95**, 95-111.

Eagleson, K. W., Lenat, D. L. *et al.* (1990). Comparison of measured instream biological responses with responses predicted using the *Ceriodaphnia dubia* chronic toxicity test. *Environmental Toxicology and Chemistry* **9**, 1019-1028.

Eberhardt, L. L. (1978). Appraising variability in population studies. *Journal of Wildlife Management* **42**, 207-238.

Efron, B. & Tibshirani, R. (1993). *An introduction to the bootstrap.* Chapman & Hall, New York.

Ehnström, B., Gärdenfors, U. & Lindelöw, Å. (1993). *Rodlistade evertebrater i Sverige 1993.* Databanken för hotade arter SLU. (In Swedish).

Ellis, D. (1985). Taxonomic sufficiency in pollution assessment. *Marine Pollution Bulletin* **16**, 439.

Emery, E. B., Simon, T. P. & Ovies, R. (1998). Influence of the family Catostomidae on metrics developed for a Great Rivers index of biotic integrity. In *Assessing the sustainability and biological integrity of water resource quality using fish communities* (ed. T. P. Simon), pp. 203-224. CRC Press, Boca Raton, Florida.

Engle, V. D., Summers, J. K. & Gaston, G. R. (1994). A benthic index of environmental condition of Gulf of Mexico estuaries. *Estuaries* **17**, 372-384.

English Nature (1997). *Wildlife and freshwater. An agenda for sustainable development.* English Nature, Peterborough. 56 pp.

Environment Agency (1996). *Procedure for collecting and analysing macro-invertebrate samples for GQA surveys*. Quality Management Systems for Environmental Monitoring: Biological Techniques, BT002. Bristol, Environment Agency. 25 pp.

Environment Agency (1997a). *The quality of rivers and canals in England and Wales 1995*. Environment Agency, Bristol. 36 pp.

Environment Agency (1997b). *Procedures for collecting and analysing macro-invertebrate samples*. Quality Management Systems for Environmental Monitoring: Biological Techniques. BT001, Environment Agency, Bristol. 164 pp

Environment Agency (1999). *Procedure for quality assurance for RIVPACS compatible macro-invertebrate samples analysed to the taxonomic level needed for the BMWP-score system*. Quality Management Systems for Environmetal Monitoring: Biological Techniques. BT003, Environment Agency, Bristol. (In preparation).

Environment Canada (1995). *Fraser River Action Plan. Measuring the health of the river*. Environmental quality program. 1995 status report. Environment Canada, Vancouver, British Columbia. Government of Canada Cat. No. EN37-99/1-1995E. 28 pp.

Environmental Protection Agency (1995). *Water quality monitoring in Australia*. Aquatech Pty Ltd. Report prepared for the Australian Environmental Protection Agency, February 1995. 278 pp.

Extence, C. A., Bates, A. J. *et al.* (1987). Biologically based water quality management. *Environmental Pollution* **45**, 221-236.

Faith, D. P. & Norris, R. H. (1989). Correlation of environmental variables with patterns of distribution and abundance of common and rare freshwater macroinvertebrates. *Biological Conservation* **50**, 77-98.

Faith, D. P., Minchin, P. R. & Belbin, L. (1987). Compositional dissimilarity as a robust measure of ecological distance: a theoretical model and computer simulations. *Vegetatio* **69**, 57-68.

Farrell, D. H. (1993). Bioassessment in Florida. In *A proceedings: estuarine and near coastal bioassessment and biocriteria workshop, Annapolis, Maryland*, pp. 17-26. USEPA Office of Science and Technology, Washington DC.

Fausch, K. D., Lyons, J. *et al.* (1990). Fish communities as indicators of environmental degradation. In *Biological indicators of stress in fish* (ed. S. M. Adams), pp. 123-144. American Fisheries Society Symposium **8**, Bethesda, Maryland.

Fore, L. S., Karr, J. R. & Wisseman, R. W. (1996). Assessing invertebrate responses to human activities: evaluating alternative approaches. *Journal of the North American Benthological Society* **15**, 212-231.

Franklin, J. F. (1988). Structural and functional diversity in temperate forests. In *Biodiversity* (ed. E. O. Wilson), pp. 166-175. National Academy Press, Washington DC.

French, S. & Smith, J. Q. (1997). *The practice of Bayesian analysis*. Arnold, London.

Friberg, N., Kronvang, B. *et al.* (1998). Long-term habitat-specific response of a macroinvertebrate community to river restoration. *Aquatic Conservation: Marine and Freshwater Ecosystems* **8**, 87-99.

Furse, M. T. (1996). *The faunal richness of headwater streams. Stage 4 – development of a conservation strategy*. R&D Note 455, National Rivers Authority, Bristol. 89 pp.

Furse, M. T. (1997). *Operational mechanisms for the protection and enhancement of headwaters. Scoping study*. R&D Technical Report E25, Environment Agency, Bristol. 121 pp.

Furse, M. T. (1998). *The faunal richness of headwater streams*. Unpublished PhD thesis, University of Reading.

Furse, M. T., Clarke, R. T. *et al.* (1995). *Biological assessment methods: controlling the quality of biological data. Package 1. The variability of data used for assessing the biological condition of rivers.* R&D Note 412, Environment Agency, Bristol. 139 pp.

Furse, M. T., Moss, D. *et al.* (1984). The influence of seasonal and taxonomic factors on the ordination and classification of running-water sites in Great Britain and on the prediction of their macro-invertebrate communities. *Freshwater Biology* **14**, 257-280.

Furse, M. T., Moss, D. *et al.* (1986). *A practical manual for the classification and prediction of macroinvertebrate communities in running water in Great Britain.* Preliminary version, FBA River Laboratory, Wareham. 147 pp.

Furse, M. T., Symes, K. L. *et al.* (1995). *The faunal richness of headwater streams. Stage 3 – impact of agricultural activities.* R&D Note 392, National Rivers Authority, Bristol. 149 pp.

Furse, M. T., Winder, J. M. *et al.* (1991). *The faunal richness of headwater streams.* A preliminary report (R&D Document 08Y) to the National Rivers Authority by the IFE, R&D Project 242 (NRA publication reference P-96). National Rivers Authority, Bristol. 135 pp.

Furse, M. T., Winder, J. M. *et al.* (1993). *The faunal richness of headwater streams. Stage 2 – catchment studies.* R&D Note 221, National Rivers Authority, Bristol. 126 pp.

Furse, M. T., Wright, J. F. *et al.* (1981). An appraisal of pond-net samples for biological monitoring of lotic macro-invertebrates. *Water Research* **15**, 679-689.

Garcia de Jalón, D. & González del Tánago, M. (1980). *Estimación de la contaminación de las aguas mediante indicadores biológicos: aplicación al río Jarama.* Diputación Provincial de Madrid.

García de Jalón, D. & González del Tánago, M. (1986). *Métodos biológicos para el estudio de la calidad de las aguas. Aplicación a la cuenca del Duero.* ICONA, Monografia 45, Madrid. 244 pp.

Gauch, H. G. (1982). *Multivariate analysis in community ecology.* Cambridge University Press, Cambridge. 298 pp.

Gauch, H. G. & Whittaker, R. H. (1981). Hierarchical classification of community data. *Journal of Ecology* **69**, 537-557.

Gerritsen, J. (1995). Additive biological indices for resource management. *Journal of the North American Benthological Society* **14**, 451-457.

Gerritsen, J. & White, J. (1997). *Development of a biological index for Florida lakes.* Florida Department of Environmental Protection, Tallahassee, Florida.

Gerritsen, J., Carlson, R. E. *et al.* (1997). *Lake and reservoir bioassessment and biocriteria: technical guidance document.* USEPA Office of Water, Washington DC.

Ghetti, P. F. (1997). *Manuale di applicazione. Indice Biotico Esteso (I.B.E.). I macroinvertebrati nell controllo della qualità degli ambienti di acque correnti.* Provincia Autonoma di Trento. Agenzia Provinciale per la Protezione dell'Ambiente. Trento. 222 pp.

Ghetti, P. F., Bernini, F. *et al.* (1983). *Mappagio biologico di qualità dei corsi d'acqua della provincia di Piacenza.* Administrazione Provincia di Piacenza, CNR progetto finalizzato "Promozione della qualità dell'ambiente-progetto di transferismento". 29 pp.

Giarratano, J. & Riley, G. (1989). *Expert systems – principles and programming.* PWS-Kent, Boston.

Gibson, G. R., Barbour, M. T. *et al.* (1996). *Biological criteria: technical guidance for streams and small rivers (revised edition).* EPA 822-B-96-001. USEPA Office of Water, Washington DC.

Gibson, G. R., Bowman, M. L. *et al.* (1997). *Estuarine and coastal marine waters bioassessment and biocriteria technical guidance.* USEPA Office of Water, Washington DC.

Giles, N., Phillips, V. E. & Barnard, S. (1991). *The current crisis: ecological effects of low flows.* Royal Society for Nature Conservation, Lincoln. 34 pp.

Giller, P. S. & Twomey, H. (1993). Benthic macroinvertebrate community organization in two contrasting rivers – between-site differences and seasonal patterns. *Proceedings of the Royal Irish Academy – Biology and Environments* **93B**, 115-126.

Goedkoop, W., Johnson, R. K. & Spånberg, E. (1999). The importance of sampling methodology for the assessment of the ecological quality of Swedish inland waters using macroinvertebrates. *Verhandlungen der Internationalen Vereinigung für theoretische und angewandte Limnologie* **27** (in press).

González del Tánago, M. & García de Jalón, D. (1984). Desarrollo de un índice biológico para estimar la calidad de las aguas de la cuenca del Duero. *Limnética* **1**, 263-272.

González del Tánago, M., García de Jalón, D. & Elcoro, I. M. (1979a). Estudio sobre la fauna de macroinvertebrados de los ríos Cigüela, Záncara y Córcoles: aplicación de índices biológicos para el estudio de la calidad de las aguas. *Boletin de la Estación Central de Ecología*, ICONA **8**, 45-59.

González del Tánago, M., García de Jalón, D. & Elcoro, I. M. (1979b). Aplicación de algunos índices biológicos a diversos ríos españoles para la estimación de la calidad de sus aguas. *Técnica, Investigación y Tratamiento del Medio Ambiente* **1**, 28-38.

Gore, J. A. (1994). Hydrological change. In *The rivers handbook, Volume 2* (eds P. Calow & G. E. Petts), pp. 33-54. Blackwell Scientific Publications, Oxford.

Green, R. H. (1979). *Sampling design and statistical methods for environmental biologists.* John Wiley & Sons, New York.

Growns, J. E., Chessman, B. C. *et al.* (1997). Rapid assessment of Australian rivers using macroinvertebrates: cost and efficiency of 6 methods of sample processing. *Journal of the North American Benthological Society* **16**, 682-693.

Guisan, A., Theurillat, J.-P. & Kienast, F. (1998). Predicting the potential distribution of plant species in an alpine environment. *Journal of Vegetation Science* **9**, 65-74.

Haapala, A. & Muotka, T. (1998). Seasonal dynamics of detritus and associated macroinvertebrates in a channelized boreal stream. *Archiv für Hydrobiologie* **142**, 171-189.

Hafernik, J. E. (1992). Threats to invertebrate biodiversity: implications for conservation strategies. In *Conservation biology: the theory and practice of nature conservation, preservation and management* (eds P. L. Fiedler & S. K. Jain), pp. 171-195. Chapman & Hall, London.

Hanes, E. C., Ciborowski, J. J. H. & Corkum, L. D. (1990). Standardized rearing materials and procedures for *Hexagenia*, a benthic bioassay organism: comparison of sediment types. In *Proceedings 1990 Ontario Ministry of the Environment Technology Transfer Conference on environmental research* (ed. Anonymous), pp. 374-382. Toronto.

Hannaford, M. J. & Resh, V. H. (1995). Variability in macroinvertebrate rapid-bioassessment surveys and habitat assessments in a northern California stream. *Journal of the North American Benthological Society* **14**, 430-439.

Hannaford, M. J., Barbour, M. T. & Resh, V. H. (1997). Training reduces observer variability in visual-based assessments of stream habitat. *Journal of the North American Benthological Society* **16**, 853-860.

Hansen, H. O., Boon, P. J. *et al.* (Editors) (1998). *River restoration: the physical dimension.* Special issue of *Aquatic Conservation: Marine and Freshwater Ecosystems,* Volume **8** (1).

Harriman, R., Likens, G. E. *et al.* (1994). Influence of management practices in catchments on freshwater acidification: afforestation in the United Kingdom and North America. In *Acidification of freshwater ecosystems: implications for the future* (eds C. E. W. Steinberg & R. F. Wright), pp. 83-101. John Wiley & Sons, Chichester.

Hastings, A., Hom, C. L. *et al.* (1993). Chaos in ecology: is mother nature a strange attractor?

Annual Review of Ecology and Systematics **24**, 1-33.

Hawkes, H. A. (1975). River zonation and classification. In *River ecology. Studies in ecology, Volume 2* (ed. B. A. Whitton), 312-374. Blackwell Scientific Publications, Oxford.

Hawkes, H. A. (1998). Origin and development of the Biological Monitoring Working Party score system. *Water Research* **32**, 964-968.

Hawkins, C. P., Hogue, J. N. *et al.* (1997). Channel morphology, water temperature, and assemblage structure of stream insects. *Journal of the North American Benthological Society* **16,** 728-749.

Hawkins, C. P., Norris, R. H. *et al.* (2000). Development and evaluation of predictive models for assessing the biological integrity of streams. *Ecological Applications* (in press).

Hawking, J. & O'Connor, R. (1997). *Quality assurance of identifications for the MRHI State Territory bioassessment program*. Final report to Land and Water Resources Research and Development Corporation, (Reference No. MDR16), September 1997.

Haykin, S. (1994). *Neural networks: a comprehensive foundation*. Macmillan. New York and Toronto.

Heck, K. L., van Belle, G. & Simberloff, D. (1975). Explicit calculation of the rarefaction diversity measurement and the determination of sufficient sample size. *Ecology* **56**, 1459-1461.

Hellawell, J. M. (1978). *The biological surveillance of rivers; a biological monitoring handbook*. Water Research Centre, Stevenage. 333 pp.

Hellawell, J. M. (1986). *Biological indicators of freshwater pollution and environmental management*. Pollution Monitoring Series. Elsevier Applied Science, London & New York. 546 pp.

Henriksen, A., Skjelvåle, B. L. *et al.* (1998). Northern European lake survey 1995. *Ambio* **27**, 80-91.

Hewitt, G. (1991). River quality investigations, Part 1: Some diversity and biotic indices. *Journal of Biological Education* **25**, 44-52.

Hildrew, A. G. (1992). Food webs and species interactions. In *Rivers handbook. Hydrological and ecological principles, Volume 1* (eds P. Calow & G. E. Petts), pp. 309-330. Blackwell Scientific Publications, Oxford.

Hildrew, A. G. & Giller, P. S. (1994). Patchiness, species interactions and disturbance in the stream benthos. In *Aquatic ecology: scale, pattern and process* (eds P. S. Giller, A. G. Hildrew & D. G. Raffaelli), pp. 21-62. Symposia of the British Ecological Society. Blackwell Scientific Publications, Oxford.

Hill, M. O. (1979a). *TWINSPAN – A FORTRAN program for arranging multivariate data in an ordered two-way table by classification of the individuals and the attributes*. Ecology and Systematics, Cornell University, Ithaca, New York. 49 pp.

Hill, M. O. (1979b). *DECORANA – A FORTRAN program for detrended correspondence analysis and reciprocal averaging*. Ecology and Systematics, Cornell University, Ithaca, New York. 52 pp.

Hill, M. O. & Gauch, H. G. (1980). Detrended correspondence analysis: an improved ordination technique. *Vegetation* **42**, 47-58.

Hilsenhoff, W. L. (1988). Rapid field assessment of organic pollution with a family-level biotic index. *Journal of the North American Benthological Society* **7**, 65-68.

Hirschfeld, H. O. (1935). A connection between correlation and contingency. *Proceedings of the Cambridge Philosophical Society* **31**, 520-524.

Holme, N. A. & McIntyre, A. D. (1971). *Methods for the study of marine benthos*. IBP Handbook No. 16, Blackwell Scientific Publications, Oxford.

Holmes, N. T. H. (1989). British rivers – a working classification. *British Wildlife* **4**, 287-295.

Holmes, N. T. H., Boon, P. J. & Rowell, T. A. (1998). A revised classification system for British rivers based on their aquatic plant communities. *Aquatic Conservation: Marine and Freshwater Ecosystems* **8**, 555-578.

Hope, A. C. A. (1968). A simplified Monte Carlo significance test procedure. *Journal of the Royal Statistical Society (Series B)* **30**, 528-598.

Hotelling, H. (1933). Analysis of a complex of statistical variables into principal components. *Journal of Educational Psychology* **24**, 417-441.

Howard-Williams, C., Pickmere, S. & Davies, J. (1986). Nutrient retention and processing in New Zealand streams: the influence of riparian vegetation. *New Zealand Agricultural Science* **20**, 104-110.

Hughes, R. M. (1995). Defining acceptable biological status by comparing with reference conditions. In *Biological assessment and criteria. Tools for water resource planning and decision making* (eds W. S. Davis & T. P. Simon), pp. 31-47. Lewis Publishers, Boca Raton, Florida.

Hughes, R. M., Johnson, C. B. *et al.* (1993). Development of lake condition indicators for EMAP – 1991 pilot. In *EMAP – surface waters 1991 pilot report*, pp. 7-90. EPA-620-R-93-003. USEPA Office of Research and Development, Corvallis, Oregon.

Hughes, R. M., Whittier, T. R. *et al.* (1992). Lake and stream indicators for the United States Environmental Protection Agency's environmental monitoring and assessment program. In *Ecological Indicators, Volume 1*, pp. 305-335. Elsevier Applied Science, New York.

Humphrey, C. L. & Thurtell, L. (1997). External QA/QC of MRHI agency subsampling and sorting procedures. In *Development and implementation of QA/QC protocols for sample processing components of the MRHI agency bioassessment program*, (eds C. L. Humphrey, A. W. Storey & L. Thurtell). Final Report to Land and Water Resources R&D Corporation, Canberra (Reference No. ARR2), December 1997.

Humphrey, C. L., Storey, A. & Doig, L. (1997). Degree of temporal variability of macroinvertebrate communities in Australian streams. In *Temporal variability of macroinvertebrate communities in Australian streams: implications for the prediction and detection of environmental change* (ed. C. L. Humphrey). Final Report to Land and Water Resources R&D Corporation, Canberra (Reference No. ARRI), December 1997.

Hunsaker, C. T. & Carpenter, D. E. (Editors) (1990). *Ecological indicators for the environmental monitoring and assessment program*. EPA 600/3-90/060. USEPA Office of Research and Development, Research Triangle Park, North Carolina.

Hurlbert, S. H. (1984). Pseudoreplication and the design of ecological field experiments. *Ecological Monographs* **54**, 187-211.

Hynes, H. B. N. (1970). *The ecology of running waters*. Liverpool University Press, Liverpool. 555 pp.

Illies, J. & Botosaneanu, L. (1963). Problémes et méthodes de la classification et de la zonation écologique des eaux courantes, considerées surtout du point de vue faunistique. *Mitteilungen der Internationale Vereinigung für Limnologie*, **12**, 1-57.

International Union for Conservation of Nature and Natural Resources (1980). *World Conservation Strategy*. Gland.

Iversen, T. M., Kronvang, B. *et al.* (1993). Re-establishment of Danish streams: restoration and maintenance measures. *Aquatic Conservation: Marine and Freshwater Ecosystems* **3**, 73-92.

Jenkins, R. A., Wade, K. R. & Pugh, E. (1984). Macroinvertebrate–habitat relationships in the River Teifi catchment and the significance to conservation. *Freshwater Biology* **14**, 23-42.

Jenson, F. V. (1996). *An introduction to Bayesian networks*. UCL Press, London.

Johnson, R. K. (1995). The indicator concept in freshwater biomonitoring. Thienemann Lecture. In *Chironomids – from genes to ecosystems* (ed. P. S. Cranston), pp. 11-27. Proceedings of the 12th International Symposium on Chironomidae, Canberra, Australia. CSIRO, Melbourne.

Johnson, R. K. (1998). Spatio-temporal variability of temperate lake macroinvertebrate communities: detection of impact. *Ecological Applications* **8**, 61-70.

Johnson, R. K. & Wiederholm, T. (1989). Classification and ordination of profundal macroinvertebrate communities in nutrient poor, oligo-mesohumic lakes in relation to environmental data. *Freshwater Biology* **21**, 375-386.

Johnson, R. K., Söderbäck, B. & Eriksson, L. (1995). *Handbok för riksinventering av bottenfauna i sjöar och vattendrag*. Department of Environmental Assessment, Swedish University of Agricultural Sciences. Stencil, 22 pp.

Johnson, R. K., Wiederholm, T. & Rosenberg, D. M. (1993). Freshwater biomonitoring using individuals, organisms, populations, and species assemblages of benthic macrovertebrates. In *Freshwater biomonitoring and benthic invertebrates* (eds D. M. Rosenberg & V. H. Resh), pp. 40-158. Chapman & Hall, New York.

Jones, B. (1996). *Sleepers wake. Technology and the future of work*. Oxford University Press, Melbourne.

Jongman, R. H. G., Ter Braak, C. J. F. & Van Tongeren, O. F. R. (1987). *Data analysis in community and landscape ecology*. Pudoc, Wageningen. 299 pp.

Jordan, S., Carmichael, J. & Richardson, B. (1992). Habitat measurements and index of biotic integrity based on fish sampling in northern Chesapeake Bay. In *A proceedings: estuarine and near coastal bioassessment and biocriteria workshop*. Annapolis, Maryland. USEPA Office of Science and Technology, Washington DC.

Kansanen, P. K., Aho, J. & Paasivirta, L. (1984). Testing the benthic lake type concept based on chironomid associations in some Finnish lakes using multivariate statistical methods. *Annales Zoologici Fennici* **21**, 55-76.

Karr, J. R. (1981). Assessment of biotic integrity using fish communities. *Fisheries* **66**, 21-27.

Karr, J. R. (1991). Biological integrity: a long-neglected aspect of water resource management. *Ecological Applications* **1**, 66-84.

Karr, J. R. (1995). Protecting aquatic ecosystems: clean water is not enough. In *Biological assessment and criteria. Tools for water resource planning and decision making* (eds W. S. Davis & T. P. Simon), pp. 7-13. Lewis Publishers, Boca Raton, Florida.

Karr, J. R. & Dudley, D. R. (1981). Ecological perspectives on water quality goals. *Environmental Management* **5**, 55-68.

Karr, J. R., Fausch, K. D. *et al.* (1986). *Assessing biological integrity in running waters: a method and its rationale*. Special Publication 5. Illinois Natural History Survey.

Keough, M. J. & Mapstone, B. D. (1995). *Protocols for designing marine ecological monitoring programs associated with BEK mills*. National Pulp Mills Research Program, Technical Report No. 11. CSIRO, Canberra. 185 pp.

Kerans, B. L. & Karr, J. R. (1994). A benthic index of biotic integrity (B-IBI) for rivers of the Tennessee Valley. *Ecological Applications* **4**, 768-785.

Kerans, B. L., Karr, J. R. & Ahlstedt, S. A. (1992). Aquatic invertebrate assemblages: spatial and temporal differences among sampling protocols. *Journal of the North American Benthological Society* **11**, 377-390.

Kingsbury, P. D. (1986). Effects of an aerial application of the synthetic pyrethroid Permethrin on a forest stream. *Manitoba Entomologist* **10**, 9-17.

Kingston, J. C. & Birks, H. J. B. (1990). Dissolved organic carbon reconstructions from diatom assemblages in PIRLA project lakes, North America. *Philosophical Transactions of the Royal Society of London (Series B)* **327**, 279-288.

Kinley, R. D. & Ellis, J. C. (1991). *The application of statistical quality control methods to macroinvertebrate sampling.* Unpublished Report for Thames Region, National Rivers Authority. WRC Report No. CO 2905. Water Research Centre, Medmenham.

Klecka, W. R. (1975). Discriminant analysis. In *SPSS. Statistical package for social sciences* (eds N. H. Nie, C. H. Hull *et al.*), pp. 434-467. McGraw-Hill, New York.

Knoben, R. A. E., Roos, C. & van Oirschot, M. C. M. (1995). *Biological assessment methods for watercourses.* UN/ECE Task Force on Monitoring and Assessment, 86 pp.

Kohonen, T. (1997). *Self-organizing maps.* 2nd edition. Springer-Verlag, Berlin.

Kruskal, J. B. (1964). Nonmetric multidimensional scaling: a numerical method. *Psychometrika* **29**, 115-129.

Kubo, T., Inoue, S. *et al.* (1975). Productivity of biotic communities in the Yurappu River. In *Productivity of communities in Japanese inland waters, Volume 10* (eds S. Mori & G. Yamamoto), pp. 287-338. University of Tokyo Press, Tokyo.

Laasonen, P., Muotka, T. & Kivijärvi, I. (1998). Recovery of macroinvertebrate communities from stream habitat restoration. *Aquatic Conservation: Marine and Freshwater Ecosystems* **8**, 101-113.

Ladle, M. & Bass, J. A. B. (1975). A new species of *Metacnephia* Crosskey (Diptera: Simuliidae) from the south of England, with notes on its habitat and biology. *Hydrobiologia* **47**, 193-207.

Lake, P. S. (1995). Of floods and droughts: river and stream ecosystems of Australia. In *Ecosystems of the world 22, river and stream ecosystems* (eds C. E. Cushing, K. W. Cummins & G. W. Minshall), pp. 659-694. Elsevier, Amsterdam.

Land and Water Resources Research and Development Commission (LWRRDC) (1997). *The third monitoring river health initiative (MRHI) bioassessment workshop.* Summary of proceedings. Land and Water Resources R&D Corporation, Canberra.

Lauritzen, S. L. & Spiegelhalter, D. J. (1988). Local computations with probabilities on graphical structures and their application to expert systems. *Journal of the Royal Statistical Society* **50**, 157-224.

Lenat, D. R. (1983). Benthic macroinvertebrates of Cane Creek, North Carolina, and comparisons with other southeastern streams. *Brimleyana* **9**, 53-68.

Lenat, D. R. (1987). The macroinvertebrate fauna of the Little River, North Carolina: taxa list and seasonal trends. *Archiv für Hydrobiologia* **110**, 19-43.

Leopold, L. B., Wolman, M. G. & Miller, J. P. (1964). *Fluvial processes in geomorphology.* Freeman & Co., San Francisco and London.

Little, W., Fowler, H. W. & Coulson, J. (1959). *The shorter Oxford English dictionary*, 3rd edition. The Clarendon Press, Oxford.

Lonergan, S. P. & Rasmussen, J. B. (1996). A multi-taxonomic indicator of acidification: isolating the effects of pH from other water-chemistry variables. *Canadian Journal of Fisheries and Aquatic Science* **53**, 1778-1787.

Long, E. R. & Chapman, P. M. (1985). A sediment quality triad: measures of sediment contamination, toxicity and infaunal community composition in Puget Sound. *Marine Pollution Bulletin* **16**, 405-415.

Lyons, J., Wang, L. & Simonson, T. D. (1996). Development and validation of an index of biotic integrity for coldwater streams in Wisconsin. *North American Journal of Fisheries Management* **16**, 241-256.

Macan, T. T. (1961). A review of running water studies. *Verhandlungen der Internationale Vereinigung für theoretische und angewandte Limnologie*, **14**, 587-602.

Macan, T. T. & Macan, Z. (1940). Preliminary notes on the Ephemeroptera and Plecoptera of the Hampshire Avon and its tributaries. *Society of British Entomology* **2**, 53-61.

Mahanalobis, P. C. (1936). On the generalized distance in statistics. *Proceedings of the National Institute of Science, India* **2**, 49-55.

Maitland, P. S. (1977). *A coded checklist of animals occurring in fresh water in the British Isles*. Institute of Terrestrial Ecology, Edinburgh. 76 pp.

Maitland, P. S. (1979). *Synoptic limnology, the analysis of British freshwater ecosystems*. Institute of Terrestrial Ecology, Edinburgh. 28 pp.

Manley, B. F. J. (1994). *Multivariate statistical methods – a primer*. Second edition. Chapman & Hall, New York.

Marchant, R. (1989). A subsampler for samples of benthic invertebrates. *Bulletin of the Australian Society of Limnology* **12**, 49-52.

Marchant, R., Barmuta, L. & Chessman, B. C. (1995). A preliminary study of the ordination and classification of macroinvertebrate communities from running waters in Victoria, Australia. *Australian Journal of Marine and Freshwater Research* **45**, 945-962.

Marchant, R., Hirst, A. *et al.* (1997). Classification and prediction of macroinvertebrate communities from running waters in Victoria, Australia. *Journal of the North American Benthological Society* **16**, 664-681.

Margalef, R. (1958). Trophic typology versus biotic typology, as exemplified in the regional limnology of Northern Spain. *Verhandlungen der Internationalen Vereinigung für theoretische und angewandte Limnologie* **13**, 339-349.

May, R. M. (1984). An overview: real and apparent patterns in community structure. In *Ecological communities* (eds D. R. Strong Jr, Simberloff, D. L. G. *et al.*), pp. 3-18. Princeton University Press, Princeton.

McMahon, T. A. (1979). *Hydrological characteristics of Australian streams*. Civil Engineering Research Report 3. Monash University, Melbourne.

McMahon, T. A., Finlayson, B. L. *et al.* (1992). *Global run-off. Continental comparisons of annual flows and peak discharges*. Catena Verlag: Cremlingen Destedt.

Metcalfe, J. L. (1989). Biological water quality assessment of running waters based on macroinvertebrate communities: history and present status in Europe. *Environmental Pollution* **60**, 101-139.

Metzeling, L. & Chessman, B. (1996). *Evaluation of rapid biological assessment for RIVPACS modelling*. Final report to the Land and Water Resources R&D Corporation, Canberra (Reference No. AWT5/EPV2).

Mingo, J. (1980). *Indices de calidad del agua*. Ministerio de Obras Públicas (MOPU). Madrid.

Minshall, G. W., Petersen, R. C. & Nimz, C. F. (1985). Species richness in streams of different size from the same drainage basin. *The American Naturalist* **125**, 16-38.

Minshall, G. W., Petersen, R. C. *et al.* (1983). Interbiome comparisons of stream ecosystem dynamics. *Ecological Monographs* **53**, 1-25.

Moller-Pillot, H. K. M. (1971). *Faunistische beoordeling van de verontreingde laaglandbeken*. Thesis, Katholieke Universiteit Nijmegan, Tilburg. 286 pp.

Moog, O. (Editor) (1995). *Fauna aquatica Austriaca*. Version 1995. Wasserwirtschaftskataster. Bundesministerium für Land- und Forstwirtschaft, Wien.

Moss, D., Furse, M. T. *et al.* (1987). The prediction of the macro-invertebrate fauna of unpolluted running-water sites in Great Britain using environmental data. *Freshwater Biology* **17**, 41-52.

Moss, D., Wright, J. F. *et al.* (1999). A comparison of alternative techniques for prediction of the fauna of running-water sites in Great Britain. *Freshwater Biology* **41**, 167-181.

Murphy, P. M. (1978). The temporal variability in biotic indices. *Environmental Pollution* **17**, 227-236.

Murray-Bligh, J. A. D., Furse, M. T. *et al.* (1997). *Procedure for collecting and analysing macroinvertebrate samples for RIVPACS*. Environment Agency, Bristol and IFE, Wareham.

National Rivers Authority (1990). *RIVPACS field sampling. Pond-net sampling.* Video recording produced by Spectrum Communication, Birmingham. National Rivers Authority, Reading.

National Water Council (1978). *River water quality, the next stage.* NWC, London. 10 pp.

National Water Council (1981). *River quality: the 1980 survey and future outlook.* NWC, London. 39 pp.

Nature Conservancy Council (1989). *Guidelines for selection of biological SSSIs.* NCC, Peterborough.

Neapolitan, R. E. (1990). *Probabilistic reasoning in expert systems.* John Wiley & Sons, New York.

Nicholls, A. O. (1989). How to make biological models go further with Generalized Linear Models. *Biological Conservation* **50**, 51-75.

Nielsen, M. B. (1996). River restoration: report of a major EU Life demonstration project. *Aquatic Conservation: Marine and Freshwater Ecosystems* **6**, 187-190.

Norris, R. H. (1994). Rapid biological assessment, natural variability and selecting reference sites. Classification of rivers and environmental health indicators. In *Proceedings of a joint South African/Australian workshop, Cape Town, South Africa* (ed. M. C. Uys), pp. 129-166. Water Research Commission, Report No. TT/63/94.

Norris, R. H. (1995). Biological monitoring: the dilemma of data analysis. *Journal of North American Benthological Society* **14**, 440-450.

Norris, R. H. (1996). Predicting water quality using reference conditions and associated communities. In *Study design and data analysis in benthic macroinvertebrate assessments of freshwater ecosystems using a reference site approach* (eds R. C. Bailey, R. H. Norris & T. B. Reynoldson), pp. 32-52. Technical Information Workshop, North American Benthological Society, 44th Annual Meeting, Kalispell, Montana.

Norris, R. H. & Georges, A. (1986). Design and analysis for assessment of water quality. In *Limnology in Australia* (eds P. De Decker & W. D. Williams), pp. 555-572. CSIRO, Melbourne and Junk Publishers, Dordrecht.

Norris, R. H. & Georges, A. (1993). Analysis and interpretation of benthic macroinvertebrate surveys. In *Freshwater biomonitoring and benthic macroinvertebrates* (eds D. M. Rosenberg & V. H. Resh), pp. 234-286. Chapman and Hall, New York.

Norris, R. H. & Norris, K. R. (1995). The need for biological assessment of water quality: Australian perspective. *Australian Journal of Ecology* **20**, 1-6.

Norris, R. H., Hart, B. & Bell, B. C. (1993). *Core indicators for biological assessment of river health*. Consultancy Report for the Monitoring River Health Initiative. Commonwealth Environment Protection Agency, Canberra. 20 pp.

North West Water (1982). *The use of biological data in river quality classification.* Unpublished report TS/BS/82-1. Technical Support Group, Scientists Dept., Rivers Division.

Noss, R. F. (1990). Indicators for monitoring biodiversity: a hierarchical approach. *Conservation Biology* **4**, 355-364.

Odum E. P. (1971). *Fundamentals of ecology.* Saunders Company, Philadelphia. 574 pp.

Odum, E. P. (1985). Trends expected in stressed ecosystems. *Bioscience* **35**, 419-422.

Ohio Environmental Protection Agency (Ohio EPA) (1987). *Biological criteria for the protection of aquatic life, Volumes I-III.* Ohio EPA, Columbus, Ohio.

Ohio EPA (1997). *1996 Ohio water resource inventory (305b report), Volume I: summary, status and trends.* OEPA Tech. Bull. MAS/1996-10-3. Division of Surface Water, Columbus, Ohio. 198 pp.

Økland, R. H. (1996). Are ordination and constrained ordination alternative or complementary strategies in general ecological studies? *Journal of Vegetation Science* **7**, 289-292.

Oksanen, J. & Minchin, P. R. (1997). Instability of ordination results under changes in input data order: explanations and remedies. *Journal of Vegetation Science* **8**, 447-454.

Omernik, J. M. (1995). Ecoregions: a spatial framework for environmental management. In *Biological assessment and criteria. Tools for water resource planning and decision making* (eds W. S. Davis & T. P. Simon), pp. 49-62. Lewis Publishers, Boca Raton, Florida.

Omernik, J. M. & Bailey, R. G. (1997). Distinguishing between watersheds and ecoregions. *Journal of the American Water Resources Association* **33**, 935-949.

Ontario Ministry of Environment (1990). *The Canadian Great Lakes basin intake outfall atlas* (8 volumes) (ed. M. Griffiths). Water Resources Branch, Toronto, Ontario.

Ormerod, S. J. (1987). The influences of habitat and seasonal sampling regimes on the ordination and classification of macroinvertebrate assemblages in the catchment of the River Wye, Wales. *Hydrobiologia* **15**, 143-151.

Ormerod, S. J. & Edwards, R. W. (1987). The ordination and classification of macroinvertebrate assemblages in the catchment of the River Wye in relation to environmental factors. *Freshwater Biology* **17**, 533-546.

Ormerod, S. J., Donald, A. P. & Brown, S. J. (1989). The influence of plantation forestry on the pH and aluminium concentration of upland Welsh streams: a re-examination. *Environmental Pollution* **62**, 47-62.

Ormerod, S. J., Rundle, S. D. *et al.* (1993). The influence of riparian management on the habitat structure and macro-invertebrate communities of upland streams draining plantation forests. *Journal of Applied Ecology* **30**, 13-24.

Ormerod, S. J., Rundle, S. D. *et al.* (1994). Altitudinal trends in the diatoms, bryophytes, macroinvertebrates and fish of a Nepalese river system. *Freshwater Biology* **32**, 309-322.

Osborne, L. L., Davies, R. W. & Linton, K. J. (1980). Use of hierarchical diversity indices in lotic community analysis. *Journal of Applied Ecology* **17**, 567-580.

Painter, S. (1992). *Regional variability in sediment background metal concentrations and the Ontario sediment quality guidelines.* NWRI Report No. 92-85. Environment Canada, Burlington, Ontario.

Palau, A. (1990). Sobre la utilización de índices de calidad del agua. *Tecnología del Agua* **71**, 24-32.

Palau, A. & Palomes, A. (1985). *Diagnóstico físico-químico y biológico del río Segre.* Departamento de Ciencias del Suelo y Departamento de Microbiologia. Escuela Técnica Superior de Ingenieros Agrícolas, Lérida. 500 pp.

Palau, A. & Palomes, A. (1986). Los macroinvertebrados bentónicos como elementos de juicio para la evaluación de la calidad biológica del Rio Segre (Lérida, EN España). *Limnética* **2**, 205-215.

Palmer, C., Palmer, A. *et al.* (1994). Macroinvertebrate community structure and altitudinal changes in the upper reaches of a warm, temperate Southern African river. *Freshwater Biology* **32**, 337-347.

Pardo, I. (1992). *Estudio comparado de la macrofauna bentónica (ambientes lóticos) de los ríos Louro y Tea (Pontevedra).* Tesis doctoral, Universidad de Santiago de Compostela. 443 pp.

Pardo, I. & Armitage, P. D. (1997). Species assemblages as descriptors of mesohabitats. *Hydrobiologia* **344**, 111-128.

Parsons, M. & Norris, R. H. (1996). The effect of habitat-specific sampling on biological assessment of water quality using a predictive model. *Freshwater Biology* **36**, 419-434.

Pearl, J. (1988). *Probabilistic reasoning in intelligent systems: network of plausible inference.* Morgan Kaufmann. San Mateo, California.

Pearson, R. G., Benson, L. J. & Smith, R. E. W. (1986). Diversity and abundance of the fauna in Yuccabine creek, a tropical rainforest stream. In *Limnology in Australia* (eds P. de Dekker & W. D. Williams), pp. 329-342. CSIRO, Melbourne and Junk Publishers, Dordrecht.

Peet, R. K. (1980). Ordination as a tool for analyzing complex data sets. *Vegetatio* **42**, 171-174.

Pennak, R. W. (1971). Towards a classification of lotic habitats. *Hydrobiologia* **38**, 321-324.

Perry, J. A. (1994). Water quality in the 21st century: proactive management at the ecosystem level. *Limnética* **10**, 5-13.

Persoone, G. (1979). Proposal for a biotypological classification of watercourses in the European communities. *Biological Indicators of Water Quality* **7**, 17-32.

Pettigrove, V. (1990). The importance of site selection in monitoring the macroinvertebrate communities of the Yarra River, Victoria. *Environmental Monitoring and Assessment* **14**, 297-313.

Plafkin, J. L., Barbour, M.T. *et al.* (1989). *Rapid bioassessment protocols for use in streams and rivers. Benthic macroinvertebrates and fish.* EPA 440-4-89-001. USEPA Office of Water Regulations and Standards, Washington DC.

Polls, I. (1994). How people in the regulated community view biological integrity. *Journal of the North American Benthological Society* **13**, 598-604.

Prat, N., Munét, T. & Rieradevall, M. (1997). *La calidad ecológica de las aguas.* Dentro de un seminario sobre bioindicación y calidad de las aguas, Universidad del Valle, Cali, Colombia, Febrero 1997.

Prat, N., Puig, M. A. & González, G. (1983). *Predicció i control de la qualitat de les aigües dels rius Besòs i Llobregat. II. El poblament faunístic i la seva relació amb la qualitat de les aigües.* Estudis i Mongrafies Servei del Medi Ambient Diputació de Barcelona, 9, 1-164.

Prat, N., Rieradevall, M. & Munét, T. (1996). *La qualitat ecològica del Besòs i el Llobregat. Estudis de la qualitat ecològica dels rius: I (Informe 1994-1995).* Area del Medi Ambient de la Diputació de Barcelona.

Prentice, I. C. & Helmisaari, H. (1991). Silvics of north European trees: compilation, comparisons and implications for forest succession modeling. *Forest Ecology and Management* **42**, 79-93.

Preston, F. W. (1962). The canonical distribution of commonness and rarity: part 1. *Ecology* **43**, 185-215.

Pujante, A. (1993). *Macroinvertebrados y calidad de aguas de los ríos de la Comunidad Valenciana.* PhD Thesis, Universitat de València. 239 pp.

Pujante, A. M., Furse, M. T. *et al.* (2000). The performance of a British predictive technique (RIVPACS) in some Mediterranean rivers of Spain. (In preparation).

Queralt, R., Godé, L. X. *et al.* (1995). Indice automático de calidad de aguas. Un nuevo índice para aplicar a la red automática de control de aguas. *Tecnología del Agua* **143**, 17-24.

Quinn, J. M., Williamson, R. B. *et al.* (1992). Effects of riparian grazing and channelisation on streams in Southland. 2. Benthic invertebrates. *New Zealand Journal of Marine and Freshwater Research* **26**, 259-273.

Ratcliffe, D. A. (Editor) (1977). *A nature conservation review.* Cambridge University Press, Cambridge.

Raven, P. J., Fox, P. *et al.* (1997). River Habitat Survey: a new system for classifying rivers according to their habitat quality. In *Freshwater quality: defining the indefinable?* (eds P. J. Boon & D. L. Howell), pp. 215-234. The Stationery Office, Edinburgh.

Raven, P. J., Holmes, N. T. H. *et al.* (1998). Quality assessment using River Habitat Survey data. *Aquatic Conservation: Marine and Freshwater Ecosystems* **8**, 477-499.

Renberg, I., Korsman, T. & Birks, H. J. B. (1993). Prehistoric increases in the pH of acid-sensitive Swedish lakes caused by land-use changes. *Nature* **362**, 824-826.

Resh, V. H. (1995). The use of benthic macroinvertebrates and rapid assessment procedures for water quality monitoring in developing and newly industrialized countries. In *Biological assessment and criteria. Tools for water resource planning and decision making* (eds W. S. Davis & T. P. Simon), pp. 167-177. Lewis Publishers, Boca Raton, Florida.

Resh, V. H. & Jackson, J. K. (1993). Rapid assessment approaches to biomonitoring using benthic macroinvertebrates. In *Freshwater biomonitoring and benthic macroinvertebrates* (eds D. M. Rosenberg & V. H. Resh), pp. 195-233. Chapman & Hall, New York.

Resh, V. H. & McElravy, E. P. (1993). Contemporary quantitative approaches to biomonitoring using benthic macroinvertebrates. In *Freshwater biomonitoring and benthic macroinvertebrates* (eds D. M. Rosenberg & V. H. Resh), pp. 159-194. Chapman & Hall, New York.

Resh, V. H. & Unzicker, J. D. (1975). Water quality monitoring and aquatic organisms: the importance of species identification. *Journal of Water Pollution Control Federation* **47**, 9-19.

Resh, V. H. & Yamamoto, D. M. (1994). International collaboration in freshwater ecology. *Freshwater Biology* **23**, 613-624.

Resh, V. H., Norris, R. H. & Barbour, M. T. (1995). Design and implementation of rapid assessment approaches for water resource assessments. *Australian Journal of Ecology* **20**, 108-121.

Reynolds, C. S. (1996). The threat of algal blooms in proposed estuarine barrages: models, predictions, risks. In *Barrages: engineering design and environmental impacts* (eds N. Burt & J. Watts), pp. 83-89. John Wiley & Sons, Chichester.

Reynolds, C. S. & Glaister, M. S. (1993). Spatial and temporal changes in phytoplankton abundance in the upper and middle reaches of the River Severn. *Archiv für Hydrobiologie, Supplement* **101**, 1-22.

Reynolds, C. S. & Irish, A. E. (1997). Modelling phytoplankton dynamics in lakes and reservoirs: the problem of *in-situ* growth rates. *Hydrobiologia* **349**, 5-17.

Reynoldson, T. B. & Rosenberg, D. M. (1996). Sampling strategies and practical considerations in building reference data bases for the prediction of invertebrate community structure. In *Study design and data analysis in benthic macroinvertebrate assessments of freshwater ecosystems using a reference site approach* (eds R. C. Bailey, R. H. Norris & T. B. Reynoldson), pp. 1-31. Technical Information Workshop, North American Benthological Society, 44th Annual Meeting. Kalispell, Montana.

Reynoldson, T. B. & Zarull, M. A. (1993). An approach to the development of biological sediment guidelines. In *Ecological integrity and the management of ecosystems* (eds G. Francis, J. Kay & S. Woodley), pp 177-200. St Lucie Press, Florida.

Reynoldson, T. B., Day, K. E. & Pascoe, T. (1997). A summary report on biological sediment guidelines for the Laurentian Great Lakes. NWRI Report No. 97-134. 39 pp.

Reynoldson, T. B., Thompson, S. P. & Bamsey, J. L. (1991). A sediment bioassay using the tubificid oligochaete worm *Tubifex tubifex*. *Environmental Toxicology and Chemistry* **10**, 1061-1072.

Reynoldson, T. B., Bailey, R. C. *et al.* (1995). Biological guidelines for freshwater sediment based on BEnthic Assessment of SedimenT (the BEAST) using a multivariate approach for predicting biological state. *Australian Journal of Ecology* **20**, 198-219.

Reynoldson, T. B., Norris, R. H. *et al.* (1997). The reference condition: a comparison of multimetric and multivariate approaches to assess water-quality impairment using benthic macroinvertebrates. *Journal of the North American Benthological Society* **16**, 833-852.

Rheinhardt, R. D., Rheinhardt, M. C. *et al.* (1998). Forested wetlands of low order streams in the inner coastal plain of North Carolina, USA. *Wetlands* **18**, 365-378.

Richards, C. & Minshall, G. W. (1992). Spatial and temporal trends in stream macroinvertebrate communities – the influence of catchment disturbance. *Hydrobiologia* **241**, 173-184.

Richardson, J. S. & Healey, M. C. (1996). A healthy Fraser River? How will we know when we achieve this state? *Journal of Aquatic Ecosystem Health* **5**, 107-115.

Rico, E., Rallo, A. *et al.* (1992). Comparison of several biological indices based on river macroinvertebrate benthic community for assessment of running water quality. *Annales de Limnologie* **28**, 147-156.

Rogers, K. H. & Bestbier, R. (1997). *Development of a protocol for the definition of the desired state of riverine systems in South Africa*. Department of Environmental Affairs and Tourism, Pretoria.

Rohani, P. & Miramontes, O. (1996). Chaos or quasiperiodicity in laboratory insect populations? *Journal of Animal Ecology* **65**, 847-849.

Rosenberg, D. M. & Resh, V. H. (1993a). Introduction to freshwater biomonitoring and benthic macroinvertebrates. In *Freshwater biomoitoring and benthic invertebrates* (eds D. M. Rosenberg & V. H. Resh), pp. 1-9. Chapman & Hall, London and New York.

Rosenberg, D. M. & Resh, V. H. (Editors) (1993b). *Freshwater biomonitoring and benthic macroinvertebrates*. Chapman & Hall, London and New York. 488 pp.

Rosenberg, D. M. & Resh, V. H. (1996). Use of aquatic insects in biomonitoring. In *An introduction to the aquatic insects of North America, 3rd Edition* (eds R. W. Merritt & K. W. Cummins), pp. 87-97. Kendall/Hunt, Dubuque, Iowa.

Rosenberg, D. M., Reynoldson, T. B. & Resh, V. H. (2000). *Establishing reference conditions for benthic invertebrate monitoring in the Fraser River catchment, British Columbia, Canada*. Report submitted to the Fraser River Action Plan. Environment Canada, Vancouver, British Columbia. (In review).

Rosenberg, D. M., Davies, I. J. *et al.* (1977). Ecological Monitoring and Assessment Network (EMAN) protocol for measuring biodiversity: benthic macroinvertebrates in fresh waters. EMAN Office, Environment Canada, Burlington, Ontario [EMAN website: www.cciw.ca/eman-temp/intro.html].

Rosser, Z. C. & Pearson, R. G. (1995). Responses of rock fauna to physical disturbance in two Australian tropical rainforest streams. *Journal of the North American Benthological Society* **14**, 183-196.

Roth, N. E., Allan, J. D. & Erickson, D. L. (1996). Landscape influences on stream biotic integrity assessed at multiple spatial scales. *Landscape Ecology* **11**, 141-156.

Royal Commission on Environmental Pollution (1992). *Sixteenth report: freshwater quality*. HMSO, London. 291 pp.

Ruck, B. M. (1995). *The application of artificial neural networks to the interpretation and classification of freshwater benthic invertebrate communities*. Unpublished PhD thesis, Aston University, Birmingham.

Ruck, B. M., Walley, W. J. & Reynoldson, T. B. (1993). A neural network predictor of benthic community structures in the Canadian Waters of the Laurentian Great Lakes. In *Water pollution II: modelling, measuring and prediction* (eds L. C. Wrobel & C. A. Brebbia), pp.

287-294. Computational Mechanics Publications.

Rushton, S. P. (1987). A multivariate approach to the assessment of terrestrial sites for conservation. In *The use of invertebrates in site assessment for conservation. Proceedings of a meeting held at the University of Newcastle upon Tyne, 7 January 1987* (ed. M. L. Luff), pp. 62-75. Agricultural Environment Research Group, University of Newcastle upon Tyne.

Rutt, G. P., Pickering, T. D. & Reynolds, N. R. M. (1993). The impact of livestock-farming on Welsh streams: the development and testing of a rapid biological method for use in the assessment and control of organic pollution from farms. *Environmental Pollution* **81**, 217-228.

Rutt, G. P., Weatherley, N. S. & Ormerod, S. J. (1989). Microhabitat availability in Welsh moorland and forest streams as a determinant of macroinvertebrate distribution. *Freshwater Biology* **22**, 247-261.

Rutt, G. P., Weatherley, N. S. & Ormerod, S. J. (1990). Relationships between the physico-chemistry and macroinvertebrates of British upland streams: the development of modelling and indicator systems for predicting fauna and detecting acidity. *Freshwater Biology* **24**, 463-480.

Ryder, R. A. & Edwards, C. J. (Editors) (1985). *A conceptual approach for the application of biological indicators of ecosystem quality.* Great Lakes Science Advisory Board, International Joint Commission and Great Lakes Fishery Commission, Windsor, Ontario, Canada. 169 pp.

Sanz, S. & Pinkster, S. (2000). Biogeographical patterns of epigean amphipods in the Eastern Iberian Peninsula with description of a new species, *Echinogammarus baeticus*. *Contributions to Zoology* (in press).

SAS (Statistical Analysis System) Institute (1995). *SAS/STAT guide for personal computers, version 6.11*. SAS Institute, Carey, North Carolina.

Savage, N. L. & Rabe, F. W. (1979). Stream types in Idaho: an approach to classification of streams in natural areas. *Biological Conservation* **15**, 301-315.

Schluter, D. & Ricklefs, R. E. (1993). Species diversity: an introduction to the problem. In *Species diversity in ecological communities* (eds R. E. Ricklefs & D. Schluter), pp. 1-10. University of Chicago Press, Chicago.

Schofield, N. J. & Davies, P. E. (1996). Measuring the health of our rivers. *Water* **May/June 1996**, 39-43.

Scott, D., White, J. W. *et al.* (1994). Invertebrate fauna of three streams in relation to land use in Southland, New Zealand. *New Zealand Journal of Marine and Freshwater Research* **28**, 277-290.

Scrimgeour, G. J. & Wicklum, D. (1996). Aquatic ecosystem health and integrity: problems and potential solutions. *Journal of the North American Benthological Society* **15**, 254-261.

SEPA (Swedish Environmental Protection Agency) (1990a). *Då. Nu. Sedan – En resultat – och framtidesanalys av milöarbetet*. Naturvårdsverket Informerar. 63 pp. (In Swedish).

SEPA (Swedish Environmental Protection Agency) (1990b). *Miljöövervakningen inför 2000-talet*. Naturvardsverket Rapport. 41 pp. (In Swedish).

Shafer, G. & Pearl, J. (1990). *Readings in uncertain reasoning*. Morgan Kaufmann, San Mateo, California.

Shannon, C. E. & Weaver, W. (1949). *The mathematical theory of communication*. University of Illinois Press.

Shirt, D. B. (Editor) (1987). *British red data books. 2. Insects*. Nature Conservancy Council, Peterborough.

Sibley, P. K., Kaushik, N. K. & Kreutzweiser, D. P. (1991). Impact of a pulse application of Permethrin on the macroinvertebrate community of a headwater stream. *Environmental Pollution* **70**, 35-55.

Simons, D. B. (1979). Effects of stream regulation on channel morphology. In *The ecology of regulated streams* (eds J. V. Ward & J. A. Stanford), pp. 95-111. Plenum Press, New York.

Simpson, E. H. (1949). Measurement of diversity. *Nature, London* **163**, 688.

Simpson, J. C. (1995). *The effect of subsampling method on the efficiency, accuracy and precision of a predictive model for the assessment of aquatic ecosystem health.* Unpublished thesis, University of Canberra.

Simpson, J. C., Norris, R. H. *et al.* (1997). AusRivAS Web page
[http://ausrivas.canberra.edu.au/ausrivas].

Sivaramakrishnan, K. G., Hannaford, M. J. & Resh, V. H. (1996). Biological assessment of the Kaveri River catchment, South India: applicability of water quality monitoring approaches developed in other countries. *International Journal of Ecology and Environmental Sciences* **22**, 113-132.

Smith, C. M. (1992). Riparian afforestation effects on water yields and water-quality in pasture catchments. *Journal of Environmental Quality* **21**, 237-245.

Smith, I. & Lyle, A. (1979). *Distribution of freshwaters in Great Britain.* Institute of Terrestrial Ecology, Edinburgh. 44 pp.

Spindler, P. (1996). *Using ecoregions for explaining macroinvertebrate community distribution among reference sites in Arizona, 1992.* Arizona Department of Environmental Quality, Tucson, Arizona.

Stoner, J. H., Gee, A. S. & Wade, K. R. (1984). The effects of acidification on the ecology of streams in the Upper Twyi catchment in West Wales. *Environmental Pollution (Series A)* **35**, 125-157.

Storey, A. W. & Humphrey, C. L. (1997). Further refinement of QA/QC acceptance criteria for MRHI sorting procedures: additional analyses based on UPGMA within to between group dissimilarities. In *Development and implementation of QA/QC protocols for sample processing components of the MRHI agency bioassessment program* (eds C. L. Humphrey, A. W. Storey & L. Thurtell), Final Report to Land and Water Resources R&D Corporation, Canberra (Reference No. ARR2), December 1997.

Strahler, A. N. (1952). Hypsometric (area-altitude) analysis of erosional topograph. *Bulletin of the Geological Society of America* **63**, 117-142.

Strahler, A. N. (1957). Quantitative analysis of watershed geomorphology. *Transactions of the American Geophysical Union* **38**, 913-920.

Sutcliffe, D. W. (Editor) (1994). *Water quality and stress indicators in marine and freshwater systems: linking levels of organisation.* Freshwater Biological Association, Ambleside.

Suter, G. W. (1993). A critique of ecosystem health concepts and indexes. *Environmental Toxicology and Chemistry* **12**, 1533-1539.

Sweeting, R. A., Lowson, D. *et al.* (1992). 1990 Biological assessment of rivers in the UK. In *River water quality: ecological assessment and control* (eds P. J. Newman, M. A. Piavaux & R. A. Sweeting), pp. 319-326. Publication EUR 14606 EN-FR. Commission of the European Communities, Luxembourg.

Tansley, A. G. (1920). The classification of vegetation and the concept of development. *Journal of Ecology* **8**, 118-149.

Tausch, R. J., Charlet, D. A. *et al.* (1995). Patterns of ordination and classification instability resulting from changes in input data order. *Journal of Vegetation Science* **6**, 897-902.

Ter Braak, C. J. F. (1985). *CANOCO–A FORTRAN program for canonical correspondence analysis and detrended correspondence analysis.* IWIS-TNO, Wageningen, The Netherlands.

Ter Braak, C. J. F. (1986). Canonical correspondence analysis: a new eigenvector technique for multivariate direct gradient analysis. *Ecology* **67**, 1167-1179.

Ter Braak, C. J. F. (1987). *CANOCO–A FORTRAN program for canonical community ordination by [partial] [detrended] [canonical] correspondence analysis, principal component analysis and redundancy analysis (version 2.1).* TNO Institute of Applied Computer Science, Wageningen, The Netherlands. 95 pp.

Ter Braak, C. J. F. (1988). *CANOCO–A FORTRAN program for canonical community ordination by correspondence analysis, principal components analysis, and redundancy analysis.* Version 2.1, Agricultural Mathematics Group, Wageningen, The Netherlands. 95 pp.

Ter Braak, C. F. J. (1990). *Update notes: CANOCO version 3.10.* Agricultural Mathematics Group, Wageningen, The Netherlands. Microcomputer Power, Ithaca, New York. 35 pp.

Ter Braak, C. J. F. & Looman, C. W. N. (1986). Weighted averaging, logistic regression and the Gaussian response model. *Vegetatio* **65**, 3-11.

Ter Braak, C. J. F. & Prentice, I. C. (1988). A theory of gradient analysis. *Advances in Ecological Research* **18**, 271-317.

Ter Braak, C. J. F. & Verdonschot, P. F. M. (1995). Canonical correspondence analysis and related multivariate methods in aquatic ecology. *Aquatic Sciences* **57**, 255-289.

Thienemann, A. (1955). *Die binnengewasser in natur und kultur.* Springer-Verlag, Berlin. 156 pp.

Thoma, R. F. (1998). Biological monitoring and an IBI application to Lake Erie's nearshore waters. In *Assessing the sustainability and biological integrity of water resource quality using fish communities* (ed. T. P. Simpson), pp. 203-224. CRC Press, Boca Raton, Florida.

Thompson, B. A. & Fitzhugh, G. R. (1986). *A use attainability study and an evaluation of fish and macroinvertebrate assemblages of the lower Calcasieu River, Louisiana.* Report LSU-CFI-29. Louisiana State University, Center for Wetland Resources, Coastal Fisheries Institute, Baton Rouge, Louisiana.

Townsend, C. R., Hildrew, A. G. & Schofield, K. (1987). Persistence of stream invertebrate communities in relation to environmental variability. *Journal of Animal Ecology* **56**, 597-613.

Townsend, C. R., Scarsbrook, M. R. & Dolédec, S. (1997). The intermediate disturbance hypothesis, refugia, and biodiversity in streams. *Limnology and Oceanography* **42**, 938-949.

Trayler, K. M. & Davis, J. A. (1998). Forestry impacts and the vertical distribution of stream invertebrates in south-western Australia. *Freshwater Biology* **40**, 331-342.

Trueman, J. W. H., Lee, W. *et al.* (1996). *Key to Australian aquatic invertebrates.* CD-ROM. CSIRO Division of Entomology.

Tuffery, G. & Verneaux, J. (1967). Une méthode zoologique practique de determination de la qualité biologique des eaux courantes. Indices biotiques. *Annales Scientifiques Université Besançon, Zoologie* **3**, 79-90.

Tüxen, R. (1955). Das System der nordwestdeutschen Pflanzengesellschaften. *Floristische Soziologische Arbeitsgemeinschafts Mitteilungen N.F.* **5**, 155-176.

Underwood, A. J. (1991). Beyond BACI: experimental designs for detecting human environmental impacts on temporal variations in natural populations. *Australian Journal of Marine and Freshwater Research* **42**, 569-587.

Underwood, A. J. (1997) *Experiments in ecology: their logical description and interpretation using analysis of variance.* Cambridge University Press, Cambridge. 528 pp.

United Kingdom Acid Waters Review Group (1989). *Acidity in United Kingdom fresh waters.* Second report of the UK Acid Waters Review Group. HMSO, London. 61 pp.

United States Environmental Protection Agency (USEPA) (1990). *Biological criteria: national program guidance for surface waters.* EPA 440-5-90-004. USEPA Office of Water

Regulations and Standards, Washington DC.

United States Environmental Protection Agency (USEPA) (1997). *Guidelines for preparation of the comprehensive state water quality assessments (305(b) reports) and electronic updates.* EPA 841-B-97-002A. USEPA Office of Water, Washington DC.

Van der Maarel, E. (1979). Transformation of cover-abundance values in phytosociology and its effects on community similarity. *Vegetatio* **39**, 97-114.

Van Dijk, P. (1994). *Analytical quality control for macroinvertebrate enumeration.* R&D Note 331. National Rivers Authority, Bristol.

Van Groenewoud, H. (1992). The robustness of correspondence, detrended correspondence, and TWINSPAN analysis. *Journal of Vegetation Science* **3**, 239-246.

Vannote, R. L., Minshall, G. W. *et al.* (1980). The river continuum concept. *Canadian Journal of Fisheries and Aquatic Sciences* **37**, 130-137.

Van Tongeren, O. (1986). FLEXCLUS, an interactive flexible cluster program. *Acta Botanica Neerlandica* **35**, 137-142.

Ventura, M. & Harper, D. (1996). The impacts of acid precipitation mediated by geology and forestry upon upland stream invertebrate communities. *Archiv für Hydrobiologie* **138**, 161-173.

Verdonschot, P. F. M. (1984). The distribution of aquatic oligochaetes in the fenland area of N. W. Overijssel (The Netherlands). *Hydrobiologia* **115**, 215-222.

Verdonschot, P. F. M. (1990). *Ecological characterization of surface waters in the province of Overijssel (The Netherlands).* Thesis, Agricultural University, Wageningen. 255 pp.

Verdonschot, P. F. M. (1991). The web approach: a tool in water management. In *Ecological water management in practice.* Proceedings of the Technological Meeting, CHO-TNO **45**, 59-76.

Verdonschot, P. F. M. (1992a). Macrofaunal community types in ponds and small lakes (Overijssel, The Netherlands). *Hydrobiologia* **232**, 111-132.

Verdonschot, P. F. M. (1992b). Macrofaunal community types of ditches in the province of Overijssel (The Netherlands). *Archiv für Hydrobiologie, Supplement* **90**, 133-158.

Verdonschot, P. F. M. (1992c). Typifying macrofaunal communities of larger disturbed waters in The Netherlands. *Aquatic Conservation: Marine and Freshwater Ecosystems* **2**, 223-242.

Verdonschot, P. F. M. (1994). Water typology: a tool for water management and nature conservation. *Verhandlungen der Internationalen Vereinigung für theoretische und angewandte Limnologie* **25**, 1911-1913.

Verdonschot, P. F. M. (1995). Typology of macrofaunal assemblages: a tool for the management of running waters. *Hydrobiologia* **297**, 99-122.

Verdonschot, P. F. M. & Schot, J. A. (1987). Macrofaunal community types in helocrene springs. *Annual Report of the Research Institute for Nature Management* **1986**, 85-103, Leersum.

Verneaux, J. (1976). Fondements biologiques et écologiques de l'étude de la qualité des eaux continentales – principales méthodes biologiques. In *La pollution des eaux continentales. Incidence sur les biocoenoses aquatiques* (ed. P. Pesson), pp. 229-285. Gauthier-Villars, Paris.

Vidal-Abarca, M. R., Suárez, M. L. & Ramírez, L. (1992). Ecology of Spanish semi-arid streams. *Limnética* **8**, 151-160.

Vinson, M. R. (1998). *Global patterns in local stream insect taxa richness.* Dissertation, Utah State University, Logan, Utah.

Vollenweider, R. A. (1975). Input-output models with special reference to the phosphorous loading concept in limnology. *Schweizerische für Hydrobiologie* **37**, 53-84.

Vuori, K.-M. & Joensuu, I. (1996). Impact of forest drainage on the macroinvertebrates of a small boreal headwater stream: do buffer zones protect lotic biodiversity? *Biological Conservation* **77**, 87-95.

Vuori, K.-M., Joensuu, I. *et al.* (1998). Forest drainage: a threat to benthic biodiversity of boreal headwater streams? *Aquatic Conservation: Marine and Freshwater Ecosystems* **8**, 745-759.

Walker, I. R., Mott, R. J. & Smol, J. P. (1991). Allerød-Younger Dryas lake temperatures from midge fossils in Atlantic Canada. *Science* **253**, 1010-1012.

Wallace, I. D. (1991). *A review of the Trichoptera of Great Britain.* Research and Survey in Nature Conservation No. **32**, Nature Conservancy Council, Peterborough. 61 pp.

Wallace, J. R. & Webster, J. R. (1996). The role of macroinvertebrates in stream ecosystem function. *Annual Review of Entomology* **41**, 115-139.

Walley, W. J. (1993). Artificial intelligence in river water quality monitoring and control. In *Proceedings of the freshwater European symposium on river water quality monitoring and control* (eds W. J. Walley & S. Judd), pp. 179-193. Aston University, February 1993.

Walley, W. J. (1994). New approaches to the interpretation and classification of water quality data based on techniques from the field of artificial intelligence. In *Proceedings of monitoring tailor-made* (eds M. Adriaanse, J. Kraats *et al.*), pp. 195-210. RIZA, The Netherlands.

Walley, W. J. & Dzeroski, S. (1995). Biological monitoring: a comparison between Bayesian, neural and machine learning methods of water quality classification. In *Environmental software systems* (eds R. Denzer, G. Schimak & D. Russell), pp. 229-240. IFIP Conference Series, Chapman & Hall, London.

Walley, W. J. & Fontama, V. N. (1998). Neural network predictors of average score per taxon and number of families at unpolluted river sites in Great Britain. *Water Research* **32**, 613-622.

Walley, W. J. & Hawkes, H. A. (1996). A computer-based reappraisal of Biological Monitoring Working Party scores using data from the 1990 River Quality Survey of England and Wales. *Water Research* **30**, 2086-2094.

Walley, W. J. & Hawkes, H. A. (1997). A computer-based development of the Biological Monitoring Working Party score system incorporating abundance rating, biotope type and indicator value. *Water Research* **31**, 201-210.

Walley, W. J. & Martin, R. W. (1997). *Distribution of macroinvertebrates in English and Welsh rivers based on the 1995 survey.* Environment Agency Technical Report E12, Foundation for Water Research.

Walley, W. J., Boyd, M. & Hawkes, H. A. (1992a). An expert system for the biological monitoring of river pollution. In *Computer techniques to environmental studies IV* (ed. P. Zanetti), pp. 721-736. Elsevier/CMP, New York/Southampton.

Walley, W. J., Fontama, V. N. & Martin, R. (1998). *Applications of artificial intelligence for the biological surveillance of river quality.* R&D Report Technical Report E52, Environment Agency, Bristol.

Walley, W. J., Hawkes, H. A. & Boyd, M. (1992b). Application of Bayesian inference to river water quality surveillance. In *Applications of artificial intelligence in engineering VII* (eds D. E. Grierson, G. Rzevski & R. A. Adey), pp. 1030-1047. Elsevier/CMP, New York/Southampton.

Walsh, C. J. (1997). A multivariate method for determining optimal subsample size in the analysis of macroinvertebrate samples. *Marine and Freshwater Research* **47**, 241-248.

Ward, J. V. (1986). Altitudinal zonation in a Rocky Mountain stream. *Archiv für Hydrobiologie,*

Supplement **74**, 133-199.

Warn, A. E. (1997). *Assessing the performance of a nation in improving river water quality: planning for the future.* Environment Agency, unpublished.

Warren, C. E., Allen, M. & Haeffner, J. W. (1979). Conceptual frameworks and the philosophical foundations of general living systems theory. *Behavioural Sciences* **24**, 296-310.

Warwick, R. M. (1988a). Analysis of community attributes of the macrobenthos of Frierfjord/Langesundfjord at taxonomic levels higher than species. *Marine Ecological Progress Series* **46**, 167-170.

Warwick, R. M. (1988b). The level of taxonomic discrimination required to detect pollution effects on marine benthic communities. *Marine Pollution Bulletin* **19**, 259-268.

Washington, H. G. (1984). Diversity, biotic and similarity indices. A review with special relevance to aquatic ecosystems. *Water Research* **18**, 653-694.

Wasson, B., Banens, B. *et al* (1996). Inland waters. In *State of the environment, Australia 1996* (State of the Environment Advisory Council), Chapter 7, pp. 7.1-7.54. CSIRO Publishing, Collingwood, Australia.

Weatherley, N. S. & Ormerod, S. J. (1990). The constancy of invertebrate assemblages in soft-water streams: implications for the prediction and detection of environmental change. *Journal of Applied Ecology* **27**, 952-964.

Wells, S. M., Pyle, R. M. & Collins, N. M. (1983). *The IUCN invertebrate red data book.* International Union for Conservation of Nature and Natural Resources. Gland.

Whiles, M. R. & Wallace, J. B. (1992). 1st-year benthic recovery of a headwater stream following a 3-year insecticide-induced disturbance. *Freshwater Biology* **28**, 81-91.

Whittaker, R. H. (1978). *Classification of plant communities.* Handbook of vegetation sciences No. 4. Junk Publishers, The Hague. 104 pp.

Wiederholm, T. & Johnson, R. K. (1997). Monitoring and assessment of lakes and watercourses in Sweden. In *Monitoring tailor-made II. Information strategies in water* (eds J. J. Ottens, F. A. M. Claessen *et al.*), pp. 317-329. Nunspeet, The Netherlands.

Wiederholm, T., Johnson, R. K. *et al.* (1992). *Freshwater environmental monitoring in Sweden – Proposals from a working group.* SEPA report. 156 pp.

Wiegleb, G. (1981). Application of discriminant analysis on the analysis of the correlation between macrophyte vegetation and water quality in running waters of Central Europe. *Hydrobiologia* **79**, 91-100.

Wiens, J. A. (1981). Single-sample surveys of communities: are the revealed patterns real? *American Naturalist* **117**, 90-98.

Wiggins, G. B. & Mackay, R. J. (1978). Some relationships between systematics and trophic ecology in Nearctic aquatic insects, with special reference to Trichoptera. *Ecology* **59**, 1211-1220.

Wilander, A., Johnson, R. K. *et al.* (1998). *Riksinventering 1995, En synoptisk studie av vattenkemi och bottenfauna i svenska sjöar och vattendrag.* Naturvårdsverket Rapport. 191 pp. (In Swedish).

Williams, C. (1996). *Rapid biological assessment of water quality: comparison of analysis options and use of different mesh sizes.* Unpublished thesis, University of Canberra.

Wishart, M. J., Davies, B. R. *et al.* (2000). Global disparities in river conservation: "first-world" values and "third-world" realities. In *Global perspectives on river conservation: science, policy and practice* (eds P. J. Boon, B. R. Davies & G. E. Petts) (in press). John Wiley & Sons, Chichester.

Wold, H. (1982). Soft modeling: the basic design and some extensions. In *Systems under indirect observations II, North-Holland* (eds K. G. Joreskog & H. Wold), pp. 1-54.

Amsterdam.

Woodiwiss, F. S. (1964). The biological system of stream classification used by the Trent River Board. *Chemistry and Industry* **11**, 443-447.

Wright, J. F. (1994). Development of RIVPACS in the UK and the value of the underlying data-base. *Limnética* **10**, 15-31.

Wright, J. F. (1995). Development and use of a system for predicting the macroinvertebrate fauna in flowing waters. *Australian Journal of Ecology* **20**, 181-197.

Wright, J. F., Armitage, P. D. & Furse, M. T. (1981). *Analysis of natural river communities in Great Britain. Phase 1 (October 1977–September 1981).* A report to the Department of the Environment.

Wright, J. F., Furse, M. T. & Armitage, P. D. (1993). RIVPACS – a technique for evaluating the biological quality of rivers in the UK. *European Water Quality Control* **3**, 15-25.

Wright, J. F., Furse, M. T. & Armitage, P. D. (1994). Use of macroinvertebrate communities to detect environmental stress in running waters. In *Water quality and stress indicators in marine and freshwater systems: linking levels of organisation* (ed. D. W. Sutcliffe), pp. 15-34. Freshwater Biological Association, Ambleside.

Wright, J. F., Furse, M. T. & Moss, D. (1998a). River classification using invertebrates: RIVPACS applications. *Aquatic Conservation: Marine and Freshwater Ecosystems* **8**, 617-631.

Wright, J. F., Moss, D. & Furse, M. T. (1998b). Macroinvertebrate richness at running-water sites in Great Britain: a comparison of species and family richness. *Verhandlungen der Internationalen Vereinigung für theoretische und angewandte Limnologie* **26**, 1174-1178.

Wright, J. F., Armitage, P. D. *et al.* (1984). *Analysis of natural river communities in Great Britain. Phase 2. October 1981–March 1984.* Report to the Department of the Environment, The Scottish Development Department and The Welsh Office.

Wright, J. F., Armitage, P. D. *et al.* (1985). The classification and prediction of macroinvertebrate communities in British rivers. *Annual Report of the Freshwater Biological Association* **53**, 80-93.

Wright, J. F., Armitage, P. D. *et al.* (1988). A new approach to the biological surveillance of river quality using macroinvertebrates. *Verhandlungen der Internationalen Vereinigung für theoretische und angewandte Limnologie* **23**, 1548-1552.

Wright, J. F., Armitage, P. D. *et al.* (1989). Prediction of invertebrate communities using stream measurements. *Regulated Rivers: Research and Management* **4**, 147-155.

Wright, J. F., Blackburn, J. H. *et al.* (1996). Macroinvertebrate frequency data for the RIVPACS III sites in Great Britain and their use in conservation evaluation. *Aquatic Conservation: Marine and Freshwater Ecosystems* **6**, 141-167.

Wright, J. F., Furse, M. T. *et al.* (1991). *Testing and further development of RIVPACS.* IFE interim report (R&D 243/1/Y) to the National Rivers Authority, Bristol. 141 pp.

Wright, J. F., Furse, M. T. *et al.* (1992). *Invertebrate survey and classification of rivers for nature conservation.* SNH Research, Survey and Monitoring Report No. 1. Scottish Natural Heritage, Edinburgh.

Wright, J. F., Furse, M. T. *et al.* (1995). *Testing and further development of RIVPACS. Part 1 – Main Report,* 72 pp., *and Part 2 – Tables and Figures.* NRA R&D Note 453, National Rivers Authority, Bristol. 110 pp.

Wright, J. F., Gunn, R. J. M. *et al.* (1995). *Extension of RIVPACS to Northern Ireland.* Final report to the Department of the Environment (Northern Ireland).

Wright, J. F., Hiley, P. D. *et al.* (1984). The invertebrate fauna of a small chalk stream in Berkshire, England, and the effect of intermittent flow. *Archiv für Hydrobiologie* **99**, 176-199.

Wright, J. F., Moss, D. *et al.* (1984). A preliminary classification of running-water sites in Great Britain based on macro-invertebrate species and the prediction of community type using environmental data. *Freshwater Biology* **14**, 221-256.

Wright, J. F., Moss, D. *et al.* (1997). Biological assessment of river quality using the new version of RIVPACS (RIVPACS III). In *Freshwater quality: defining the indefinable?* (eds P. J. Boon & D. L. Howell), pp. 102-108. The Stationery Office, Edinburgh.

Wright, J. F., Welton, J. S. *et al.* (1988). The macroinvertebrate fauna of the Moors River and Uddens Water in Dorset. *Proceedings of the Dorset Natural History and Archaeological Society* **110**, 127-135.

Yoder, C. O. (1991). The integrated biosurvey as a tool for evaluation of aquatic life use attainment and impairment in Ohio surface waters. In *Biological criteria: research and regulation, proceedings of a symposium, 12-13 December 1990, Arlington, Virginia*, pp. 110-122. EPA-440-5-91-005. USEPA Office of Water, Washington DC.

Yoder, C. O. & Rankin, E. T. (1995a). Biological criteria program development and implementation in Ohio. In *Biological assessment and criteria. Tools for water resource planning and decision making* (eds W. S. Davis & T. P. Simon), pp. 109-144. Lewis Publishers, Boca Raton, Florida.

Yoder, C. O. & Rankin, E. T. (1995b). Biological response signatures and the area of degradation value; new tools for interpreting multimetric data. In *Biological assessment and criteria. Tools for water resource planning and decision making* (eds W. S. Davis & T. P. Simon), pp. 263-286. Lewis Publishers, Boca Raton, Florida.

Yoder, C. O. & Rankin, E. T. (1998). The role of biological indicators in a state water quality management process. *Journal of Environmental Monitoring and Assessment* **51**, 61-88.

Yorkshire Water Authority (1978). *The Yorkshire interpretive index for biological quality assessment of rivers in Yorkshire*. Unpublished manuscript.

Zamora-Muñoz, C. (1992). *Macroinvertebrados acuáticos, caracterización y calidad de las aguas de los cauces de la cuenca alta del río Genil*. Tesis doctoral, Universidad de Granada.

Zamora-Muñoz, C. & Alba-Tercedor, J. (1996). Bioassessment of organically polluted Spanish rivers, using biotic index and multivariate methods. *Journal of the North American Benthological Society* **15**, 332-352.

Zamora-Muñoz, C., Sáinz-Cantero, C. E. *et al.* (1995). Are biological indices BMWP' and ASPT' and their significance regarding water quality seasonally dependent? Factors explaining their variations. *Water Research* **29**, 285-290.

Zarull, M. A. & Reynoldson, T. B. (1992). A management strategy for contaminated sediments: assessment and remediation. *Water Pollution Research Journal of Canada* **27**, 871-882.

Zwick, P. (1992). Contamination of streams and rivers by insecticides. *Natürwissenschaften* **79**, 437-442.

INDEX TO SCIENTIFIC NAMES (TAXA)

INDEX TO SELECTED TOPICS

Selected topics appear below under the following bold headings: Named lakes; Named rivers/streams; Countries/regions/places named in the text; Organisations; Legislation; Regional surveys/programmes; Methodology; Reference condition/sites; Field sampling; Laboratory sorting; Level of identification/analysis; Conservation/biodiversity; Environmental variables; Major conclusions/recommendations.

Swedish national survey of lakes and
   streams (1995) 230

WPA (Watershed Protection Approach) 283

Methodology

Abundance-based index (see Q14)
Acidity index 232
AI (Artificial Intelligence) 263-79, 327,
   330-2
Alatalo index 258
ANOVA (ANalysis Of VAriance) 47, 186
AQC (Analytical Quality Control) 72-7
ASPT (Average Score Per Taxon) xxiv, 8,
   11, 17-18, 31, 33-4, 39-41, 45-8, 52-4,
   57, 59-66, 79, 83-91, 93, 96, 104-9, 118,
   128, 141, 213, 229, 232-5, 269-78, 305-7
ASTM (American Society for Testing and
   Materials) 175-6
AUSRIVAS (AUStralian RIVer Assessment
   Scheme) 113, 119-63, 166, 182, 195,
   197-8, 204-5, 305-9

BACI (Before-After-Control-Impact) 117,
   160
Bayesian classifier 273-9
BBN (Bayesian Belief Networks) 268-9,
   278-9
BEAST (BEnthic Assessment of SedimenT)
   165-6, 177-205, 298-9
ß-functions 328, 330
BIDB (Biotic Index of the Duero Basin)
   208
BILL (Llobregat and Besòs Index) 208, 215
Biotic Index (Chandler) 208
BIRC (Benthic Information system for
   Reference Conditions) 179
BMWP (Biological Monitoring Working
   Party) xxiv, 5-20, 26, 30-40, 44-57, 72,
   75, 83-91, 93, 96, 104-9, 118, 207-10,
   215, 238, 263-78, 302, 305-7, 317-8,
   322, 324
BMWP (Spanish adaptation of BMWP)
   209-11, 213, 215
Bonferroni correction 200
Bray-Curtis dissimilarity measure 148-9
Bray-Curtis similarity coefficient
   (association measure) 32, 51, 127, 170,
   186

CA (Correspondence Analysis) 325-8
CANOCO (computer program) 32-8, 243,
   329
CCA (Canonical Correspondence Analysis)
   233, 238-9, 328-9
Chi-squared test 14, 29, 33-6
Cluster analysis 165, 170, 243-4, 327-8
CoG (Confidence of Grade) 67-8
COINSPAN (Constrained-Indicator-
   Species-Analysis) 329
CONCLASS (computer program) 63
Confidence limits 53-4
CV (Coefficient of Variation) 150, 175-6,
   185, 187, 199-201, 204
Czekanowski Coefficient 257-8

DCA (Detrended Correspondence Analysis)
   233, 327-8
DCCA (Detrended Canonical
   Correspondence Analysis) 32-7, 243-5,
   256-7
DECORANA (DEtrended CORrespondence
   ANAlysis) 30-2
Dempster-Shafer theory of evidence 268
DFA (Discriminant Function Analysis) 324,
   327-30
DFMs (Discriminant Functions Models)
   218-26

EKOO (computer program) 241, 256-7
EQI (Ecological Quality Index) xxiv, 57,
   60-5, 83-90, 93, 264, 267-9, 274-7
Euclidean distance 257-8

Face bands/values 53-4, 63
Family Biotic Index 199, 201, 203
FLEXCLUS (computer program) 243-5
FUSE (computer program) 32-7, 149
Fuzzy logic 258

Gaussian logistic regression 330
GFRs (Genus to Family Ratios) 219-20,
   223, 226
GIS (Geographic Information System) 22,
   330
GPS (Global Positioning System) 167
GQA (General Quality Assessment) 57, 60-
   9, 72, 74-5, 82, 94, 265, 270-7

HMDS (Hybrid Multi-Dimensional
   Scaling) 118, 170